WHAT'S THIS? The Runaway Locomotive? The Wabash Cannonball? No. It's the Backyard and Birdbath Express chugging mightily down the high iron. The engineer and his passenger look like they wouldn't swap their loco for a real Boeing 707. You can establish a division of the B&B R.R. in your backyard. The plans are on page 2752

UNDERWATER PHOTO bugs can make waterproof cases for their cameras after reading page 2824

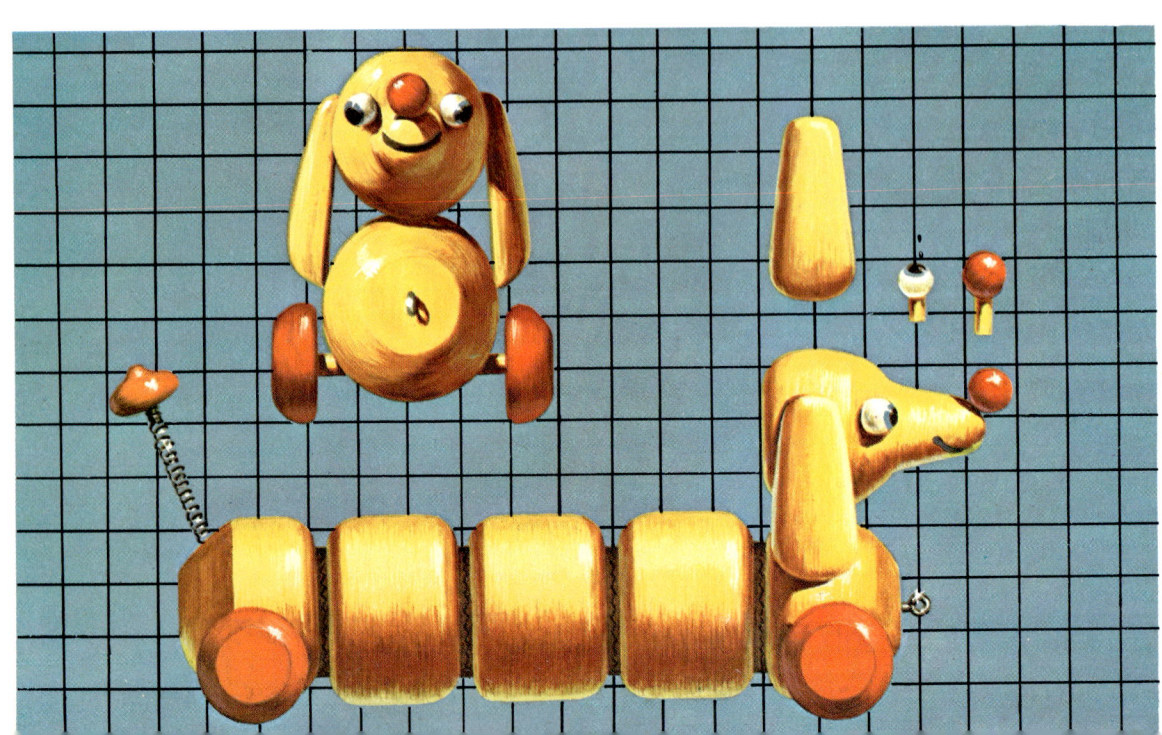

THE PLANS on page 2720 are straight from the workshops of Santa Claus' elves. They show you how to make some great pull-apart pull toys. These colorful toys have top kid-appeal, but are easy to make in any workshop

Photo courtesy of The Coleman Company, Inc.

DON'T START OUT on a vacation trip with your trailer—any kind of trailer—until you check page 2737. The article tells you how to service the trailer before a trip. It's good advice, and could save you breakdowns

THAT LAKE in the background of the picture below is for real, because this man is building a vacation home for his family. Perhaps you're thinking of building one, too. Read the stories on pages 2840, 2848 and 2856 for some ideas

Photos courtesy of Eastman Kodak Co.

PLAN FOR BETTER COLOR PICTURES

DO THE GUESTS look around for the exits when you bring out your motion-picture projector? It's probably because they're expecting the ordinary amateur production on your screen. Fool 'em next time with titles that look like professional work. Two stories, pages 2700 and 2702, give you the know-how

Popular Mechanics
Do-It-Yourself Encyclopedia

in 16 volumes

A complete guide to

- home maintenance
- home improvement
- hand-tool skills
- craft projects
- power-tool know-how
- hobbies
- automotive upkeep
- automotive repair
- shop shortcuts
- boating
- fishing
- hunting
- model making
- outdoor living
- radio, TV and electronics

Volume 15

Book Division, Hearst Magazines, New York, N.Y. 10019

© 1968, The Hearst Corporation
All Rights Reserved

No part of the text or illustrations in this work may be used without written permission by the Hearst Corporation.

Printed in the United States of America

VOLUME 15

tires
    Your tires take a beating   2693
titles, movie
    How to backlight movie titles   2700
    Titling tricks add appeal to home movies   2702
toasters
    How to fix a toaster   2704
toboggan
    Build a toboggan for family fun   2706
toolpost grinder
    Toolpost grinder does a mirror-bright job   2712
tools, boat
    Stow-aboard tool kit for outboards   2716
tool tray, lathe
    Tray keeps lathe tools in easy reach   2718
toys
    Pull-apart pull toys   2720
    Kick-powered forklift truck   2723
    Boxers play for a knockout   2724
    Humpty-dumpty takes the tumble   2726
    Quick-change cardboard play mounts   2727
    A train for small-fry engineers   2728
tracing projector
    Tracing projector makes anyone an artist   2732
trailers
    Service your trailer before you go   2737
    Roadside chuck wagon   2742
    Handy trailer for yard tracs   2748
train, children's
    Backyard railroad   2752
transistor radios
    How to buy a good transistor radio   2764
    Build a portable radio in minutes   2769
    Table-model power for a transistor radio   2772
transmitter, FM
    Wireless FM mike in a cigarette case   2775
transmitter meter
    Pocket CB meter for walkie-talkies   2778
tree felling
    Rule-of-three in felling trees   2781

tree houses
    Every kid should have a tree house   2782
tree stumps
    Get rid of that tree stump   2788
trinket boxes
    Trinket boxes made from napkin rings   2790
tripods
    Dolly-in on action with a rolling tripod   2792
    Sliding camera mount for stereo shots   2794
trolling motor
    Build a trolling motor   2796
tubes, television
    The plain truth about tube testing   2798
tumbler
    Trampoline doubles as wading pool   2802
tumbling machines
    Tumbling machine gives a high-polish finish   2805
    Gang tumbler for small parts   2809
tuners, FM
    Give your tuner a longer reach   2812
    Stay on the beam with tuning indicators   2814
    FM listening with no amplifier   2818
underwater camera cases
    Waterproof camera for underwater movies   2820
    Camera case for scuba shutterbugs   2824
unicycle
    For fun, try a unicycle   2827
upholstery
    Uplift for tired old chairs   2828
    Reupholstering with foam rubber   2830
used car reconditioning
    How to get more for your old car   2834
vacation homes
    Three year-round vacation homes   2840
    Weekend projects for hideaway homes   2844
    Ideas for your vacation home   2849
    Start your vacation home at home   2856

Project-a-plans   2879

How to use your Encyclopedia

Browse. Glance through this volume, or any other volume of the Encyclopedia. Likely you will find the solution to a particular home-maintenance problem that has been bothering you, or a shop project so appealing that you will immediately head for your bench. Browsing not only is enjoyable, but is a source of ideas.

Seek specific information. Perhaps you want to find out how to cure that leak in your basement, how to keep the exterior paint from peeling, or how to tune and set the carburetor on your car.

Four reader aids, all cross-referenced, will enable you to find specific information:

1. *Alphabetical headings*. Located at the top of the page, these headings cover broad classifications of information. If you are looking for information on how to keep paint from peeling, for example, look up "Paints" alphabetically, then find the particular section dealing with peeling paint.

2. *Alphabetical cross-references*. These are shown in a box at the bottom of the page. Some material can logically be classified under more than one alphabetical heading, so if you don't find what you are seeking alphabetically (as described above), be sure to check the *alphabetical cross-references* at the bottom of the page; there you may find precisely the classification you are seeking. For example, you and your son decide to build a model airplane, and are looking for plans. You look up "Model airplanes" and find nothing under that alphabetical heading. However, if you glance at the bottom *of that same page* you will find an alphabetical cross-reference that reads: **model airplanes,** see airplane models.

3. *See also references*. These are shown at the end of many articles. They refer you to related articles which may also be of interest.

4. *Instant index*. Located at the end of Volume 16, it is thoroughly cross-referenced to help you find information under any heading.

1 *Alphabetical headings*

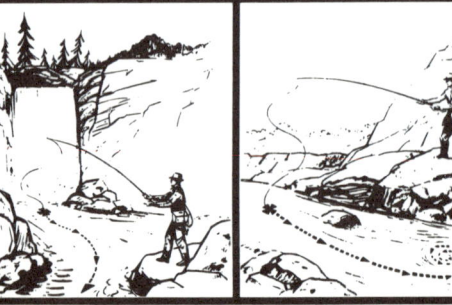

bait, fishing

When nothing else works, try worms

On those days when all you can do with an artificial lure is beat the water to a froth—you'll still catch fish with the lowly worm

BY STUART JAMES

■ WORM FISHING, according to the most avid anglers, is poor sportsmanship.

This is true if you are the type who wants to make his sport as difficult as possible. But if you go fishing to catch fish this is a left-handed accolade for the worm.

Competing against plugs, lures, dry and wet flies, or whatever else might come out of a tackle box, the lowly, unglamorous worm proves a time-honored fact—it will catch fish when nothing else will work.

The body wall of the worm secretes a mucus for keeping the skin soft. This has an odor that fish recognize, according to worm proponents. A worm must be fished slowly to allow the fish to get the scent. However, this scent washes off, so bait must be changed every half hour or so.

Casting a worm upstream (without a weight) permits it to drift like natural bait. Where the current eddies into a pool (right), cast above the pool and work the worm to the outer edge so it will move in a circle, presenting itself to the fish in a natural way, as if drifting

balancing wheels: see wheel alignment, auto
balancing beams: see playground equipment

148

2 *Alphabetical cross-references*

Adding a small section of worm to a wet fly gives the fly an odor, and also looks as though the fly has been injured and is trailing a section of gut. This is an added incentive for the game fish to attack.

How the hook is baited with the worm depends upon the fish you wish to attract. Bluegills and crappies will nibble at the worm, so it should cover the hook with the barb going clear to the tip. For bass or trout, which are smarter and require a natural bait, you must consider the anatomy of the worm. The worm's body wall is made up of a thin layer of circular muscles and a thicker layer of longitudinal muscles that make it possible to contract and expand in moving. In the water it naturally activates these muscles, so the hook is placed through the tip to allow the worm free movement so it will appear natural to the larger fish that can take it all in one gulp.

The worm is a natural food for almost all fish. After a rain, particularly, worms are washed into streams and fish gorge themselves. To fish a worm properly, you cast above the pool where the fish lurk and let it drift down. You can check the current by tossing a twig into the water.

A light fly line or light monofilament is the best for fishing worms. It is not so easily seen, and it allows the worm natural movement.

You can cast a worm on a light line into a pool—without weight on the line—and it will slowly sink to the bottom as though it just fell from a bank.

If you encounter a pool where the current moves in a circular direction, it is ideal to bring the worm in with the current and let it swirl slowly.

It is estimated that 50,000 worms exist in an average acre of land. Only a foolish angler ignores this ready source of bait.

See also: bass fishing; fishing; fly-casting; ice fishing; lures; trolling motor.

3 *See also references*

A killer for lakes and ponds—thread worm on long-shank hook with salmon eggs fore and aft; add salmon eggs on treble hook. A section of worm on a wet fly looks like trailing viscera. For bass and trout, hook a small section of worm and cast without weight, letting it wriggle naturally

149

4 *Instant index*

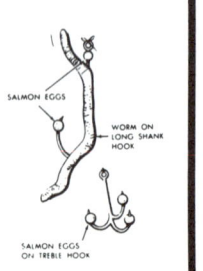

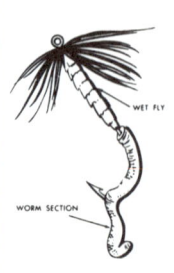

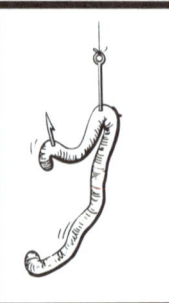

Your tires take a beating

BY MORTON J. SCHULTZ

■ MANY OF THE CONDITIONS that affect tire life and wear can be controlled. But there also are several that cannot. If you understand some of the intricacies of a tire's operation, if you know which influences are controllable and how to control them, you can squeeze safe extra miles from your car's rubber "shoes."

Your geography, for example, is beyond control. And hilly areas where roads climb, wind

Just one more important precaution than those you now practice against extreme tire wear can mean a thousand more miles—or even five thousand more—of life for the rubber "shoes" on your car

Would you guess that at a speed of about sixty the tires of your car look like this? Probably you never gave it a thought. And even though this tire looks like a blowout about to happen, it's performing in a normal fashion. But you can see the forces of distortion at work trying to pull it apart

tires

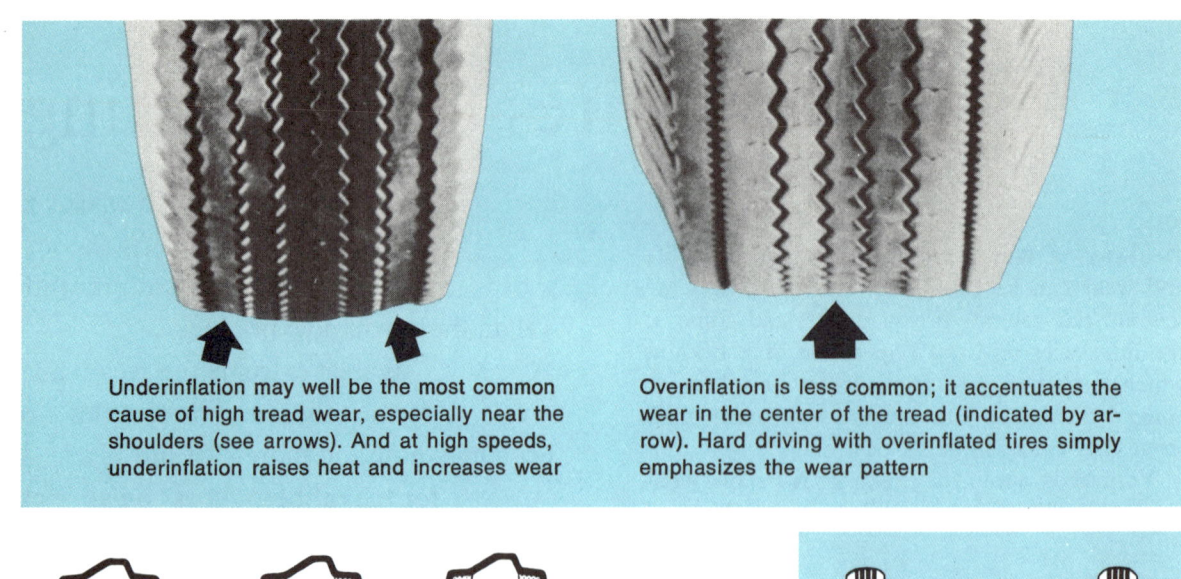

Underinflation may well be the most common cause of high tread wear, especially near the shoulders (see arrows). And at high speeds, underinflation raises heat and increases wear

Overinflation is less common; it accentuates the wear in the center of the tread (indicated by arrow). Hard driving with overinflated tires simply emphasizes the wear pattern

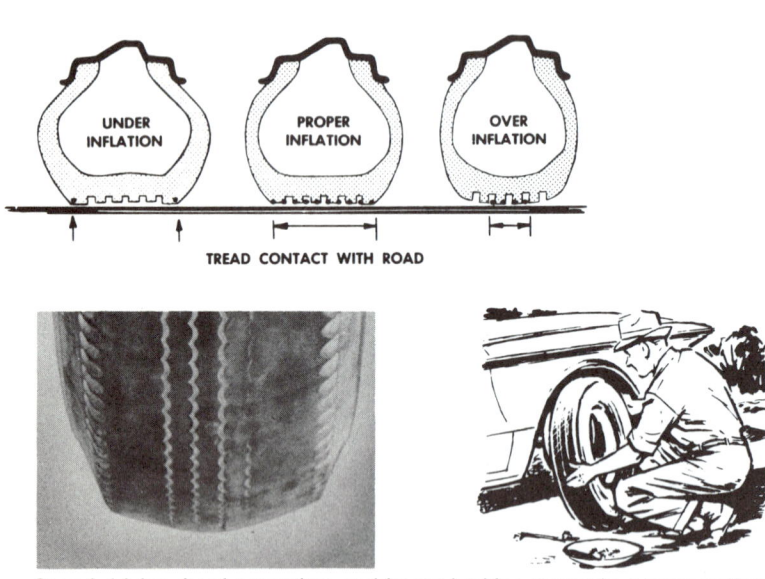

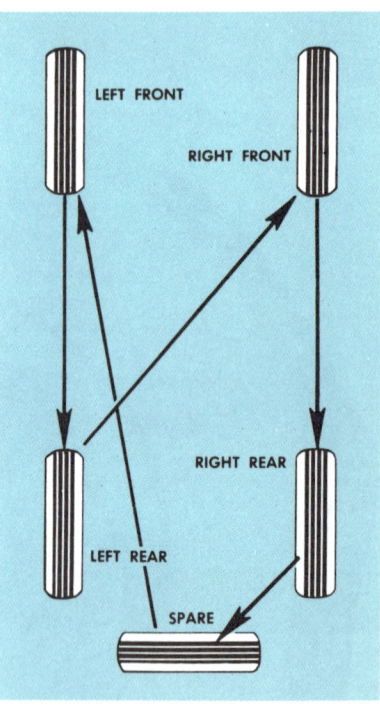

Speed driving, hard cornering, and heavy braking generate a wear pattern similar to that from underinflation. Tire rotation (right) spreads wear

tires take a beating, continued

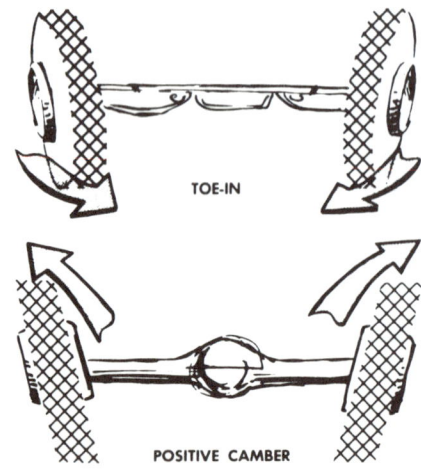

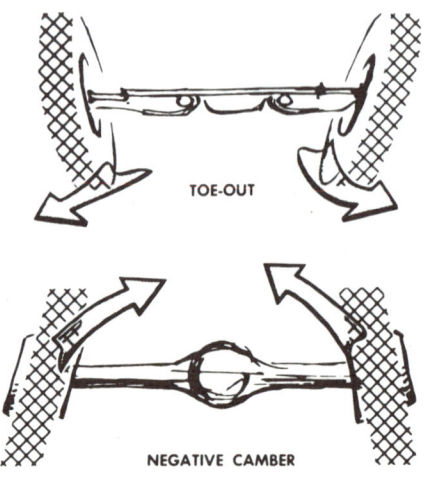

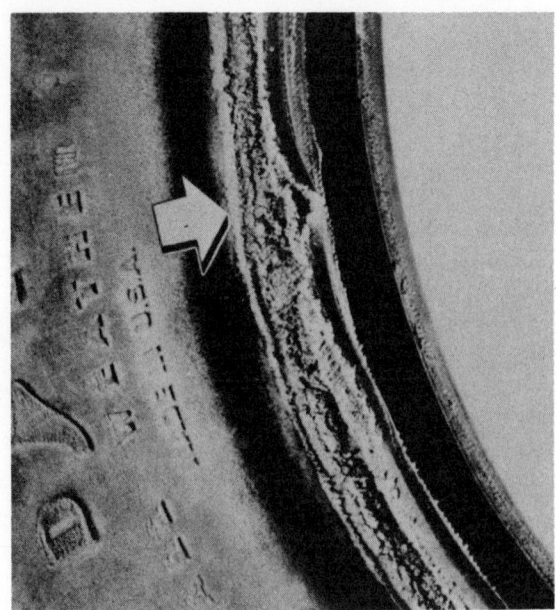
Careless tire mounting such as forcing the tire over a bent, defective, or improper-size rim can cause serious damage to the bead

The bald tire at the left should be discarded; it's dangerous. The one at the right, still with a uniform tread, should get its cap now

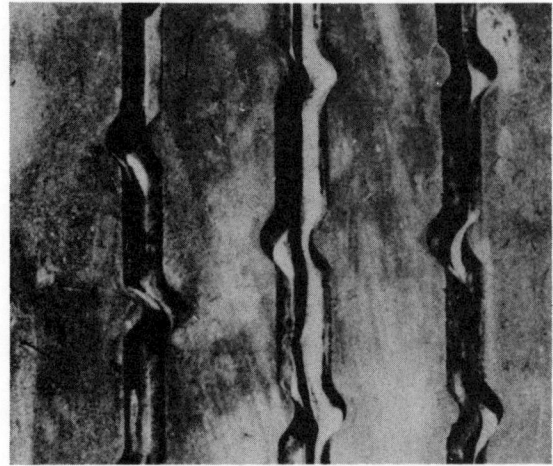
Long channel cracks between the ribs, especially at the center of the tread area, usually indicate a tire that is defective or, at best, inferior

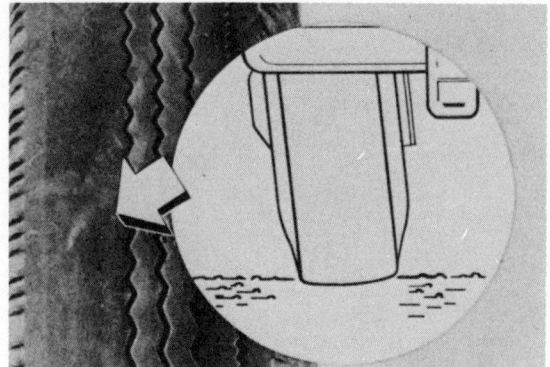
One-sided tread wear is usually caused by improper caster or camber of the front wheels, excessive tow-in, or a bent frame, making front-end alignment impossible

tightly, and descend steeply are harder on tires than miles over relatively straight, level roads.

Road surface is another condition you can't do much about, although you should avoid deep chuckholes whenever possible. Gravel and other loose surfacing material often contains small, sharp stones that can cut tread rubber. Deep ruts and chuckholes can break down sidewalls.

Remember that the apparent size of a cut or break is no sure clue to its seriousness. The depth is what concerns you. Thus, any significant cut should be investigated carefully. Probe it with a screwdriver blade, being sure you don't make it wider or deeper. If it reaches or approaches the cord, it's best to scrap the tire before it blows out at a critical moment.

The fabric layers, made of cord sandwiched deep within the rubber, are also vulnerable, but damage may be hard to detect. A straight-line break can easily be missed although the classic X-break is more obvious. The result can be a long-delayed blowout or flat, so if such a break is irreparable, discard the tire. In tubeless tires, a slow leak is the common result of a carcass break. But in the older, tube-type tires the break inside the carcass chafes the tube and can even pinch it, eventually causing a blowout.

Another environmental condition injurious to tires is the grease, oil, and other petroleum products on the road and in parking areas. Where possible, avoid parking in grease or oil-soaked areas since petroleum attacks rubber. Inspect tires periodically and wipe off any grease or oil. It is good practice to inspect the tires every time your car is greased.

Mechanical maladjustments directly affecting tire wear are out-of-balance wheels, excessive or

2695

tires

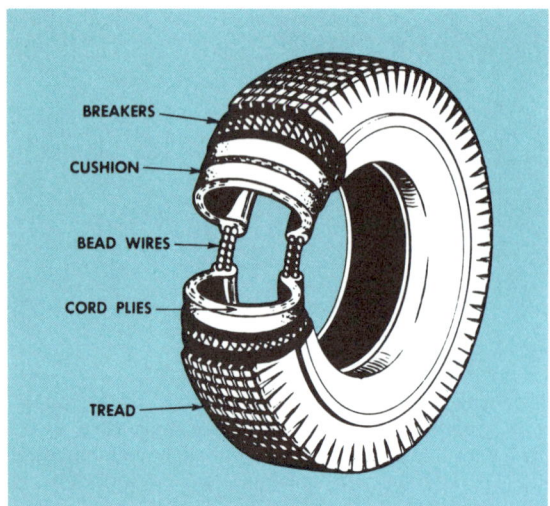

This cutaway drawing of a typical bias-ply tire shows all the construction components from the tread stock in to the cord plies and bead wires

Wear spots like this could be reduced and spread among all five tires if they were rotated. The pattern probably indicates a mechanical problem

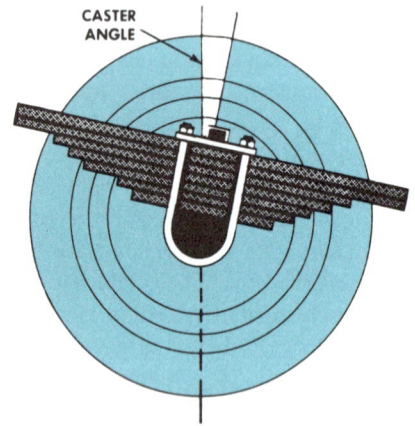

The caster angle shown here is exaggerated for clarity. Too much causes shimmy and uneven wear; too little lets the wheels wander and hampers control

improper camber, toe-in, toe-out and caster. There are two main symptoms of out-of-balance wheels:

Tramp or road shock, usually accompanied by a thumping sound, results when a heavier part of the tire moves down toward the road. Crudely described, it can be corrected by jacking up the car and allowing the heavy portion to move down —then adding weights to the light side to balance the wheel. It isn't essential that the wheel be spun, and the operation is generally called "static balancing."

A shimmy—a rapid side movement of the front wheels that vibrates the car laterally and sometimes even the steering wheel—results from a different problem. In this case, the heavier sections in the tire-wheel assembly may be on the outboard side of the wheel in one case and on the inboard side in another location around the wheel. When the wheel spins rapidly over the road, it tries to wobble—to turn inward then outward every half revolution. When the car is jacked up, the two heavy portions may seem to balance each other—unless the wheel is spun rapidly. Thus the diagnostic and repair procedure is called "dynamic balancing." It's an important job. Incidentally, a similar shimmy can result from loose steering linkage.

Camber and caster (measured in degrees) and toe-in (measured in fractions of an inch) are three vital but little-understood measurements that influence tire life.

Toe-in is the inclination of the tires toward center when measured horizontally across the front and back of the tires. It offsets the natural tendency of the wheels to rotate outward around the king pins. Toe-*out*—or too much toe-in—results in feathered edges along the grooves in the tire tread due to a wiping action on the road.

Just as the front edges of the front tires are closer together than their rear edges, the same tires should be closer together at the bottom than at the top. This tilt is measured as an angle from the vertical. It's about 1 deg. in many modern cars. Excessive camber—too much tilt— wears tires on the outside edge of the tread. Too little camber, otherwise called *negative* camber, can also be a problem. It can result from worn wheel parts or maladjustment. Result: the inside edge of the tread is worn too fast.

Caster is best understood by reference to a bicycle's front wheel or to the roller ("caster") under a furniture leg. The member that supports the wheel—the pin, in the case of the furniture caster—points to a spot in the "road" slightly forward of the center of the footprint. This distance is called "lead." The result is that the wheel tends naturally to track right behind the spot the pin points to. And this pin corresponds to the hypothetical kingpin. On a bicycle, this angle is what lets you ride "no hands." In a car, one of its effects is to bring the front wheels back to a straight-ahead position when you release the steering wheel. It doesn't have much direct effect on tire wear, but if not properly adjusted, caster influences the other angles adversely. Unequal caster will cause the car to pull to one side and cause uneven and excessive tire wear. Too little causes the wheels to wander.

Other mechanical irregularities you should watch for include grabby brakes, worn shock absorbers, sprung axles or axle housings, worn bushings, and bent wheel disks.

Tire mounting can also be important; here's how the professionals do it:

A competent serviceman will (1) inspect rim flanges for sharp dents; (2) clean flanges and bead seats with emery cloth, steel wool, or a wire brush; (3) check the butt weld in the rim and file rough spots if needed; (4) clean the valve hole area and smooth off any burrs; (5) insure cleanliness of the tire bead and sealing ridges; (6) insure that—if your tires are tubeless—the valve meets the manufacturer's size specs; (7) slosh plenty of rubber lubricant on the tire beads, rim flanges, and bead ledge areas.

listen for the "pop"

If, by the time he has blown the tire up to 40 lbs. pressure, he hasn't heard the sharp popping that indicates the beads have snapped into place on the wheel, a good tire man will start over. That means deflating the tire, relubricating it, recentering it on the rim, and inflating it again. The tire will have to be "overinflated" to seat the beads properly. Then the pressure should be reduced to normal.

If you are thinking of recapping the tires now on your car, run them only until the tread design very nearly disappears in the center or, at most, until the tread is very thin about ¾ of the way across the tire. If the tread is worn too thin, or is worn off entirely, recapping is not possible or safe. Tire manufacturers caution drivers against bad driving practices that ruin tires. These are speeding, fast starts, heavy braking at high speeds and on downgrades, high-speed turns, sharp turns at slow speeds and sudden stops.

Perhaps the chief cause of tire failure is speeding. When driving at only 50 miles per hour, a centrifugal force of two tons is acting on the tire, tending to pull it apart. At a sustained speed of 70 miles per hour, tires generate sufficient heat to boil water. When speeding, tire tread is stretched and contracted—see the photo on page 2693—setting up stresses that tend to separate the tread from the body, pull the plies apart. High-speed distortion and heat are much more damaging when tires are underinflated. Modern tires take this kind of punishment regularly and still hold together, but you can see that tire life shortens proportionally at speeds much above 50. When high sustained speeds or loads are anticipated it's good practice to increase air pressure 4 lb. above the recommended pressure.

Here are five rules to follow regarding tire inflation: 1) Keep the tires up to the recommended pressure. Many car builders only specify the *cold* pressure reading. 2) Never reduce the pressure as tires heat up. The cold-pressure recommendation is established on the assumption that it will go up as a running tire warms up. Bleeding them to the recommended cold pressure will actually leave them underinflated, flex the sidewalls excessively, and damage the tires. 3) Make sure the valve caps are screwed on finger tight to prevent unnecessary loss of air pressure. 4) Replace the core of any valve that leaks, since this is likely to be the cause of any trouble and new cores are cheap. 5) When you find pressure is often low or drops decidedly, have the tire checked for slow leaks and have it repaired at once.

turn the page

be careful with chains

A final maintenance tip concerns tire chains. Chains are made to creep on a tire, so the links won't gouge into the rubber. Make sure chains are never put on too tight and that they are the right size for the tire. Never underinflate or overinflate tires to make them fit the chain and, of course, never drive with tire chains on bare pavement; this ruins both tires and chains.

So much for maintaining today's tires; what will tomorrow's be like?

Since the late 1950s, pressure for "radial" tires has been building up in the U.S. These have the major ply cords running directly from bead to bead like extensions of radii drawn out from the hub of the wheel. Over the plies, a no-stretch belt is wrapped completely around the tire just under the tread rubber. Radials have long been popular in Europe, particularly for sports cars.

tires

Their advantages: longer wear and sharply improved roadholding.

In the early 1960s, most U.S. tire-builders began talking about building radial tires, although they actually concentrated first on importing them for smaller cars from their European plants. It appeared that the manufacturing techniques were difficult to develop here. One major manufacturer actually announced radials for U.S. cars, but then delayed their introduction for years.

Research continued especially in an effort to establish the best material for the "belt." Sears Roebuck began importing French tires that used a woven steel belt. Others continued work on rayon and fiberglass belts.

The original equipment market is, of course, the biggest market available to tire manufacturers. And the first breakthrough for the new technology came for what might be called U.S.-style radials—actually not radial tires at all.

In early 1968 Goodyear succeeded in selling its "bias belted" tire to American Motors for its new AMX sports coupe. As the name suggests, the Goodyear tire was a compromise. It carried a fiberglass belt under the tread, but the polyester plies under that were laid on an angle and alternately crisscrossing each other. Goodyear said the design gave most of the advantages of radial tires, without the slight ride harshness that some said they experienced with true radials.

Although the new designs are likely to end up on your car, the maintenance problems aren't likely to change greatly. You'll still be well advised to take good care of the "shoes," and to avoid mistreating them.

See also: steering, auto; steering, power, auto; wheel alignment, auto; wheel bearings, auto.

Feathered edges on the ribs are usually evidence of mechanical problems, especially wheel misalignment like maladjusted toe-in. The tires "wipe" the road

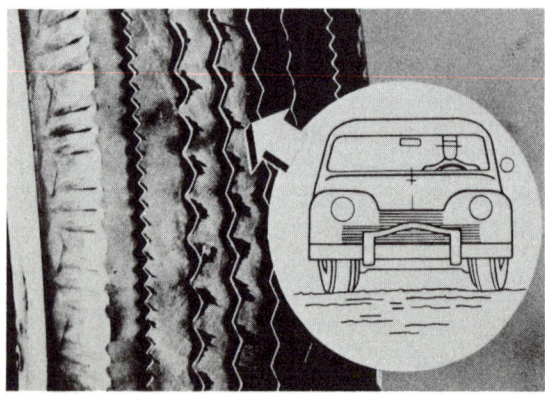

COMMON TIRE DAMAGE

MALFUNCTION	CONDITION Mechanical	CONDITION Driver	SYMPTOM	USUAL CAUSE
Cut by chains		X	Gouge marks all around tire sidewall.	Incorrect-size chains or tire underinflated.
Cut due to spin		X	Cut from lower shoulder to upper tread edge.	Spinning tire against sharp rock frozen in icy pavement or on dirt or gravel road.
Cut by obstruction on vehicle	X		Chafe marks in straight line all around tire circumference.	Tire rubbed against disengaged vehicle part, such as bolt head from loose bumper or some other loosened metal was forced against tire while driving. Also caused by spinning wheels on rough ground.
Cut through shoulder			Small, sharp clean cut in shoulder area.	Striking small sharp object with enough force to drive it into tire. Often occurs far down on sidewall.
Cut through tread			Small, sharp clean cut across tread area.	Usually caused by sharp stones or wedgelike splinters of glass.
Cracking between ribs of tread			Small cracks around tire between tread.	Considered a natural condition. Safe to continue tire in service since cracks will not grow larger.

Channel cracking		Long cracks between ribs of tread.	Usually seen at more than one point. Condition quite rare. Check with your dealer.
Sidewall cracking		Long, circumferential sidewall crack.	Condition is quite rare. There was probably an improper flow of rubber in the mold during vulcanization. Does not affect tire service. Can be removed by light buffing.
Sidewall weather cracks	X	Many small cracks on sidewall.	Improper stationary storage of tire or vehicle. Often happens to spare tire not rotated. Continue in service until cracking becomes so severe, cord body is exposed.
Radial cracks on sidewall and shoulder	X	Small cracks perpendicular to sidewall and extending to shoulder.	Rubber fatigue or improper inflation. Check with your dealer.
Outside circumferential cracks at shoulder		Several small cracks in shoulder area. Also long cracks running around tire circumference where shoulder meets sidewall.	Condition is quite rare. Indicates an improper union between sidewall rubber and shoulder rubber. Check with your dealer.
Defective sidewall splice		Long vertical splice starting at bottom of shoulder and running into sidewall. Edges of splice are smooth.	Condition is quite rare. Check with your dealer.
Open tread splice		Appears as a severe cut straight across the tread. A cut of this size, though, would have penetrated the tire completely.	Condition is quite rare. Check with your dealer.
Underinflation wear	X	Tread worn down excessively on both sides of tire between tread center and tread edges.	Underinflation.
Overinflation wear	X	Center ribs of tread are worn down considerably more than outer ribs.	Overinflation.
Spotty wear	X	Wear spots over the entire tire.	Failure to rotate tires.
One-sided wear	X	Wear evident on one side only. Could be left or right, depending on misadjustment.	Improper caster or improper camber of front wheels.
Misalignment wear	X	Feathered edges of frayed rubber along each rib of tread.	Toe-in or toe-out. Only a comparatively few miles of driving with this condition can cause severe tire damage.
Large, worn tread area	X	Large area badly worn.	Out-of-round brake drum or brakes out of adjustment. Only half the tire does all the work in braking.
Damaged bead area	X	Appears as if great friction had been applied to bead area.	Bent, defective, or improper-size rim.
Broken bead	X	Bead becomes lodged in rim well. Air pressure forces bead up on rim ledge with such impact that the bead wires are broken. Tire with a broken bead will not stay on the wheel.	Not using soap solution or recommended tire lubricant when mounting tire on rim.
Break on sidewall	X	Long jagged break at shoulder of tire.	Rim flange crushed and pinched tire sidewall against a curb or similar obstruction.
Break on sidewall	X	Long jagged horizontal break well down on sidewall and often surrounded by chafe marks.	Tire scuffed against curb or similar obstruction.

titles, movies

How to backlight movie titles

BY JAMES R. OSWALD

This double-exposure technique gives professional-looking titles easily

A progression title is made by moving an opaque card over the rear-illuminated title card during the filming (above). The image produced comes out superimposed on a previously shot scene, as shown below

■ OF THE MANY clever title effects to come from Hollywood, one of the most popular is superimposition, wherein the title copy is "wiped" over an action background. While titles of this type require that two separate exposures be made—one for the background scene and one for the title copy itself—if the title is backlighted while it is shot, a sharper, better-defined image results

on the movie film. The common practice of shooting the title copy against a dull black surface and lighted from the front results in stray light reflections which tend to produce a halo effect around each letter.

In the backlighting process, the title card becomes a "stencil" so to speak, which permits the light to pass and sharply define the lettering. Of course to produce a title card, the copy is prepared in the normal manner by mounting black lettering on a white surface and making a copy negative of it by photographing it with a 4 x 5 press-type camera. The resulting negative is your transparent title card.

To backlight the title card you need to make a light box as detailed. This is nothing more than a ready-made utility box measuring 4 x 5 x 6 in. which can be purchased at radio and electronic supply houses. The front cover of the box is replaced with a piece of opaque diffusing glass held in place with masking tape. The back cover is drilled to provide ventilation for a 10-30-watt lamp mounted inside. The copy negative is taped to the front of the diffusing glass. Use tabs of black masking tape to hold it in place.

In use, the light box is propped up so it is centered with the lens of the movie camera. Shooting is done in a darkened room to kill any stray light reflection off the glass. Wiping of the title is done during the actual filming by holding a card over the full title and slowly moving it from left to right. In the example shown in the frame sequence across the bottom of these pages, an L-card is used so that the upper part of the title is disclosed first, then the lower half. Where an action background scene is not desired, only one exposure need be made with no need to rewind the film.

See also: movies, sound; tripods; underwater camera cases.

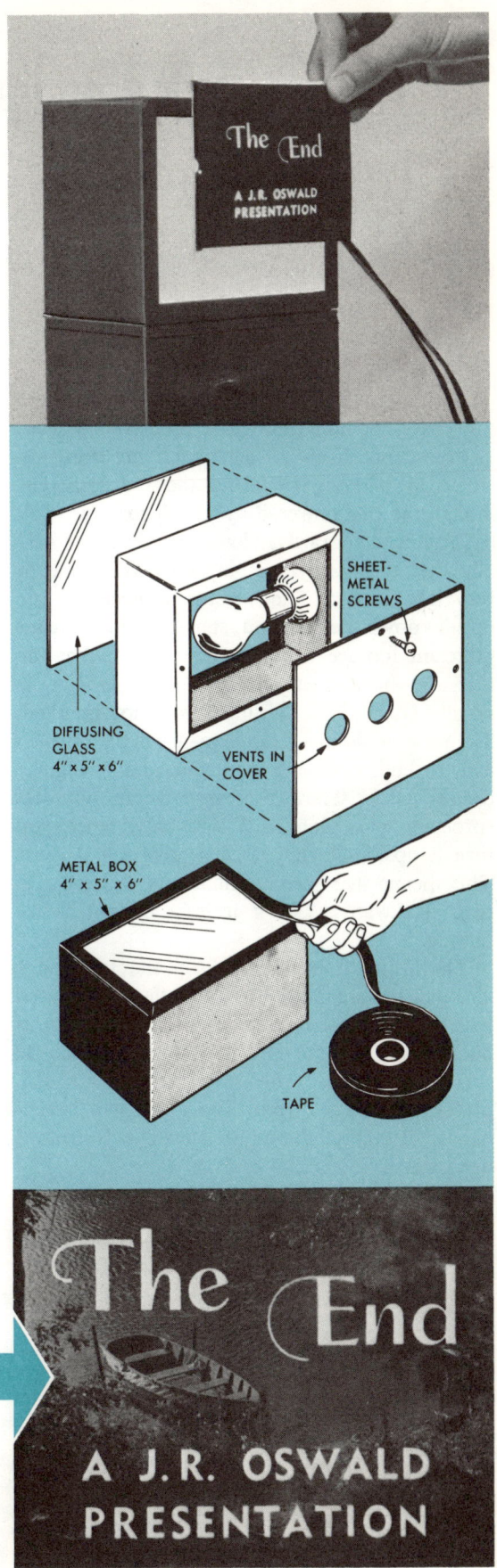

Titling tricks add appeal to home movies

BY J. R. OSWALD

■ THE INGENIOUS TITLING DEVICES shown here can give your home movies a professional look.

You're not likely to encounter any difficulty either in building or using these accessories, though the one powered by the electric fan may baffle you temporarily. How can you make certain that the dizzily spinning title will come to rest right side up? The secret is to place the title upside-down before you start shooting. After sufficient footage has been exposed so that the title will have enough screen time, the fan is switched on and the whirling title is photographed. The processed film of the sequence is then turned end for end, reversing the action and giving the desired effect. Since processed 8-mm film has sprocket holes along one side only, when you turn it upside-down you must also flip it over. This means that your original title will have to read backwards. Check it in a mirror before filming.

The whirling background on the next page gives an eerie, almost hypnotic effect. It is used with superimposed titles, where the camera is backwound and the film is double-exposed. Be sure that the disk revolves at a very slow speed, preferably about 5 rpm. The effect will be enhanced if you let the motor start slowly from a dead stop.

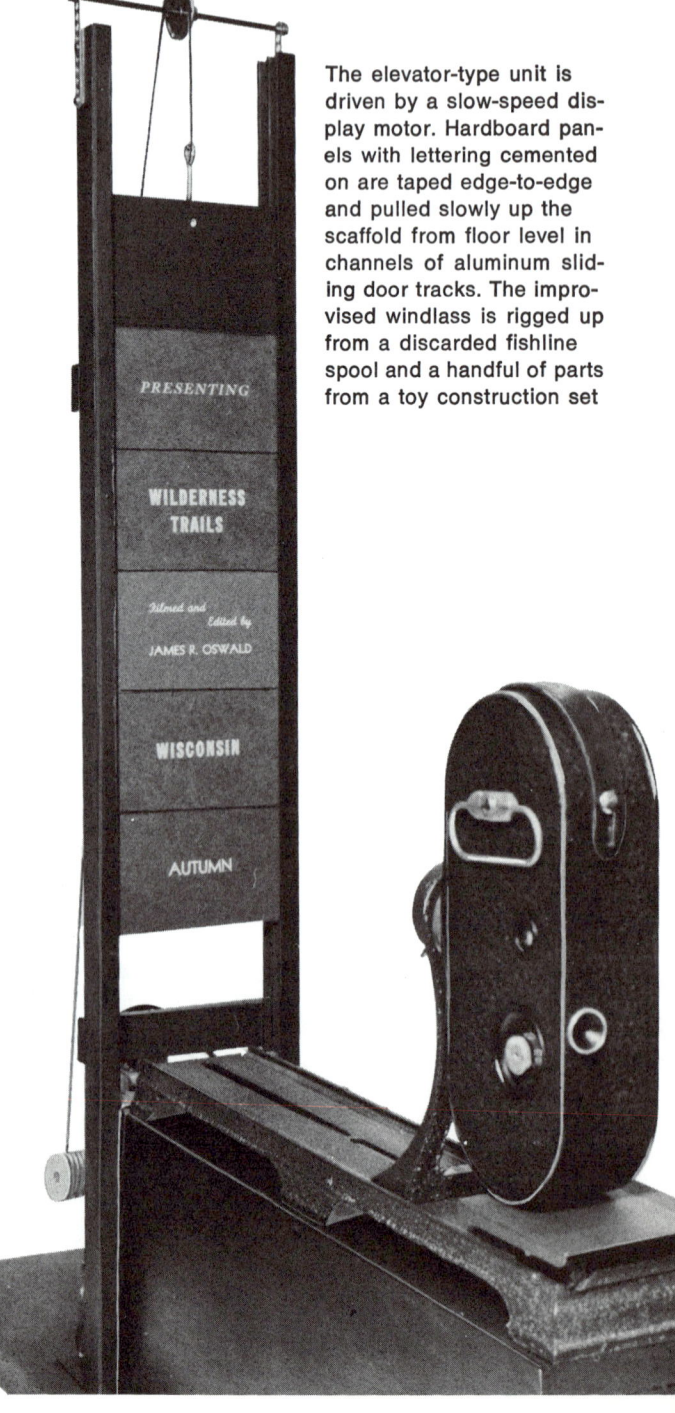

The elevator-type unit is driven by a slow-speed display motor. Hardboard panels with lettering cemented on are taped edge-to-edge and pulled slowly up the scaffold from floor level in channels of aluminum sliding door tracks. The improvised windlass is rigged up from a discarded fishline spool and a handful of parts from a toy construction set

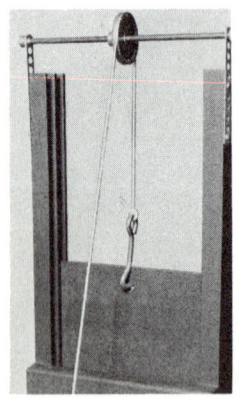 

 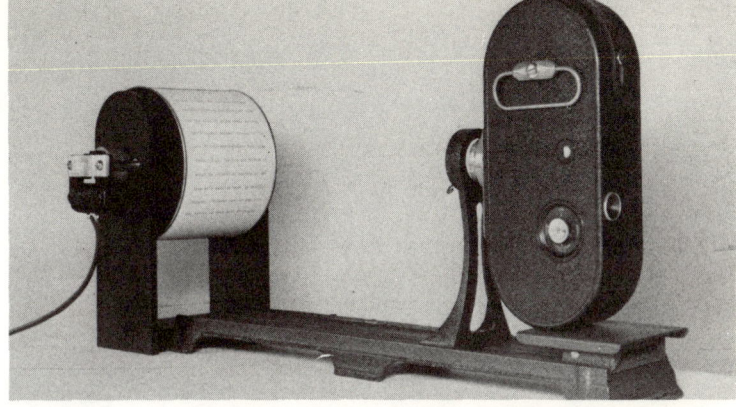

Long titles are smoothly presented through the use of a revolving drum. This is simply a tobacco can turning on an axle consisting of two stovebolts. One bolt is placed through the cover and the other through the bottom. A radio-type shaft coupling permits joining the axle to a small 4-rpm motor. The title is then typed or lettered on a sheet of paper which is taped to the drum

An intriguing background for superimposed titles is provided by a slowly revolving disk painted with a spiral design. A plastic coupling connects the disk to a 5-rpm motor. The disk, background and motor may be propped in front of the camera in any convenient way, but the titling stand shown assures proper camera alignment. An interesting effect can be produced by combining this technique with the one shown below

Attach a wooden disk to flattened fan blades with flatheaded bolts or screws so as to provide a flush mounting surface for the title. Rubber cement or a similar adhesive permitting easy removal may be used to attach the title letters to the disk. The auxiliary fan base fits on the titler track to keep the copy and the camera in perfect alignment. It is necessary to mount the title upside-down and backwards as already explained

 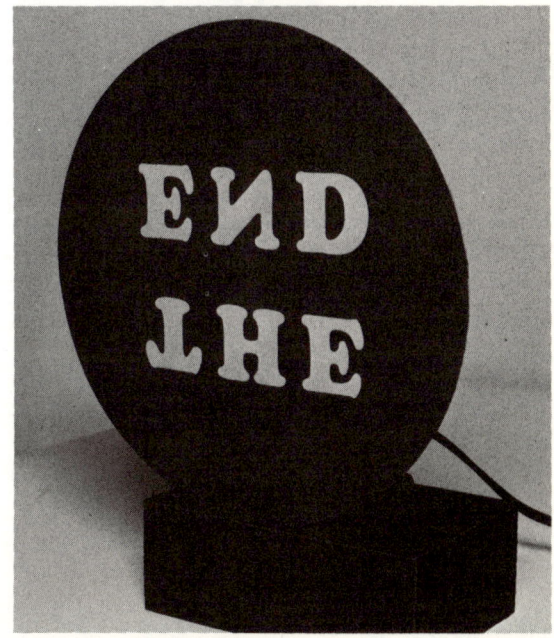

toasters

How to fix a toaster

BY JOHN PENNINGTON

On that morning when you insert
your usual two slices of bread
in the toaster
and nothing happens,
get a brush, screwdriver and wrench.
Fixing could be quite simple

■ ALL GOOD TOASTERS, automatic or not, are pretty tough gadgets and quite simple in construction and assembly, but there are certain parts that just won't take careless, rough handling or poking with a screwdriver, so take it easy when you turn your toaster upside down and begin taking things apart. Or maybe you don't turn it upside down; some toasters come apart right side up. Find out before you pull or pry too hard on something that you think should come loose.

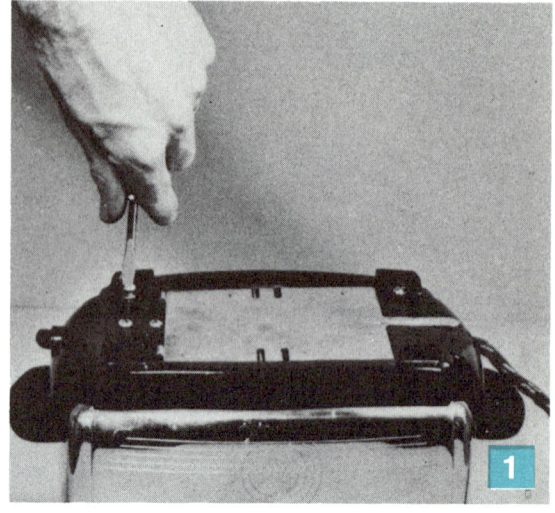

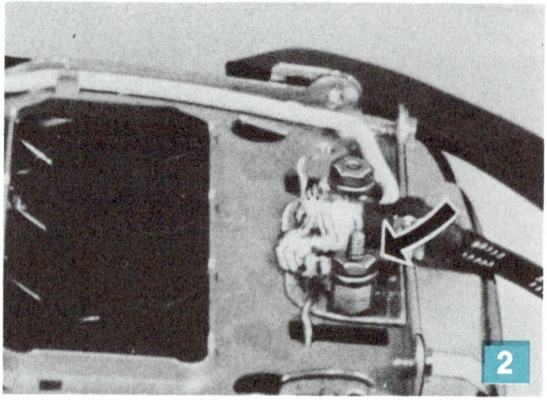

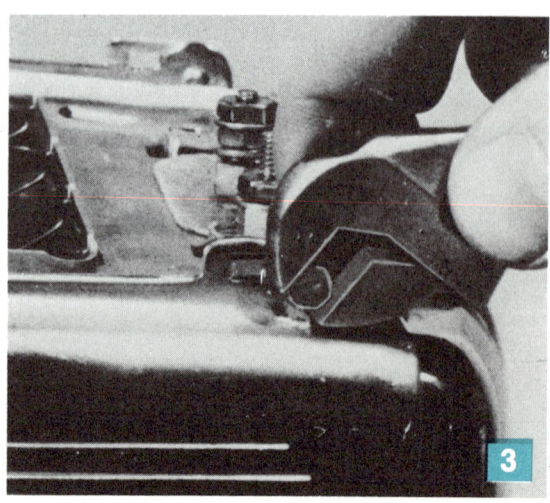

First of all, open or pull out the crumb tray and clean out everything that you can reach with a small brush, Fig. 4. When you get the bottom off, Fig. 1, take a close look at the terminals; the arrow in Fig. 2 shows these on a typical automatic toaster. Check closely for loose terminals and inspect every inch of the wires for frayed insulation.

In order to get at the operating mechanism and elements you generally have to remove the outer shell of the toaster. On the toaster pictured you do this with a wrench on small nuts and screws at the corners, Fig. 3. Again the caution —take it easy with that wrench!

When you've taken off the outer protective shell, or housing, you are likely to see something like that pictured in Fig. 5, with the arrow pointing out the thermostat and the mechanism that controls the length of the toasting cycle. These are the critical operative parts, and they should be examined closely for defects. Usually you'll find the points coated with a carbonlike deposit and possibly rather deeply pitted. If you see the latter condition, it probably will be advisable to replace the entire control unit. Otherwise, give the points a thorough cleaning.

A light (very light) touch of fine sandpaper may restore the points to working condition, at least for a time.

Heating elements can become weak with age before they actually burn out and quit for good. Look them over carefully; replacement of any that appear doubtful will pay off in the end, for if any or all of them are nearing the end of a useful life, they are likely to go at any time. Loosen the electrical connections to the elements first, then loosen the screws that hold the elements as in Fig. 6. Be careful not to damage hex heads, strip threads or bend any parts in this operation. Replace new elements in reverse order. While you have the toaster apart, clean everything thoroughly before reassembling in the reverse order.

See also: appliances; blenders, electric; clothes dryers, electric; coffeemakers; electrical wiring; floor polishers; guarantees; irons; mixers, food; testers, electric.

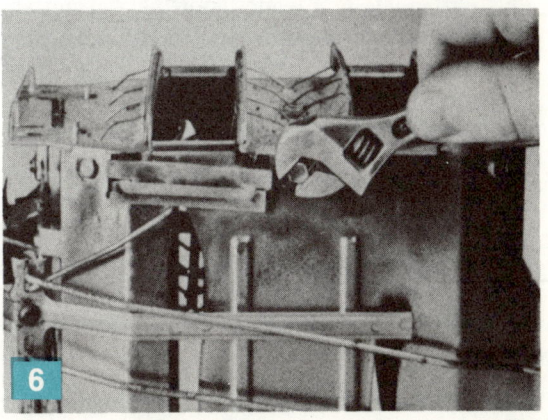

2705

toboggan

Build a toboggan for family fun

BY MANLY BANISTER

If there's an inviting hillside nearby, you'll want to add this toboggan to your family's collection of winter sports equipment. It'll go like lightning

Stack-sawing the bending caul (below) can be done on a bandsaw or by hand, using a common keyhole saw. After resawing the stock, sand the slats (photo on the opposite page) and runners to remove the saw marks. Keep the thickness uniform

■ THERE'S NOTHING LIKE a toboggan for family fun. Large enough for several members to climb aboard, a toboggan lets mom, dad and the kids participate in a winter sport as a group and brings about a togetherness which youngsters truly enjoy. Unlike a sled with runners, a toboggan rides the top of the snow with lightning speed and the added weight of four or five only seems to make it go faster.

Fun actually starts with the building of the toboggan since it involves the interesting job of bending wood. Here the ends of the four slats

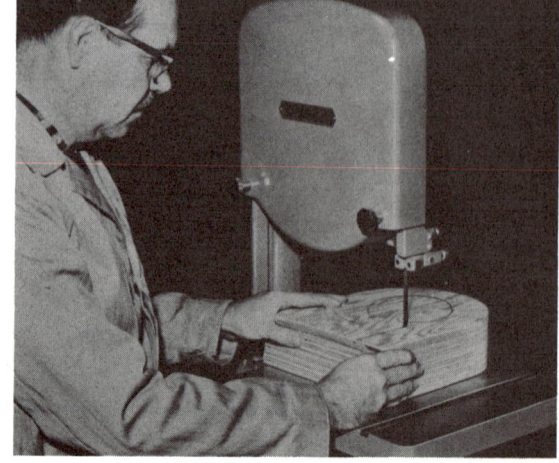

toggle bolts: see fasteners

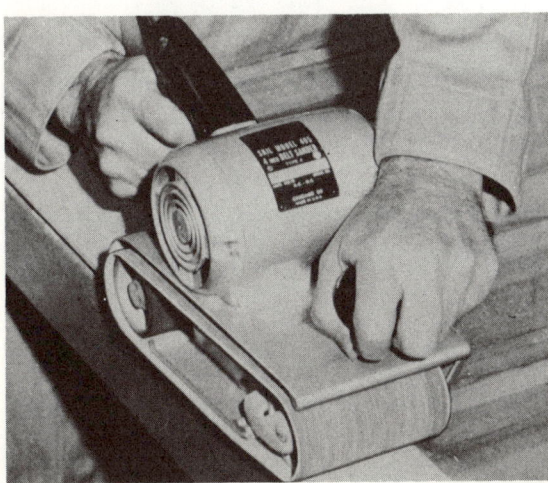

Laugh at this kooky setup if you like but it can do the bending job required on the toboggan slats and runners. Both need to be boiled from 1½ to 2 hours. Be sure to keep water level up during boiling

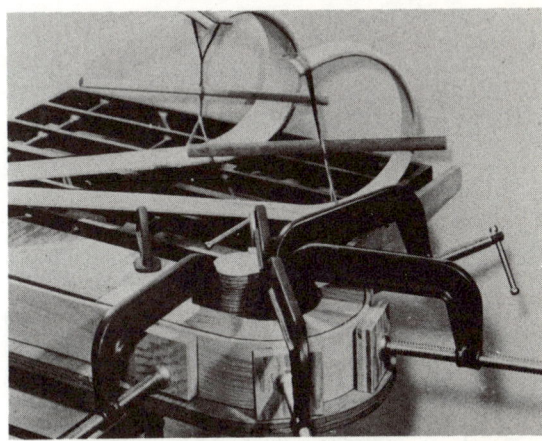

This photo shows how slats and runners are clamped in place on the bending caul. Note the position of the clamps, and note also how the finished bends look. See text for instructions on making the caul

New, free-cutting wood rasps speed up the job of making the crossbars. Use white oak or ash for the bars. Make the crossbars before you begin the bending operation so that you're ready to assemble when bending is complete

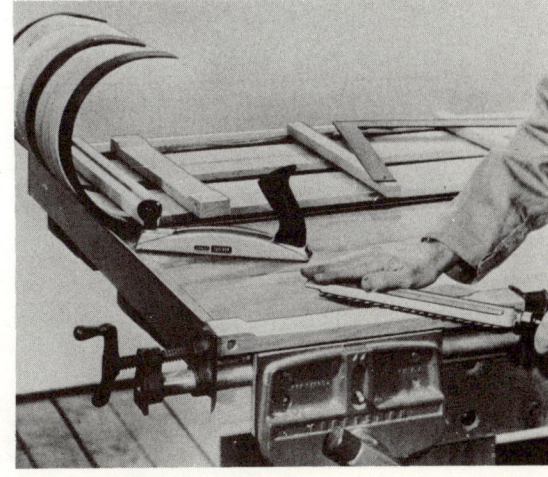

2707

toboggan

Rounding over the edges of slats and runners is quickly done with a router-shaper or sanding block

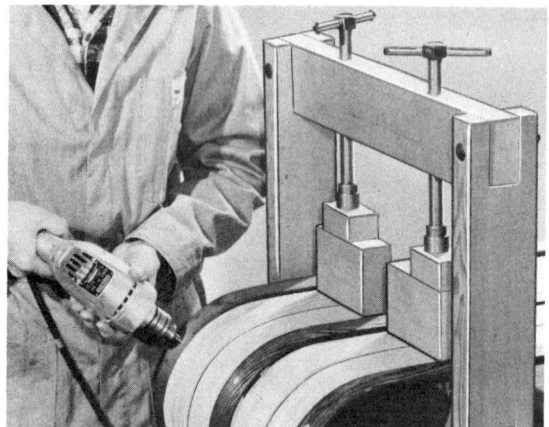

Drill and countersink the holes for screws holding the crossbars. Screwheads should be slightly below flush

and three runners are first made pliable by boiling in water and then bending and clamping around a form to dry. After the slats and runners are bent, it's a simple job of fastening them side by side to crossbars which in turn carry the stirrups that anchor the grab ropes. As for length, your toboggan can be made whatever length you wish—remembering that when it comes to carrying, it is as far back up the hill as it is down.

Before you do any boiling and bending, however, you'll need a bending caul, or form, made from a 2 x 3 and four pieces of ¾-in. plywood as in Fig. 1. Cut the plywood pieces oversize, stack them with glue on the joining faces and, when dry, saw to contour as shown in the lower right-hand photo on page 2706. The surfaces that take the slats and runners should be sanded to fine smoothness. Then assemble by screwing the two members to a ¾-in. plywood base as in Fig. 1, making sure that the 2 x 3 is lined up with the straight extension of the plywood caul. Now, note the difference in thickness between the runners and slats and that the runners are tapered from ⅜ to 3/16 in. at the ends that are to be bent. Have these items as well as the crossbars, or cleats, made and at hand. Use white oak or ash for crossbars, Fig. 2. With all this done, you're ready for bending.

White ash is also the best wood for both the

Here's a convenient way of holding runners and slats for assembly. The veneer-press clamps are homemade

2708

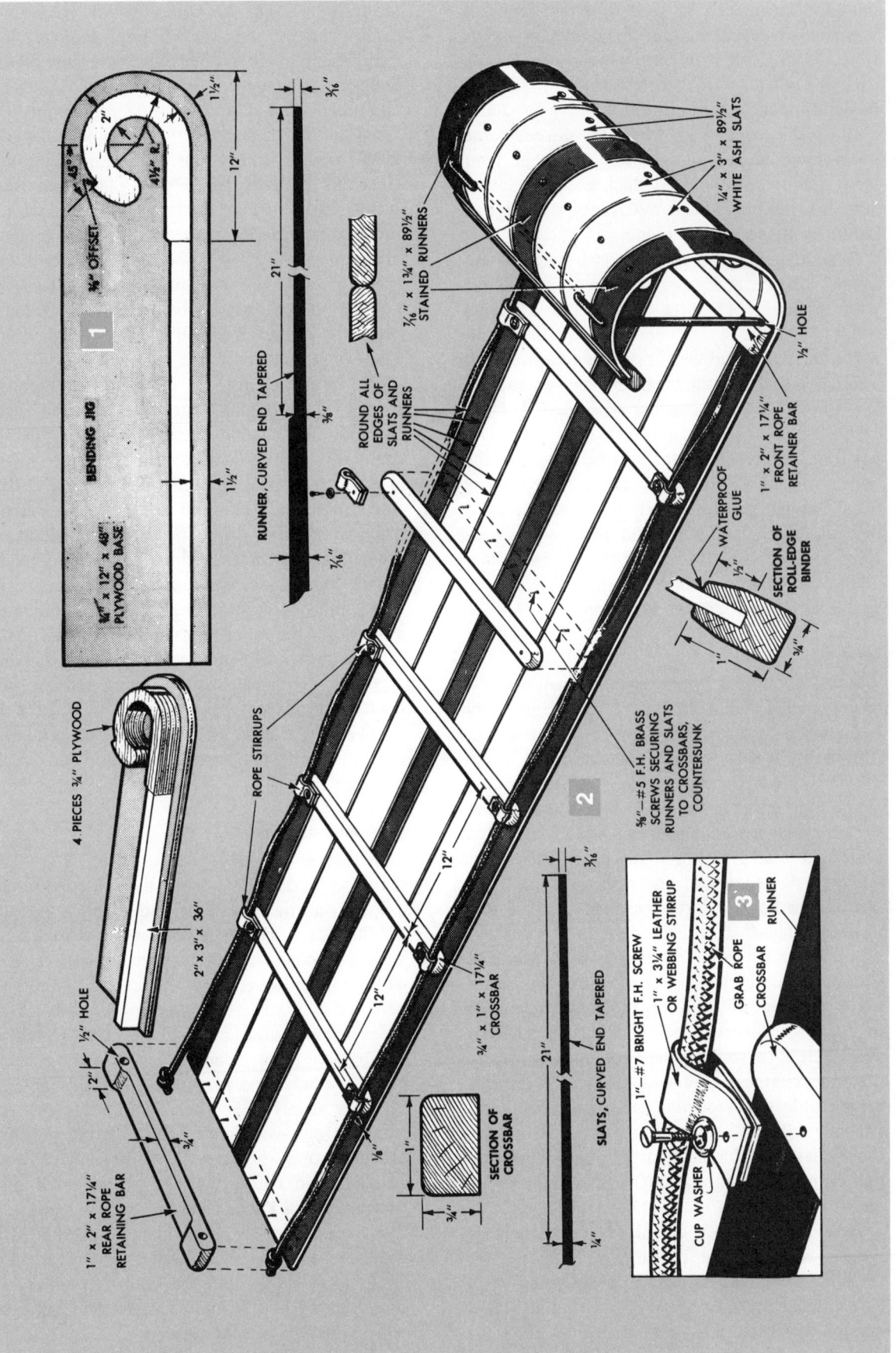

slats and runners. You need three runners and four slats. The runners are 7/16 in. thick; the slats 1/4 in. Most dealers in hard woods can supply what is known as "ski stock," which is selected, straight-grained air-dried white ash 1 in. (also 1 1/4 in.) thick and 4 in. wide. The pieces come 96 in. long. These you can easily resaw on your table saw to the required thicknesses. Allow a little for finishing the sawed faces with a belt sander or a sharp hand plane.

After the slats and runners have been sawed, sanded smooth and tapered at one end, fill the wash boiler about three-fourths full of clean water. Place the tapered end of one slat or runner in the boiler and weight it. Bring the water to a rolling boil and in the meantime heat an equivalent amount of water in other containers. It takes 1 1/2 to 2 hours of boiling to soften the wood and you'll need to replenish the original supply in the boiler, once, and perhaps twice. Keep close watch on the process for if the container boils dry, the wood will be ruined for the purpose. Keep the boiler filled to about the original level, adding only the boiling water from the supply container to maintain the temperature.

bending

After about 1 1/2 hours make a bending test of the tapered end of the runner. If it yields fairly easily when bent over the edge of the bench top, it probably is safe to bend over the caul. To do this you place the tapered end of the runner against the offset in the caul, Fig. 1, and clamp in place with a C-clamp, using a block of wood under the clamp pad. At this point make sure you have the runner in line with the caul. Then bend a few degrees farther around the caul and place another C-clamp. Proceed in this fashion clamp by clamp until the bend is complete. The clamps should be spaced as shown in the center photo on page 2707. Keep the runner clamped in place for 24 hours before releasing it. Even then there'll be some springback, so you tourniquet the bent ends by wrapping three or four turns of fairly heavy twine around the bend and twisting tight with a length of dowel. Bent ends tourniqueted in this fashion are also pictured in the center photo on page 2707. And that's it, for one runner or slat.

You can only work one slat or one runner at a time with the one bending caul, or jig. By doubling the thickness of the jig you could work two runners or two slats, given clamps large enough to reach. Or—and here's an idea for someone who wishes to make more than one toboggan, possibly for sale—if you have seven cauls (four for slats and three for runners), and a sufficient number of clamps, you can bend a complete toboggan in one operation. Using this equipment tied in with the clamping units pictured in the center and lower photos on page 2708, you're in business. The latter will hold slats and runners securely in place and make quick, easy work of the assembly. But without this equipment you can make two bar, or cross, clamps using four pieces of 2 x 2 hardwood. One piece of each pair has one face planed slightly convex so that when you clamp each pair in place the convex face will exert pressure equally throughout the length.

Assemble as in Fig. 2, beginning with the front rope-retaining bar. Drill screw holes through the slats and runners from the underside (with the curved ends overhanging the end of the bench as in the center photo, page 2708) and countersink the holes so that the screwheads are just slightly below flush with the surface. Spread a line of resorcinol (waterproof) glue on the joining face of the retainer bar and screw in place, using flathead brass screws as indicated. Proceed in the same way with all the bars, using your improvised clamps to hold the slats tightly together and in line while locating and screwing each bar in place.

The bars are spaced 12 in. apart on centers as indicated, with one screw being used for attaching each slot.

rope and stirrups

With the assembly at this stage, all that remains to be done is to make the roll-edge binder strip, install the grab rope and stirrups, and finish the wood. The edge binder is a strip shaped as in the sectional view, and grooved 3/16 x 1/4 in. This is forced over the curved ends of the runners as in Fig. 2. Use glue in the joint. Drill holes for the grab rope in the curved ends of the outside runners and adjacent slats as indicated. Attach rope stirrups to the ends of each crossbar as in Fig. 3. Then tie a knot in one end of the rope—you'll need about 15 ft. of polyethylene rope—and pass it through the stirrups and holes in the curved end as indicated. Pull tight and tie a knot in the finish end.

If desired, the three runners can be stained as indicated and the slats finished in natural color. Or you can finish both slats and runners in natural color by first applying a sealer and following with two coats of spar varnish.

See also: skiing; sleds; snow fort.

clever ideas

Make a stand for your wife's cookbook by mounting two coat hooks on a scrap of wide board. This also makes a good copy holder for use with a typewriter. Just slip a cardboard backing into the hooks and rest the book or copy against it.

Avoid marring a smooth wood surface with hammer marks by using a sheet-metal nailing shield. Notch one end of a metal strip, as shown, then bend the other end for a handle. Finish driving the nails the rest of the way home with a nailset.

Instant coffee and other products packed in jars will often be almost used up before you notice it because the label conceals the contents. Avoid this by cutting a narrow strip out of the label on the jar so you can see the level of the contents.

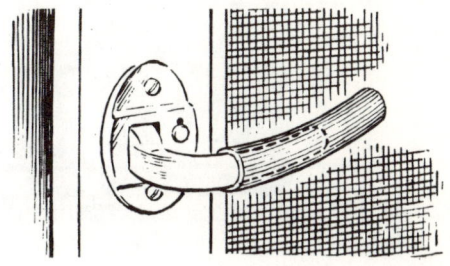

Storm door handles often catch on your coat sleeves, especially when you're trying to slip out the door with both arms full. To avoid torn sleeves, push a length of rubber tubing over the end of the handle to serve as a shield against catching sleeves.

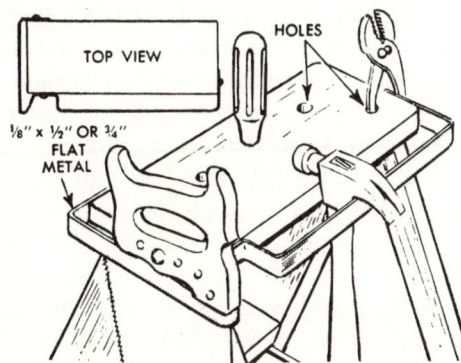

Tool holders added to the top of your stepladder will save climbing down every few minutes to get the right tool. Make them as shown, but don't drill a great number of holes in the top and legs of the ladder or you may weaken it.

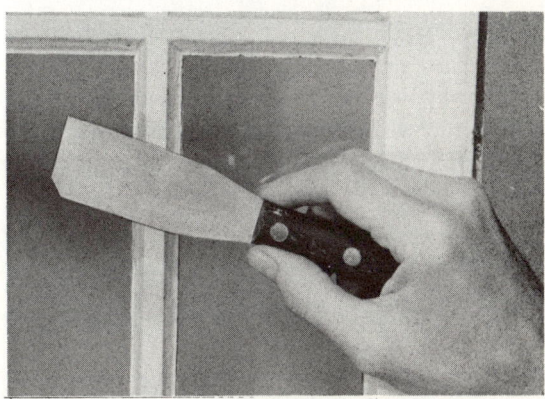

For neater glazing, grind off one corner of your putty knife to make a 45-deg. angle with the end. Run this edge into a corner after you have applied the putty and you'll produce a perfect corner joint between the putty bevels.

toolpost grinder

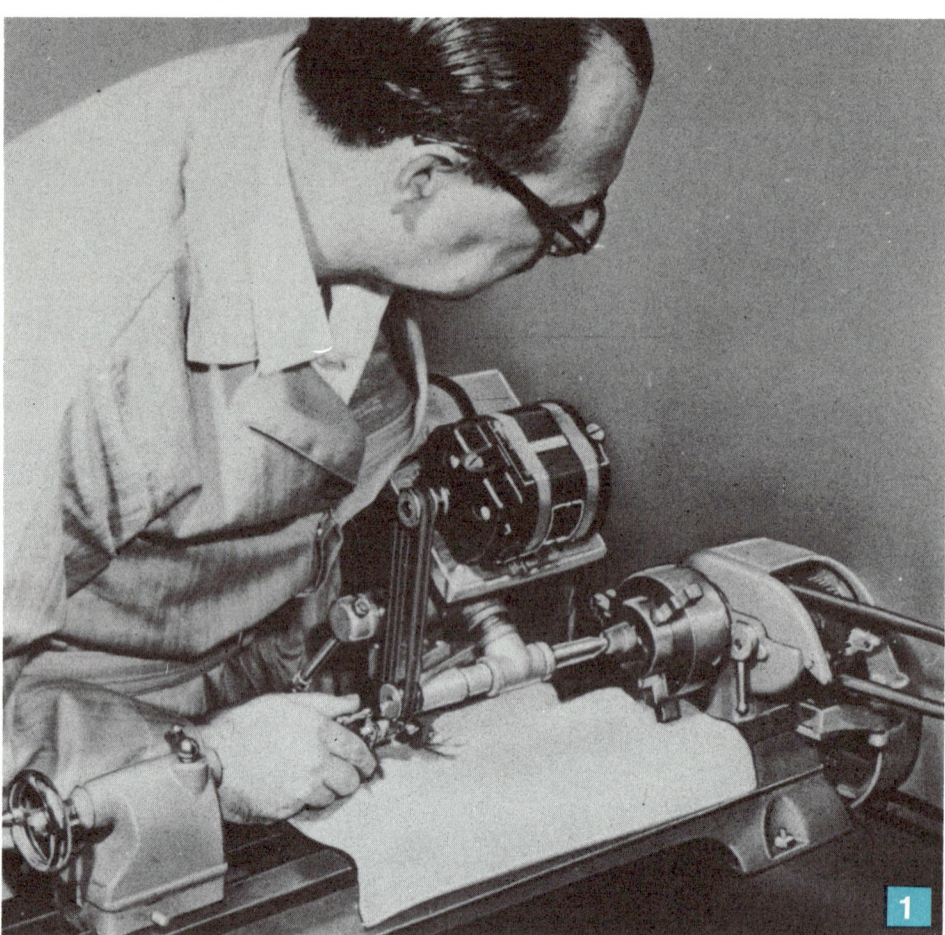

Easy to make in your shop from stock parts available anywhere, this grinder beats other finishing techniques

Toolpost grinder does a mirror-bright job

■ THAT MIRROR-BRIGHT finish you see inside and out on small metal parts designed to fit together with precision usually is done in a lathe with a toolpost grinder. In the toolpost-grinder setup, both the wheel and the work are rotated simultaneously in opposite directions, a procedure that produces a finish on metals that just can't be equaled by any other common finishing process.

The frame of the small toolpost grinder pictured in Fig. 1 is made from ordinary steel pipe fittings and obviously does not have the refinements of the precisely made commercial units. But if care is used in selecting, machining and assembling the parts, it will do very accurate work which is acceptable for all practical purposes. Figs. 2 through 5 show how the unit is put together. The motor on the original grinder pictured in use on a 6-in. lathe in Fig. 1 is a type that was salvaged from an office machine. It came with a detachable motor base shown in the pulled-apart view, Fig. 3. Any motor of similar size and power (about $1/15$ hp.) of the universal type having a speed of 3000 to 5000 rpm will serve the purpose very well. Alter the base, Fig. 3, to suit.

Before you get into the construction there are several points to be noted. Common steel pipe is made with allowable variations in inside and outside dimensions. This can mean that where an assembly of pipe or fittings like that in Fig. 3 is called for, you may not end up with precisely the dimensions you plan on. As an example of what to avoid, note the wheel-spindle as-

2712

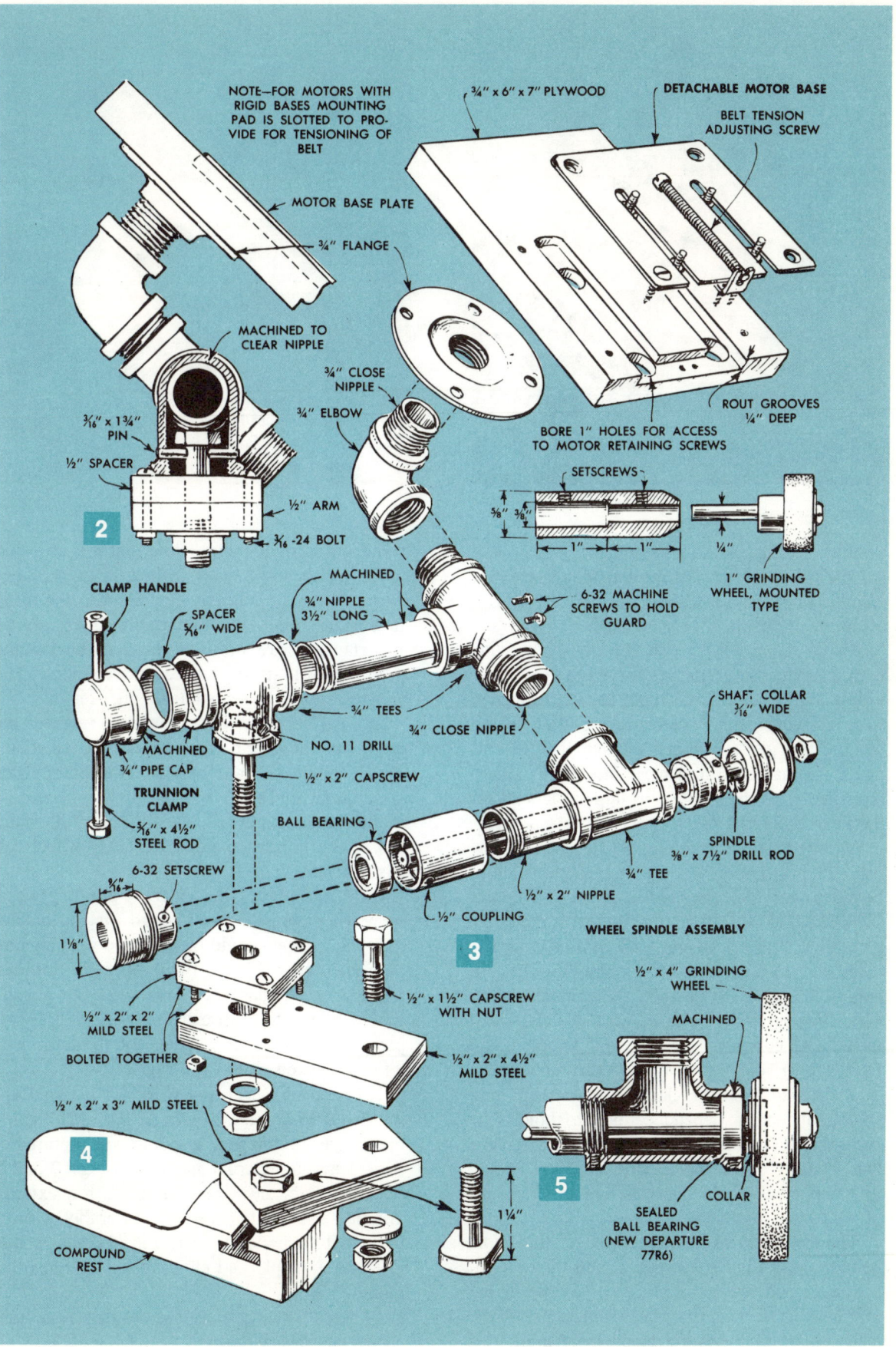

toolpost grinder

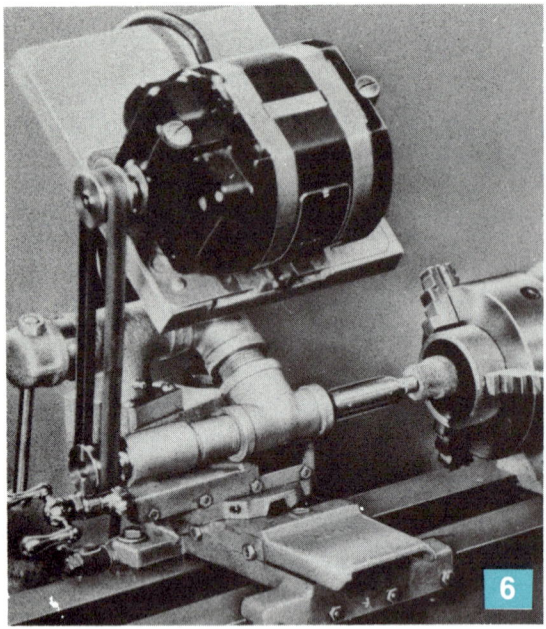

sembly in Fig. 3. The overall length of the spindle is given as 7½ in. but don't cut the spindle to length until you have made a trial assembly of the pipe-fitting housing.

Also note in Fig. 3 that the pivot, or trunnion, carrying the frame assembly is a ¾-in. pipe nipple 3½ in. long. The nipple passes through a ¾-in. tee which serves as a bearing after boring out the threads. It's important that the tee and nipple be machined to a close fit. The accuracy and rigidity of the whole unit largely depend on the fit of these two parts.

As will be seen from Fig. 4, the grinder adjusts for position on a two-part linkage which is bolted to the toolpost saddle, or boss. This arrangement, worked in conjunction with the trunnion, Fig. 3, gives a universal motion and enables you to align the grinder spindle with the axis of the lathe or position the spindle at any desired angle with the lathe centers. The trunnion clamp consists of a pipe cap, a handle made from a ¼ or 5/16-in. steel rod and two nuts, and a spacer which gives the clamp a "camming" bite so that it can be depended upon to hold. The flanged ends of the tees are machined to give a true bearing when the machined flange of the pipe cap is tightened against the spacer, the edges of which are machined.

The spindle turns on sealed ball bearings, one being mounted in the tee, Fig. 5, and the other in the outer end of the coupling as you see in the pulled-apart view of the wheel-spindle assembly. The spindle pulley is machined from mild steel round 1¼ in. in diameter. Note that it is crowned and has two low flanges with a 9/16-in. face between. A motor pulley is machined to the same dimensions. Only the dimensions given are of importance. Care must be used in boring the ball-bearing seats in the tee and coupling. The bearings should be seated in a light, press fit.

Internal grinding, Figs. 1 and 6, requires the use of mounted grinding wheels of small diameter, having ¼ or 1/8-in. arbors. The center right-hand detail in Fig. 3 shows how to machine a counterbored chuck which slips over the outer end of the grinder spindle, replacing wheel collars and nut.

In all the photos the external grinding wheel is shown without a metal guard for clarity. For safety the wheel should be provided with a guard assembled as in Fig. 8. If the operator does not regularly wear glasses, a face shield or goggles should be worn to protect the eyes. And always protect the ways and carriage of the lathe with a tightly woven cloth as in Fig. 1.

Rotation of wheel and work for external and internal grinding are shown in Fig. 10. Typical operations of internal grinding are pictured in Figs. 1 and 6, external grinding in Figs. 7 and 9.

Each time the wheel is used for external grinding it must be dressed, preferably with an industrial-diamond dresser. Fig. 11 shows how to make a simple and effective holder for a diamond dresser.

See also: grinding; lathe accessories; lathe techniques; tumbling machines.

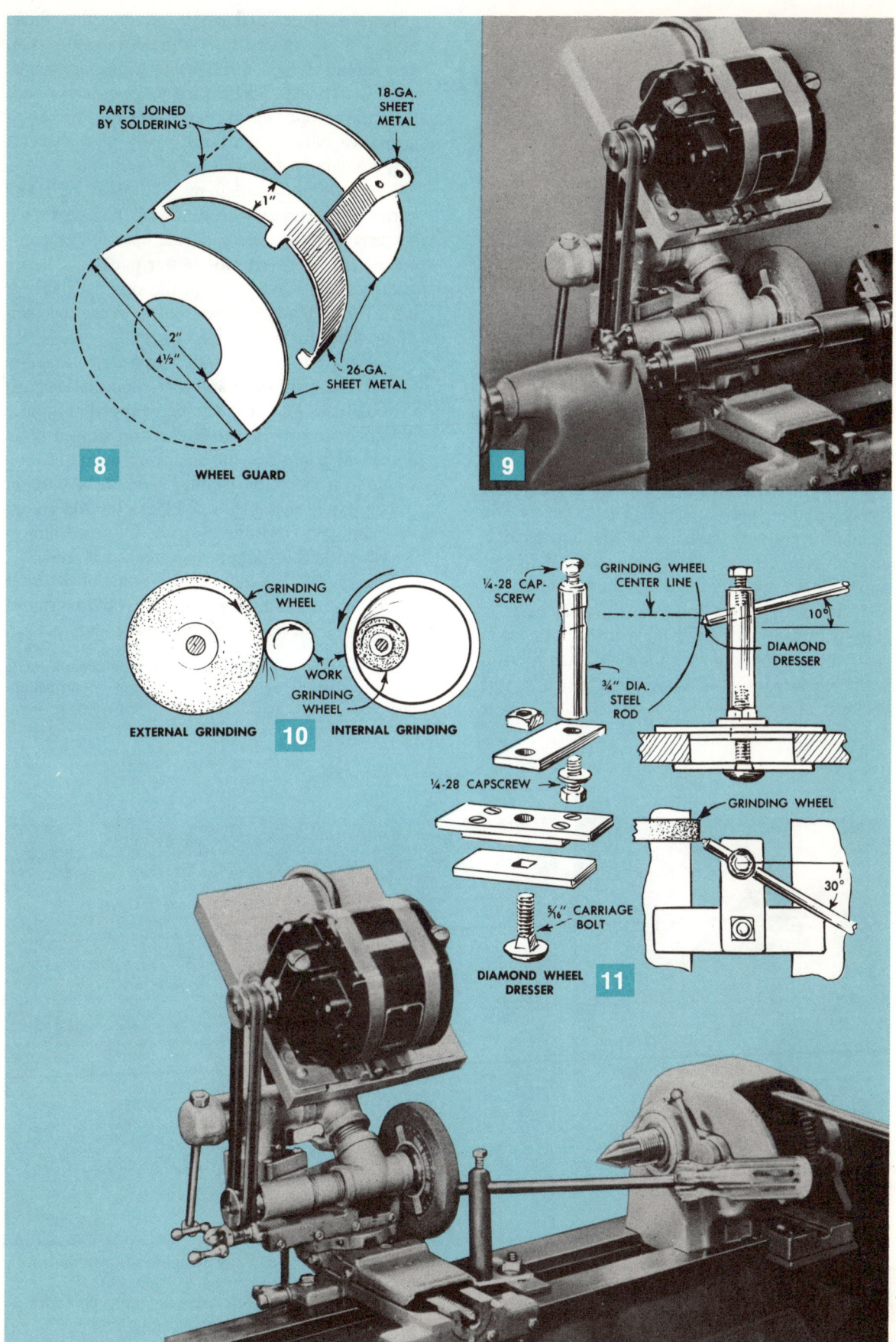

tools, boat

Stow-aboard tool kit for outboards

BY HENRY B. NOTROM

■ IT'S BOUND TO HAPPEN. No matter how carefully you maintain your motor, something is almost sure to go haywire when you're out on the water, even if it's only a sheared pin. And when this occurs, you ought to have enough tools aboard to make on-the-spot repairs that will get you home.

Of course your kit needn't include everything listed on the opposite page. The point is you should have a well-thought-out selection of tools aboard your boat at all times, instead of relying on an old screwdriver and an extra shear pin.

A fiberglass tackle box makes a great place to stow your tools. It's light, inexpensive and won't rust. If you want to do the job right, lash it down with shock cord in a convenient place in the cockpit.

Another thing to keep in mind is that those tools will be exposed to a lot more moisture than they would if they were sitting in the drawer of your workbench, so be sure to give each one a thin coat of light oil to prevent rusting. For extra insurance, wrap each individually in a sheet of that clinging-type plastic wrap.

Keep all the small items like shear pins and cotter pins in a plastic sandwich bag so they'll be easy to find. Most marine sparkplugs come encased in a waterproof blister pack, and it's a good idea to leave them in the original package until you're ready to install them. Wrap the fuel-pump diaphragm in plastic wrap.

There are two items which aren't mentioned in the list—a spare prop and a first-aid kit designed for boat use. The prop can be wrapped in a piece of canvas to protect the blades and stowed in an underseat compartment or at any other location where you won't be tripping over it. A number of companies make storage blocks to hold an extra prop, and since these can be mounted almost anywhere in the cockpit, you might try one.

Finally, the first-aid kit. Like some of the tools listed, you may never use it, but you'd be out of luck if you did need it and it wasn't aboard.

See also: boat repair; carburetors, outboard; magnetos, outboard; outboard motors, repair; propellers, boat; sparkplugs, marine.

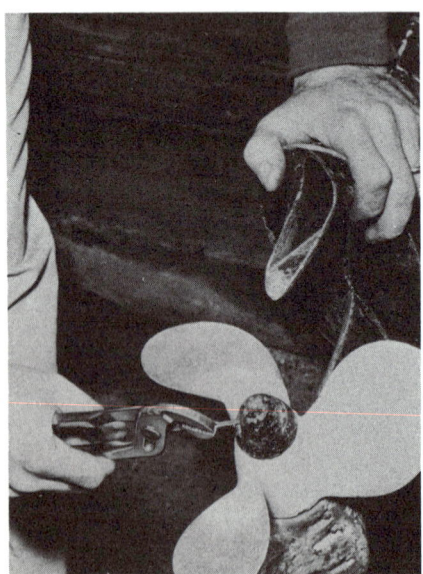

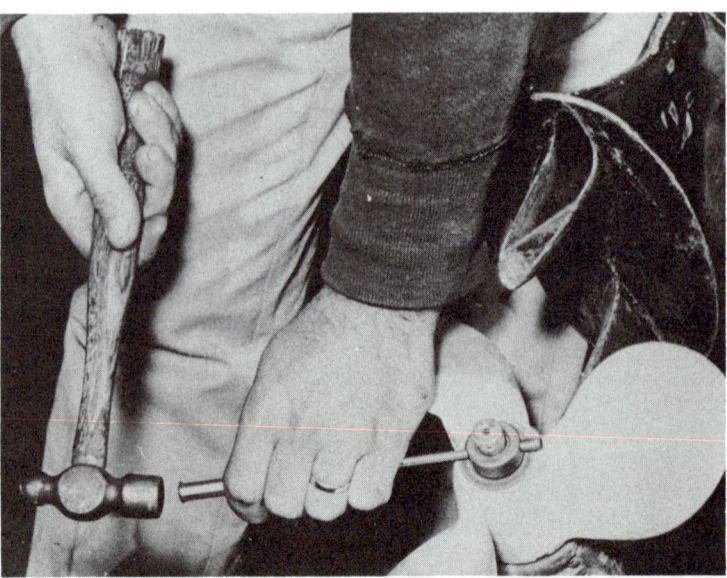

Changing a prop isn't any complicated mechanical operation, but it can be next to impossible if you don't have those few necessary tools on board. If you don't believe it, try to change a prop sometime with your bare hands

tools, garden: see garden tools
tools, power: see power tool storage

On-board troubleshooting chart

Trouble	Probable Cause	Cure	Trouble	Probable Cause	Cure
Plenty of revs but no push	A sheared pin	Replace the pin	Engine floods and won't start, or starts but stalls (check for a wet plug)	Damaged fuel-pump diaphragm	Remove housing cover, replace diaphragm
Wheel moves but the boat won't steer	Steering line snapped	Splice the line with No. 16 wire		Choke stuck closed	Open it by hand
Engine isn't getting fuel	No fuel in tank	Fill the tank		Carburetor float stuck	Tap float chamber sharply with handle of screwdriver
	Loose tank cap	Tighten the cap	Engine isn't getting spark (ground plug against head and rev engine; if it's getting spark, you'll hear it snapping)	Plugs shot	Replace
	Fuel valve closed	Open it		Break in plug wire	Tape the break
	Kink in fuel line	Straighten the line		Corrosion on plug terminals or battery posts and terminals	Rub it clean with crocus cloth
	Break in fuel line (usually near a connection)	Tape up the break		Foul-up in the magneto	Reach for the paddle
	Fuel filter clogged	Remove the filter and run without it (but only in an emergency)			
	Air leak around fuel-pump housing	Tighten up screws			

Tools you'll want to have on board

Items	Comments	Items	Comments
	A *hammer* comes in handy on even the simplest jobs, like changing a prop or replacing a shear pin. You don't need a sledge — an 8-oz. ball-peen will do. A solid *punch* (¾-in. taper) or *ice pick* is also useful. And *pliers*, by all means, either thin-nose, combination or adjustable.		Spare *sparkplugs* can mean the difference between top performance and putt-putt-putt.
			Chances are you won't need it, but carry a *spare fuel-pump diaphragm* just in case.
	To pull plugs, you'll need a *sparkplug wrench*. A 6- or 12-point box works fine. Or get a reversible ratchet with 6- or 12-point deep-drive socket.		Probably there isn't anything more frustrating than to lose your *ignition* key. Carry a spare.
			The *owner's manual* will help to refresh your memory about what's what.
	You're bound to run into a situation requiring a *screwdriver*, and a standard medium-sized head (⅜ in.) is a good compromise. If you don't have one, you're sure to need it, so toss in a Phillips-type, too.		A roll of 1-in. *plastic electrical tape* can patch leaky gas lines or parted wires.
			Throw in a coil of No. 16 *solid-strand wire*. It's great for splicing steering lines.
	An *adjustable wrench* is absolutely necessary. Get one that opens to 2 in.		Use *crocus cloth* to remove corrosion from plug terminals, battery posts and terminals.
	Carry a *pocketknife* for cutting tape and make sure it's sharp.		Rags are fine for cleaning up (and rattleproofing your tool kit).
	A *flashlight* is a lifesaver for dark corners and dark evenings.		Lack of *fuel* is one of the most common causes of engine failure. Carry a spare can plus *extra oil*.
	Have at least two *spare shear pins and cotter pins* in your tool kit.		A *paddle* may not be very powerful, but it will move the boat. Have one aboard.

2717

tool tray, lathe

Tray keeps lathe tools in easy reach

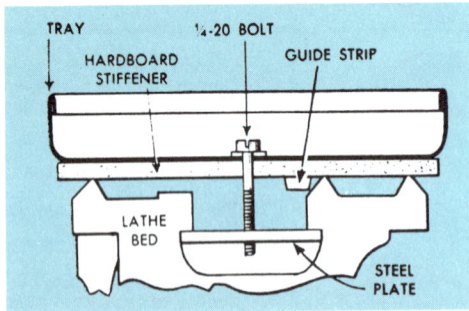

The tray is held by clamping screw and steel plate, the latter of same size as tailstock plate

■ HERE'S A DIVIDED TRAY that clamps onto the bed ways of the lathe and allows you to reach the tools and holders you want without scooping up grease, cutting oil and metal chips along with them. Just slice off the side of a gallon can, leaving about 1 in. of wall, and solder in dividers to take the tools and holders you need most often.

Roll the edges of the tray sides and ends, and reinforce the bottom with a piece of ¼-in. hardboard cut slightly smaller than the overall size of the tray. Then center a hole through the bottom of the tray and through the hardboard for a ¼-in. screw or stovebolt of sufficient length to reach through the steel clamping plate. Cut the latter from ¼ or ⅛-in. flat steel to the same overall size as the tailstock clamping plate, center-drill it and tap for the clamping screw. Notice also the hardwood guide strip screwed to the bottom of the tray and riding alongside the inside V-way of the lathe bed. This keeps the tray lined up with the bed and prevents it from sliding sidewise when you loosen the clamping screw.

Arrangement of the dividers pictured suited the owner of the original tray, but you'll want to install these to fit your own requirements. Usually you can cut dividers from what's left of the gallon can. Roll the edges over on themselves just as you did with the edges of the tray. This eliminates raw metal edges.

See also: lathe accessories; lathe techniques.

torch, brazing: see welders
torches, propane: see propane torches
touch alarm: see electronics
touchswitch: see switches, light
towing skin divers: see skin diving

clever ideas

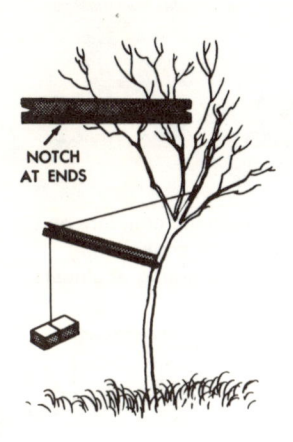

A notched stick, some twine and a brick will eventually straighten a young tree that has grown at an angle. Simply hang the brick as shown, placing it opposite the bend where it will exert a constant pull. Better than staked guy wires, this off-the-ground method of bracing makes for convenient mowing around the tree. The outboard weight will often straighten a tree in a single growing season.

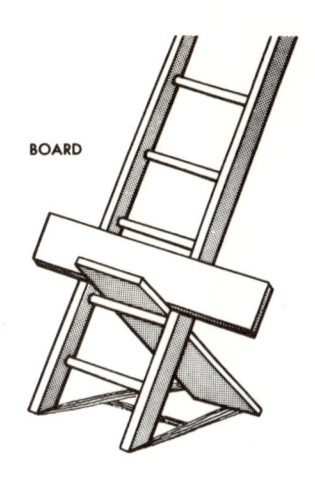

When you're working outdoors with a ladder and need a sawhorse to trim a board or two, remember this simple on-the-spot stunt: Place a scrap board on the second rung of the ladder in the manner shown so it rests at an angle to form a sawbuck. In this position, the slanting board will cradle the board to be cut when it is placed against the ladder. Saves looking around for something on which to rest the board.

After making several trips up and down a tall ladder when cleaning your gutters, you'll probably wish there was a way to lower a full bucket to the ground and then rehook another one. Here it is: Slit a hollow ball and slip it over the handle of the bucket. Clamp it in place with a skewer through both halves. This will support the handle above the edge of the bucket and make it easy to catch with a hook.

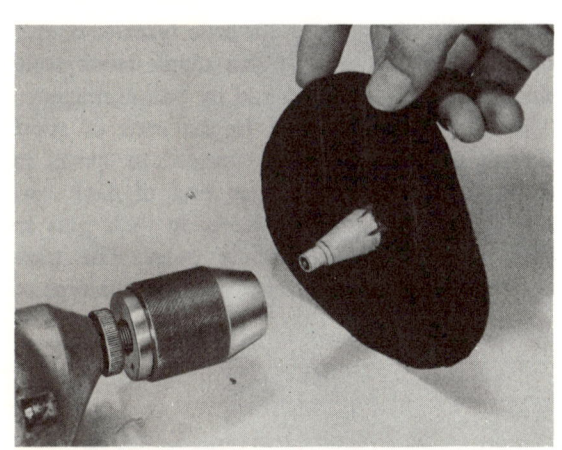

You can make a dandy flexible sanding disk for use in your portable electric drill and it won't cost you a cent. Simply round up an old inner tube, cut out a disk around the valve stem, cement an abrasive disk to it and chuck it in your drill.
If the stem happens to be rubber covered, cut away to the metal core so it will fit the chuck. Rubber cement is used to attach the abrasive to the disk. You also can use the standard sanding disks that you buy at a hardware store.

Like having two extra hands, a pair of permanent magnets will prove most useful in holding sheet-metal parts for soldering. A good example is shown above where two magnets are being used to hold the sides of a metal box in alignment for soldering the corners. Here the magnets are attached to blocks fastened to a wooden base, which gives free access. Horseshoe magnets are ideally suited for this purpose, because they are easy to fasten where needed, but you'll find that any magnets come in handy.

2719

toys

pull toys, continued

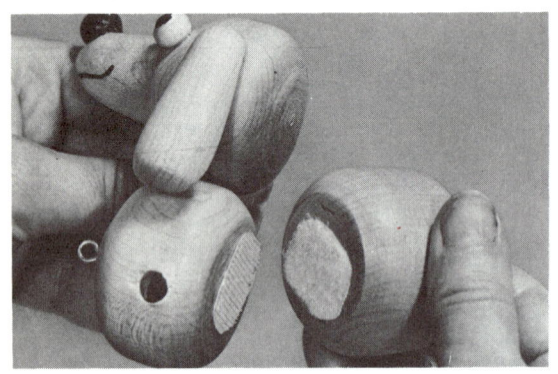

A slight pull separates the body sections to make a long or short pooch. The hook side of Velcro is glued to one face and the nap side to the other. Velcro can be bought at notions counters

■ STICKY DOG will help teach little hands co-ordination. The body is made from smooth blocks of splinter-free maple, all turned alike on the lathe. One-inch disks of Velcro, which are used to stick the sections together, are glued to 1-in. disks of felt. Color-key the end surfaces of the turned parts, then cement the Velcro disks in the center of the painted spots so exposed color around edges will indicate the proper ends to press together to assemble the train.

See also: cannons, toy; children's furniture; dollhouses; dolls; games, children's; kitchen, play; machine gun, toy; magic; puppet theaters; shovel, power, toy; stage coach.

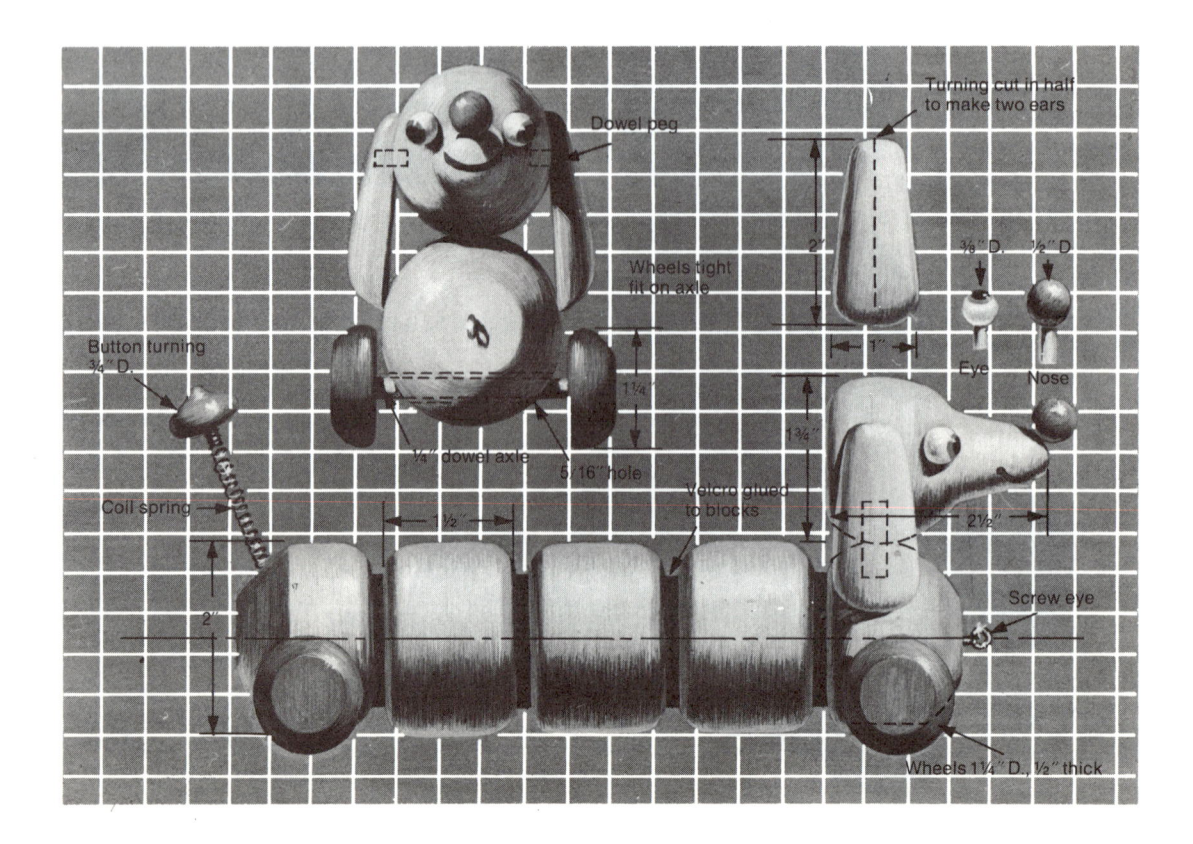

2722

Kick-powered forklift truck

BY MERTON H. SLUTZ

■ THE PAYLOAD is just a few empty cartons, but maneuvering this pint-sized truck will sharpen Junior's coordination and give him plenty of exercise as well.

Turning the double-handled crank raises or lowers the fork assembly, which slides in dadoes cut in the two uprights. For easy operation, the dadoes should be cut about 3/16-in. wider than the fork backboard. It's also a good idea to double-check the location of the crank to make sure that the operator won't skin his knuckles. In the drawing below, the fork is hinged to the backboard. If storage space at your home is no problem, the fork and back may be screwed together. The truck may be painted any color; the real models are usually yellow with black trim.

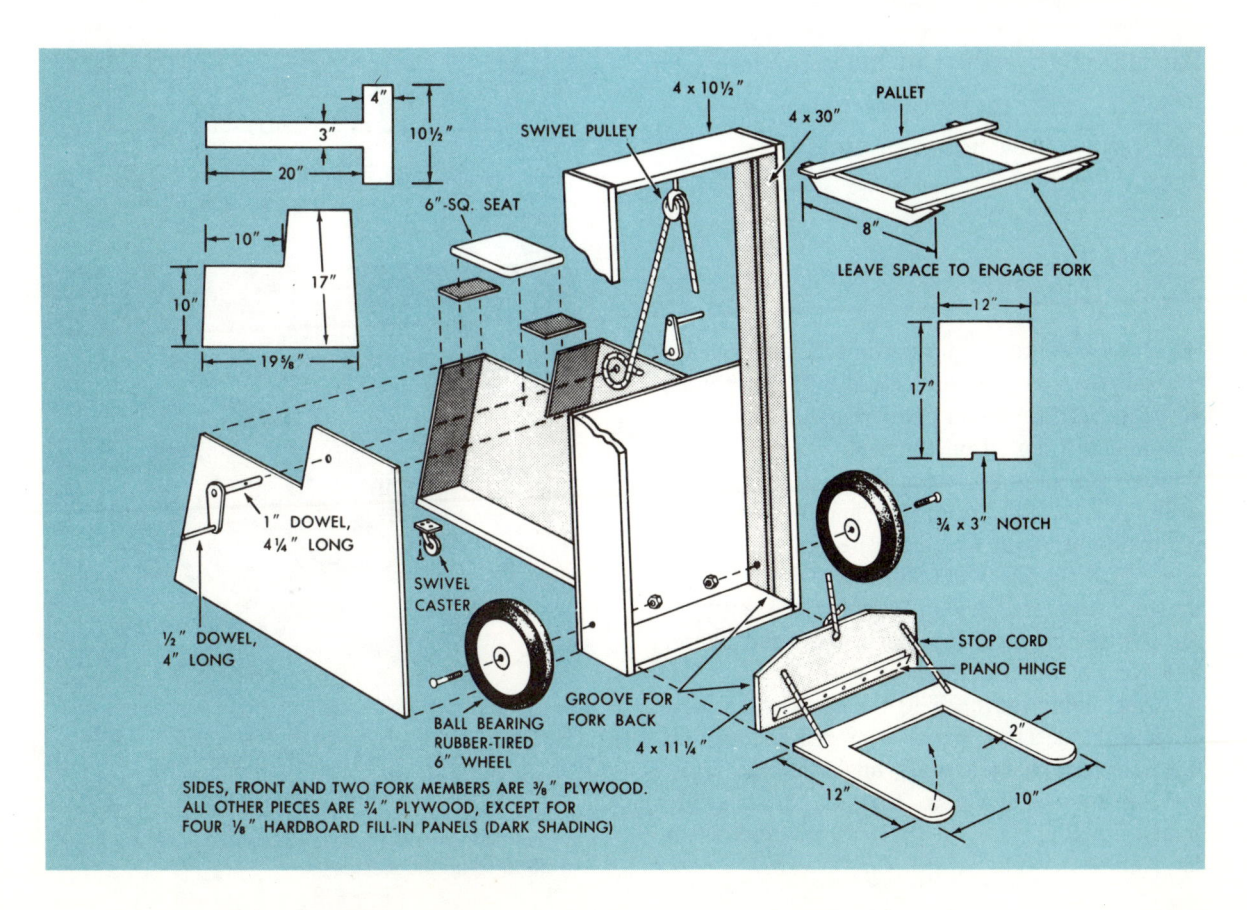

toys

Boxers play for a knockout

BY WILLARD and ELMA WALTNER

An action toy you can make
with inexpensive materials
and only a few hours of time

■ IT'S A KNOCKOUT, this battling-boxers toy. By pressing the compression base at different points, you can produce anything from a cautious sparring match to an all-out slugfest.

Turn the parts as shown in the drawing, then drill holes in the body, legs and base for the stringing cord with which the figures are assembled. Fishing line works fine for this. Thread the line from the bottom, running the ends up through the compression block, base and figure, and tying them off at the neck.

After gluing the head to the body attach the arms with pieces of piano wire passed through the body and bent to right angles at the ends, leaving enough space so that the arms swing freely. Finally, paint in the features and when the paint is dry finish with clear varnish.

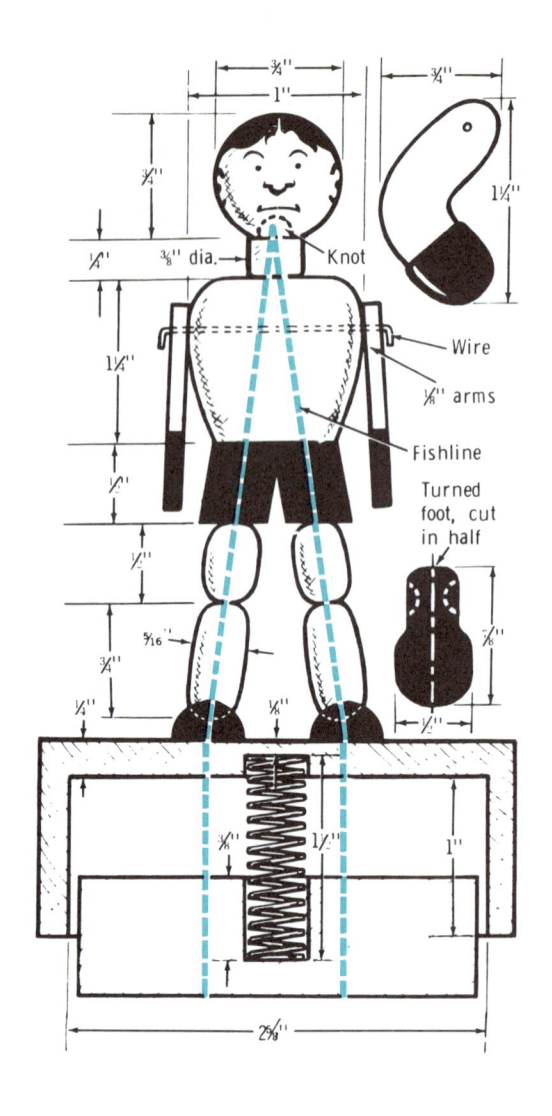

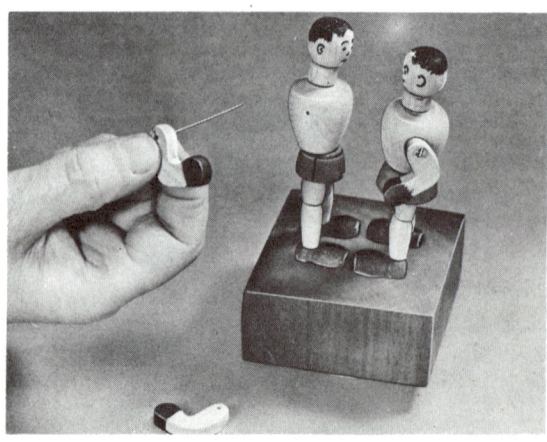

Slugging power for the boxers' arms is a matter of gravity. Mounted on pieces of piano wire that pass through the body, the arms are held in place by right-angle bends in ends of the wire that allow enough clearance for arms to swing freely. Depressing the disk causes fighters to lean, making the arms swing in round-house loops

A knockdown is produced by depressing the compression disk under one fighter. This relieves the spring tension on the stringing cord and causes the figure to collapse realistically

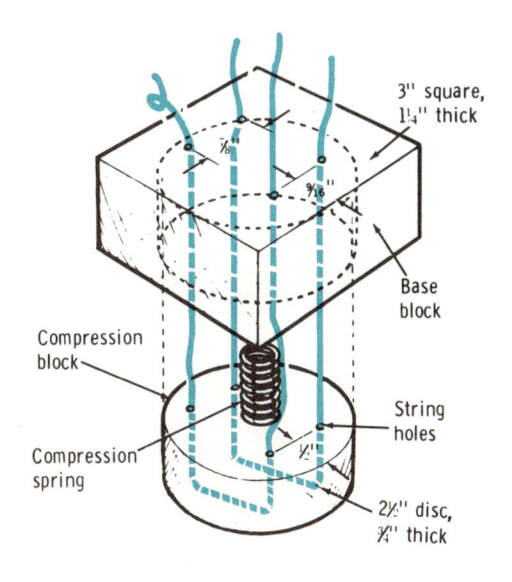

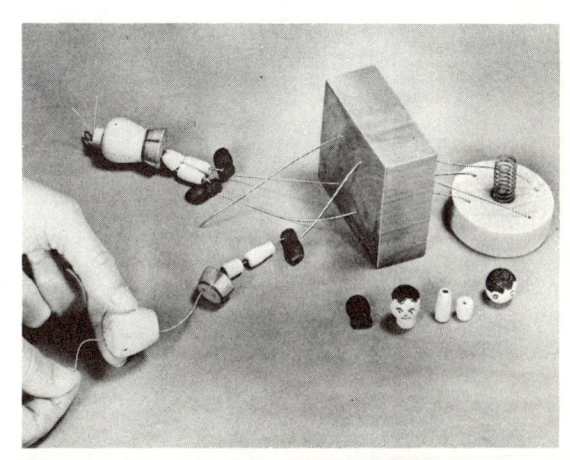

Threading the parts of the fighter on fishing line may look like a cat's-cradle operation, but it is actually simple. It's a good idea to paint all the parts before the final assembly operation is started. Pull the line tight, tie it, and you're finished

toys

Humpty-dumpty takes the tumble

BY MERTON H. SLUTZ

■ SURE TO DELIGHT your toddler, this easy-to-make toy re-enacts the famous nursery rhyme over and over again, complete with a shattering fall each time Humpty is knocked from the wall.

The operating principle is simple. When the rubber ball passes through the gate beneath Humpty-dumpty's feet, it hits the trigger panel which is hung on nail pivots. The panel swings back, carrying with it the four dowel-pin supports which hold Humpty-dumpty's four parts together on top of the wall. Result? A "great fall" which brings giggles of delight from the youngster who scores a bullseye.

A blind hole is made in the back of the four parts of Humpty's body to correspond with the spacing of the four supporting dowels.

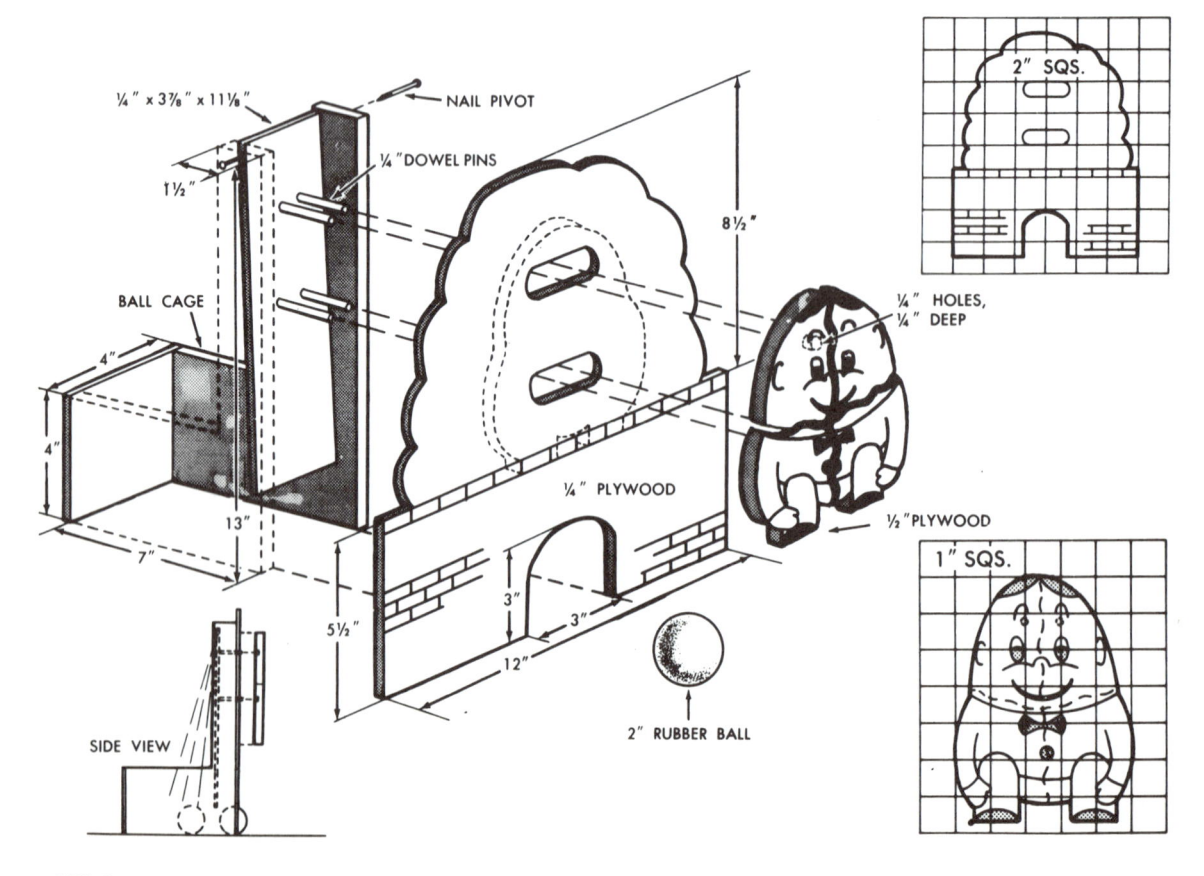

2726

Quick-change cardboard play mounts

BY MERTON H. SLUTZ

■ HERE'S A TOY that lets your youngster's imagination run wild. One minute he's a cowboy galloping over the range on his trusty pinto. A change of mood, a change of cardboard panels and he can become a tiger hunter lurching through the jungle on the back of an elephant or an Arab loping across the desert on a camel.

All three animals attach to a light plywood-and-dowel center frame with rubber crutch tips. The youngster simply slips into this frame with the rope straps over his shoulders.

Animals for the original toy were made 42 in. long, but you may scale them and the frame to fit your child. After cutting out the panels, add the features with poster paints and finish with clear shellac to preserve the cardboard.

SEE PAGE 2879 FOR PROJECT-A-PLAN

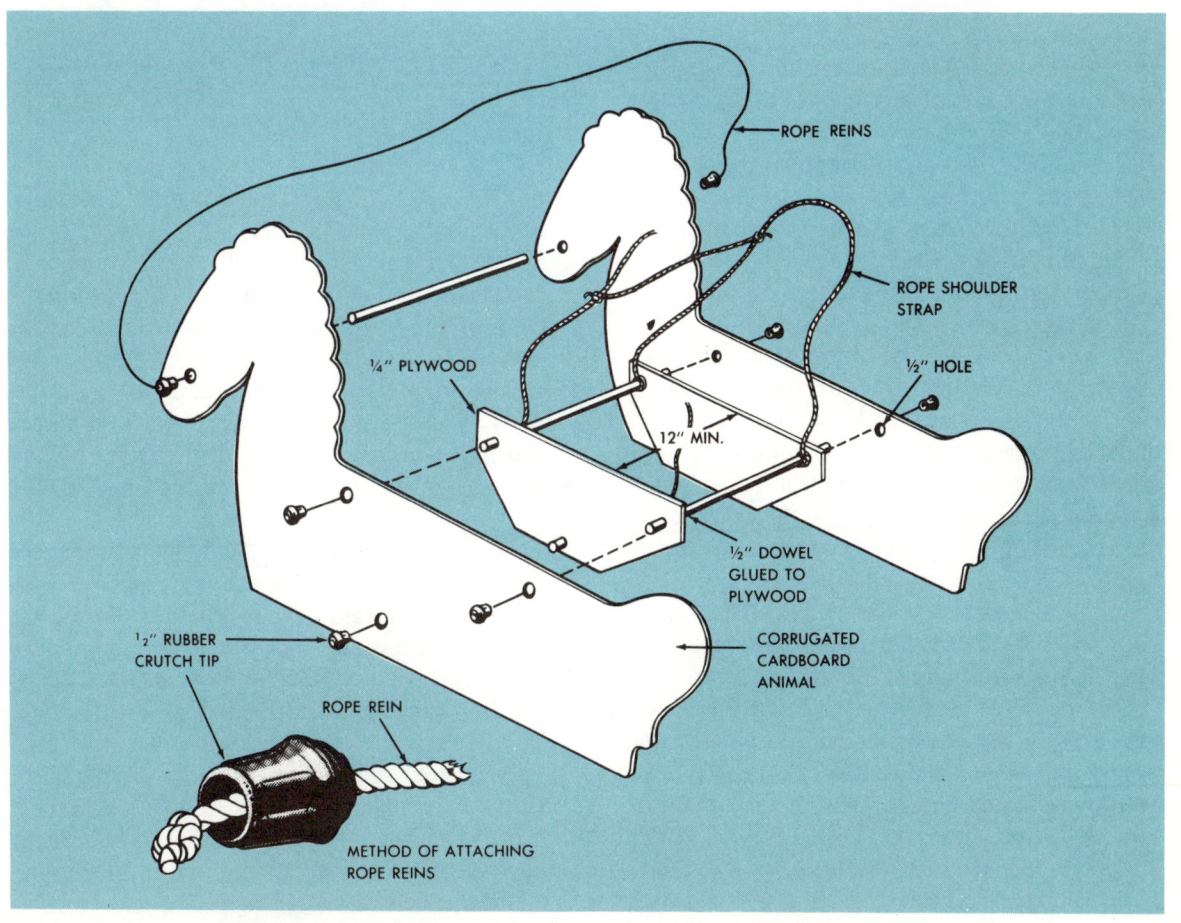

toys

A train for small-fry engineers

BY ELMA WALTNER

It huffs and puffs as it's pulled along, and it's realistic enough to please any junior railroad buff

■ THIS ANIMATED PULL-TOY train will puff its way into the heart of any toddler lucky enough to get it for Christmas.

Using Figs. 7 through 10 as the starting point, note closely in Fig. 10 the assembly of the mechanism that animates the brakeman. It's a simple parallelogram-type affair actuated by two pegs, or lugs, placed 180 deg. apart on the rear axle of the caboose. The axle is a 6¾-in. length (cut it a trifle longer to begin with) of ⅜-in. dowel and the actuating lugs are ½-in. lengths of ⅛-in. dowel glued into the holes in the axle with the ends projecting about ¼ in. Note in the sectional view, Fig. 10, that one arm of the parallelogram pivots on a screw while the other pivots on a dowel which passes through a clearance hole in the base of the caboose, the upper end being glued into a hole drilled into the body of the brakeman. The lower end of the pivot is a force fit in a hole centered through the arm.

Two pieces of coat-hanger wire with the ends bent at right angles and forced into holes in the wood arms connect the ends of the parallel arms as you see in the bottom view of the assembly, Fig. 10. When bent, the U-shaped connectors must be exactly the same length.

The brakeman is turned from a 2½-in. length of 1-in. dowel, the arms and lantern from ½-in. dowel stock. Note in Fig. 10 that washers are placed between moving and stationary parts to provide smoother operation and offset any tendency of the parts to bind. The balance of the caboose is easy boxlike construction as you see in Figs. 7, 8 and 10. Wheels are cut to a width of ¾ in. from 1½-in. round stock. Two wheels are center-drilled for roundheaded screws which serve as axles. The rear wheels are center-drilled ⅜ in. and are glued to the axle.

Now the locomotive. Start by turning the boiler to a length of 5 in. and a diameter of 3 in. from a short length of 4 x 4. Plane a flat on the boiler 1¾ in. wide. Then counterbore one deep hole and bore one shallow hole centered along the flat as in Fig. 11 and also Figs. 1 through 6. The latter is a clearance hole for the axle lugs. The outside diameter of both holes should be 1 in., the smaller diameter of the counterbore ¾ in., as in Fig. 13, the upper right detail. Shape the base and cut the slot through as in Fig. 12. Now, you bend a short length of clock spring to

2728

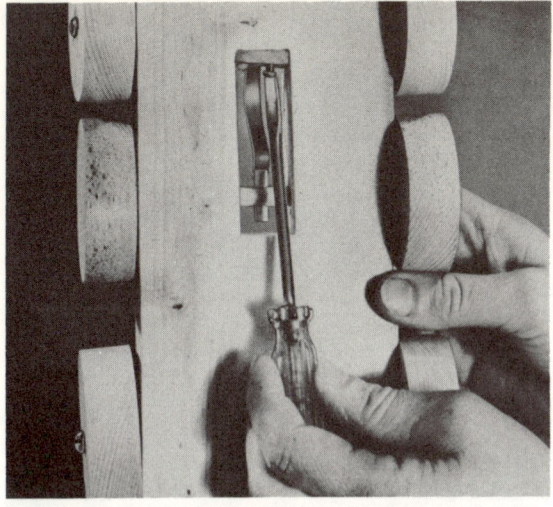

1. The noisemaker, which is a section of alarm-clock spring, is held in place with a small piece of hardboard

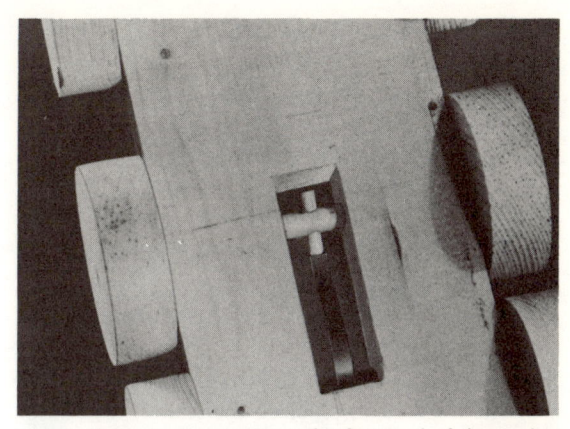

2. An axle peg engages the free end of the spring and snaps the reverse-curve bend against the sounding board

3. A sounding board about the weight of a postcard or slightly heavier is glued flush with the surface over the sound chamber

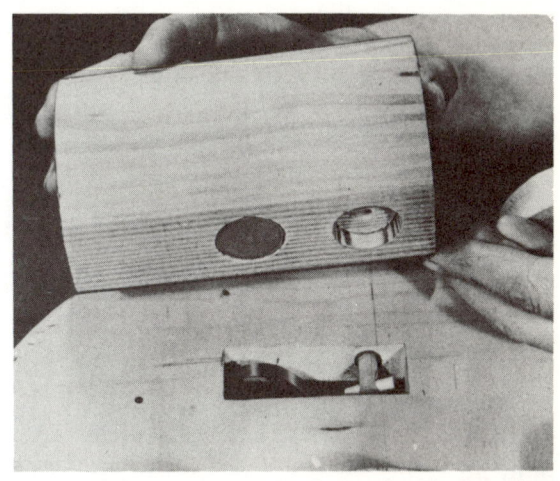

4. The center hole in the frame should allow clearance for the axle peg to turn when the wheels are turned

5. The engine bell is mounted on a U-shaped length of wire, the legs being inserted in holes in the boiler

6. The smokestack is turned to a diameter of 1½ in. and pegged into a hole in the boiler ahead of the small bell

toys

the approximate shape shown in Figs. 11 and 13 and attach it to the forward end of the slot in the locomotive base with two screws and a hardwood clamping piece as in Fig. 12. Next, you cut a disk from thin cardboard or a postcard and glue it in the counterbore as in Figs. 3 and 13. As you will note, the axle carrying the center pair of locomotive wheels actuates the spring which strikes the cardboard disk twice at each revolution of the wheels. The center axle is a length of ⅜-in. dowel center-drilled for a short length of 3/16-in. dowel, the ends of which project equally when it is glued in place in the hole in the axle. These projections depress the end of the spring and release it, the action permitting the spring to snap back and strike the cardboard disk over the counterbore, which forms a resonance chamber.

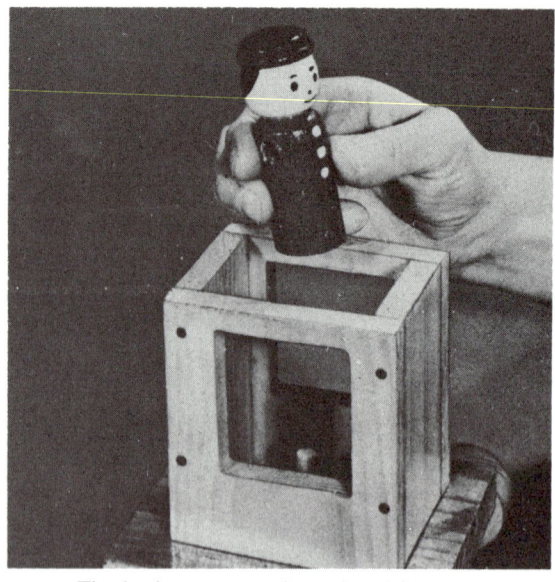

7 The brakeman must be painted (use nontoxic paint) and mounted in the caboose before the roof of the car can be attached

8 The lantern is attached to the brakeman's hand by means of a fine wire handle which allows it to swing naturally

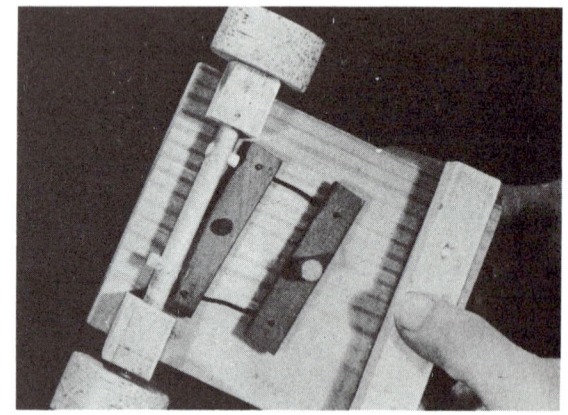

9 The drive mechanism which controls the brakeman's movement is mounted on the bottom of the caboose as detailed

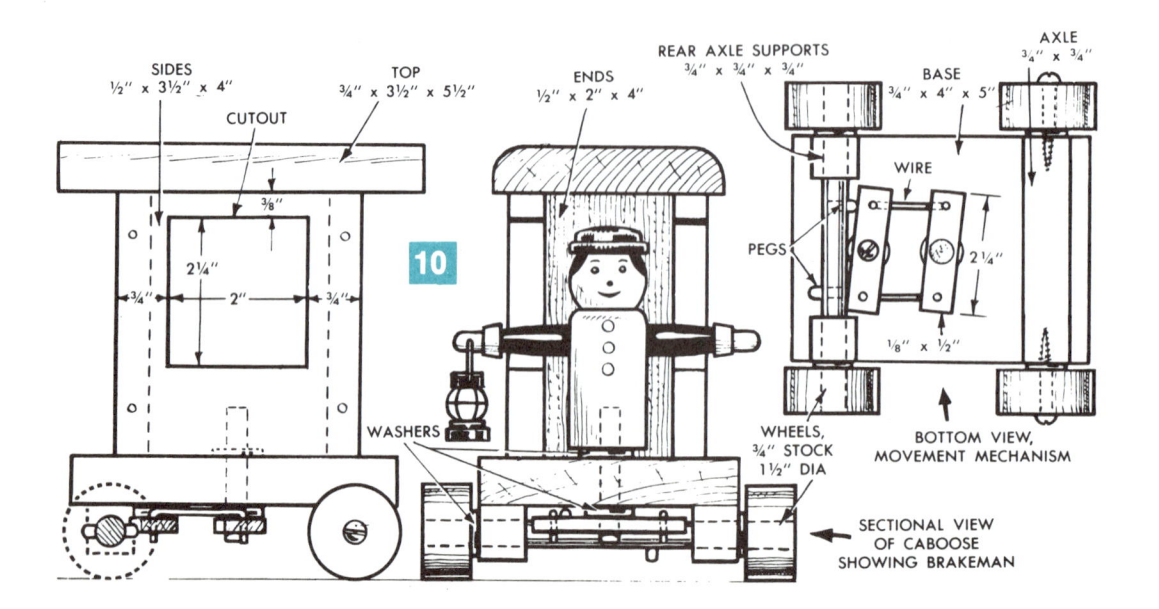

2730

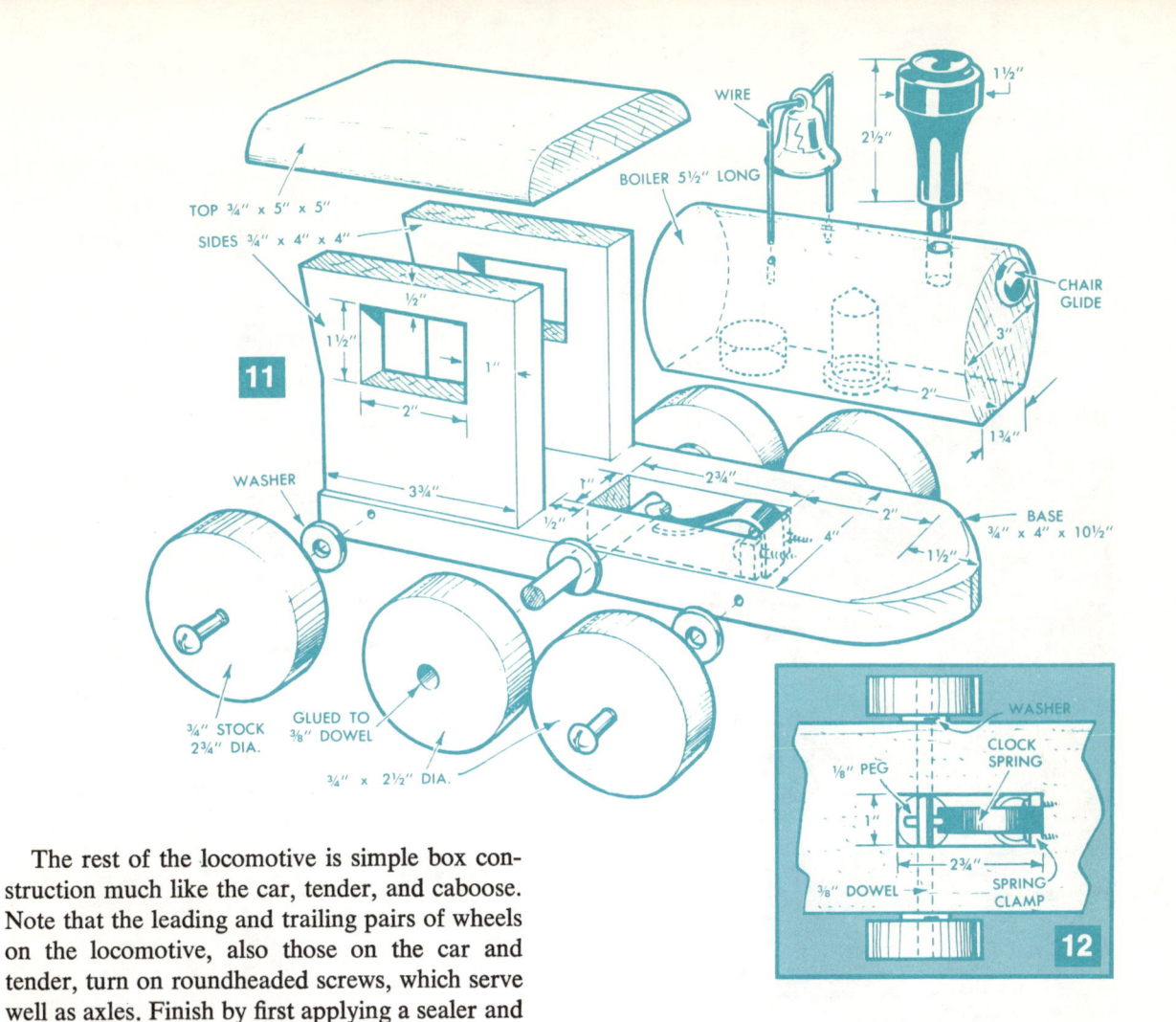

The rest of the locomotive is simple box construction much like the car, tender, and caboose. Note that the leading and trailing pairs of wheels on the locomotive, also those on the car and tender, turn on roundheaded screws, which serve well as axles. Finish by first applying a sealer and then enamels in the colors that suit your fancy. Use only enamels that do not contain lead.

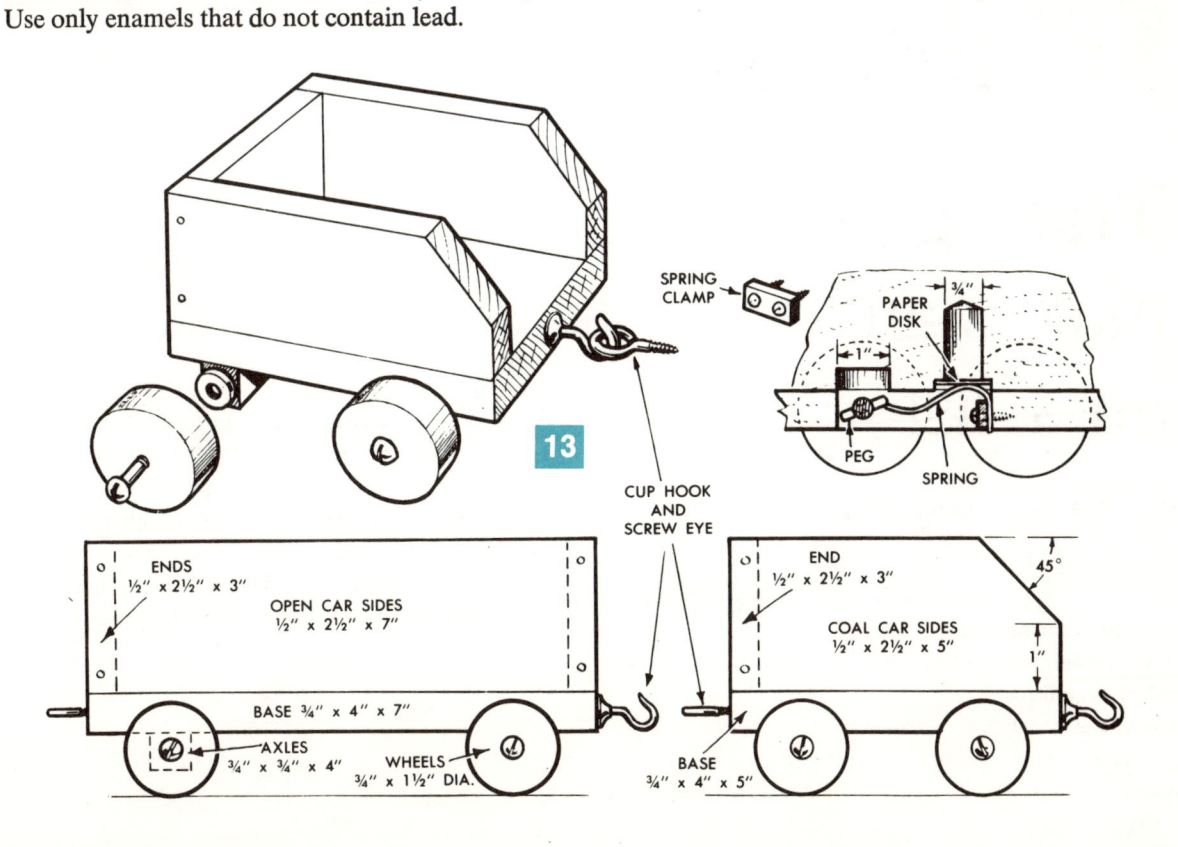

Tracing projector makes anyone an artist

BY MANLY BANISTER

■ FREE YOURSELF from tedious copying methods involving graph squares or pantographs. With a comparatively small investment in time and materials, you can build this direct-copy easel-projector that enlarges patterns or sketches up to 5½ times, or reduces them to one-third original size.

The heart of a projector is, of course, the lens—and for an artist's or draftsman's purposes, it must be of good quality to provide complete coverage of the screen without distortion. Any good camera or enlarger lens of at least 6-in.

---

track, road racing: see road racing, model
model tractor shelter: see shelters
tractor trailer: see trailers
trade-in value: see cleaning, auto; used car reconditioning

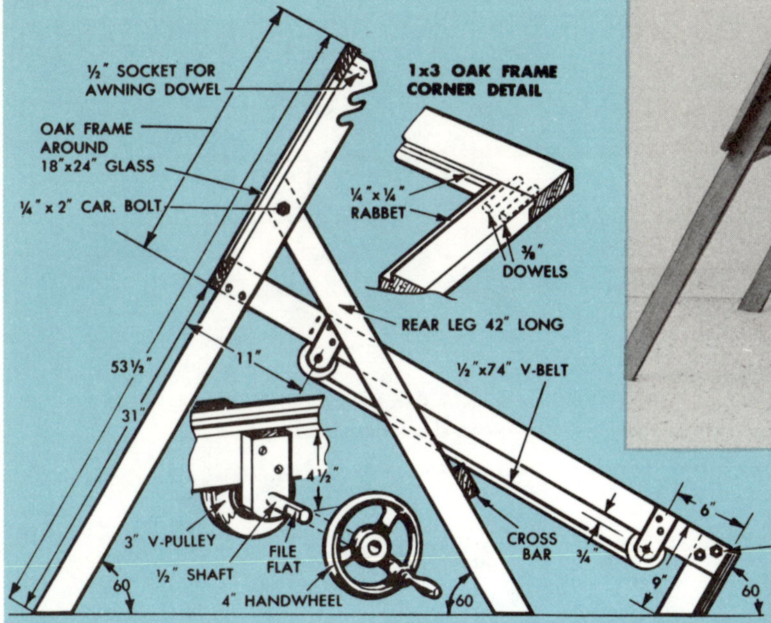
½" SOCKET FOR AWNING DOWEL
1x3 OAK FRAME CORNER DETAIL
OAK FRAME AROUND 18"x24" GLASS
¼"x¼" RABBET
¼" x 2" CAR. BOLT
⅜" DOWELS
REAR LEG 42" LONG
53½"
11"
½"x74" V-BELT
31"
4½"
6"
3" V-PULLEY
FILE FLAT
CROSS BAR
¾"
¼"x2½" CAR. BOLTS
½" SHAFT
9"
60
4" HANDWHEEL
60
60

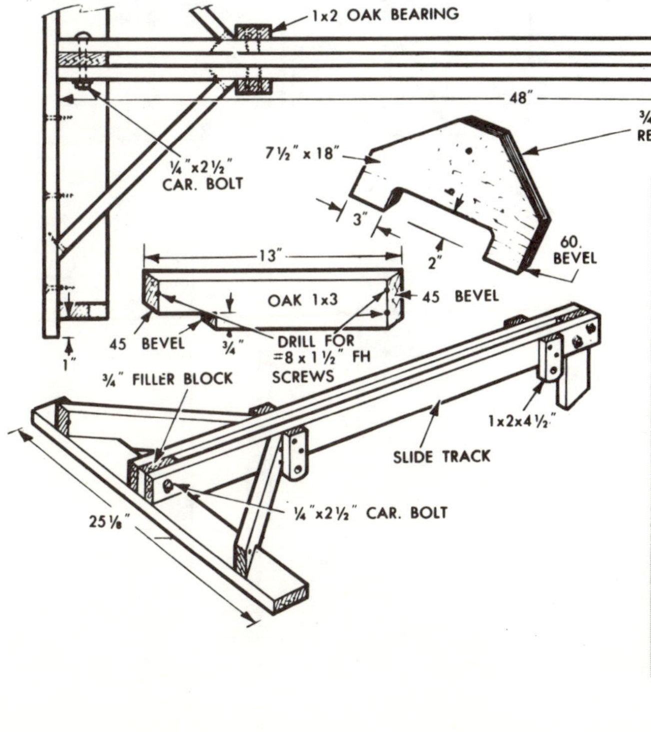
1x2 OAK BEARING
¼"x2½" CAR. BOLTS
48"
¾" PLYWOOD REAR SLIDE SUPPORT
7½" x 18"
¼"x2½" CAR. BOLT
3"
2"
60. BEVEL
13"
OAK 1x3
45 BEVEL
45 BEVEL
¾"
DRILL FOR =8 x 1½" FH SCREWS
1"
¾" FILLER BLOCK
1x2x4½"
SLIDE TRACK
25⅛"
¼"x2½" CAR. BOLT

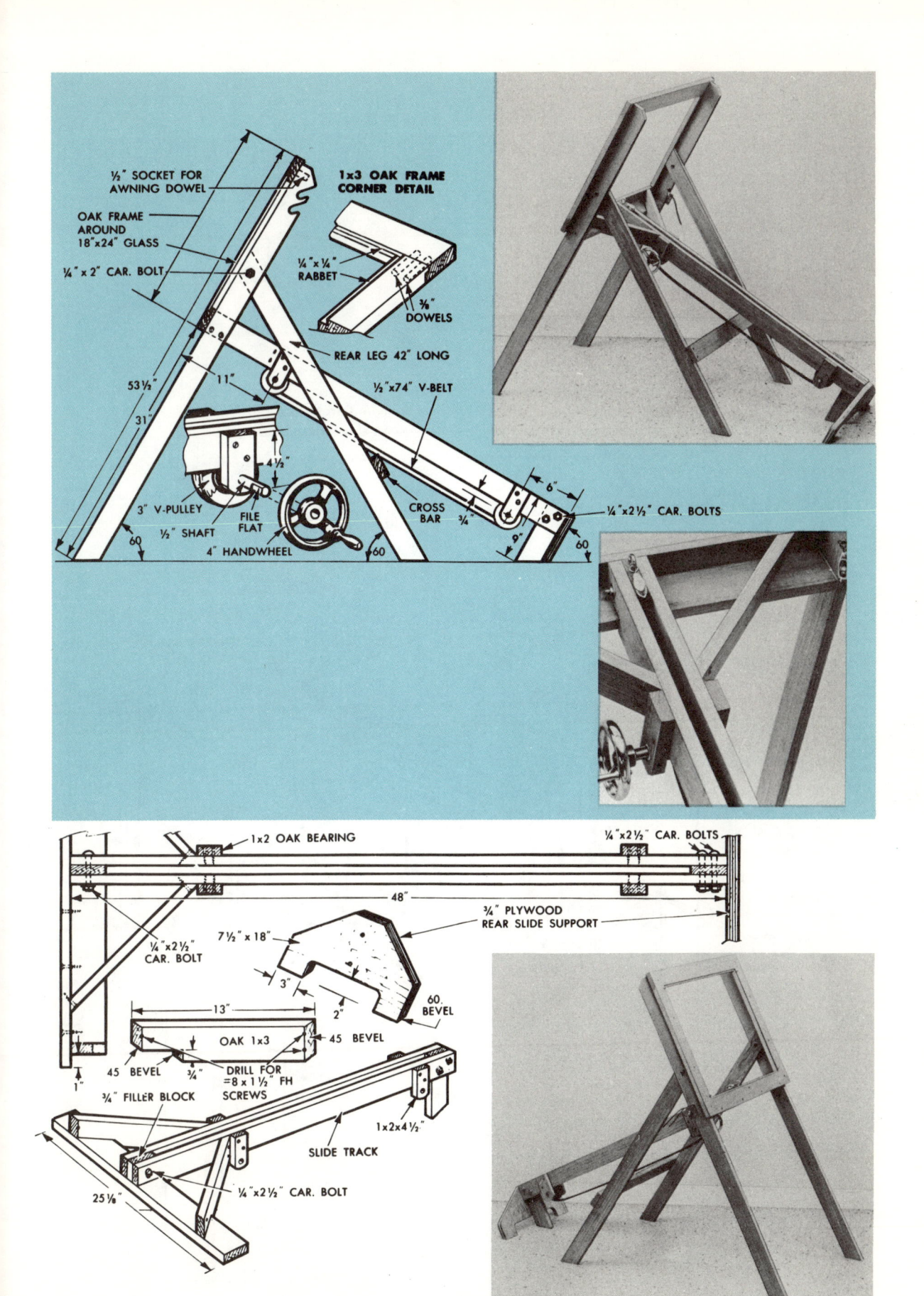

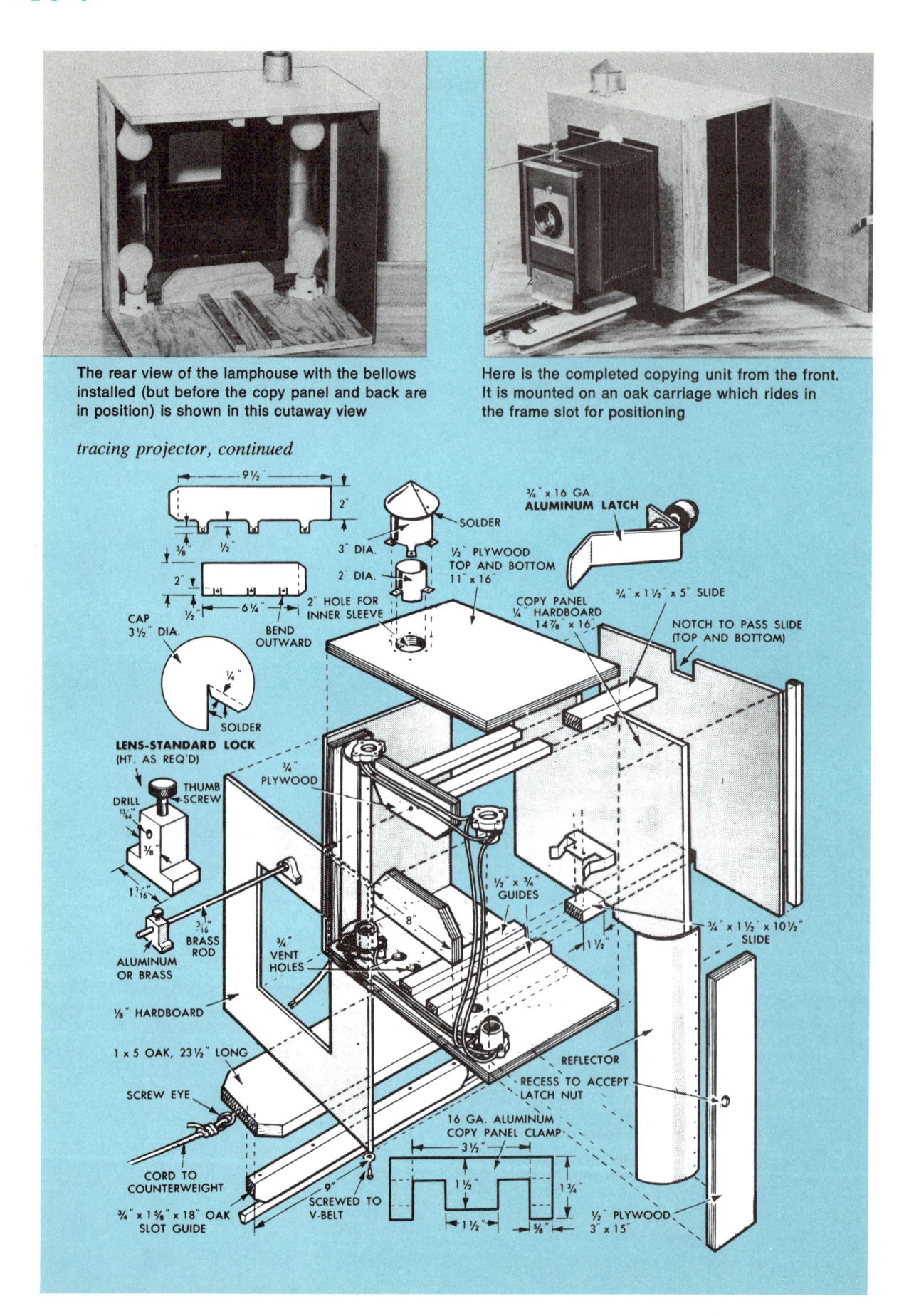

tracing projector

The rear view of the lamphouse with the bellows installed (but before the copy panel and back are in position) is shown in this cutaway view

Here is the completed copying unit from the front. It is mounted on an oak carriage which rides in the frame slot for positioning

tracing projector, continued

The framed panel door is hinged to a strip that is glued along the edge of the back of the unit. The copy-panel slides pass this through the notches. The edging strip gives support for the hinges

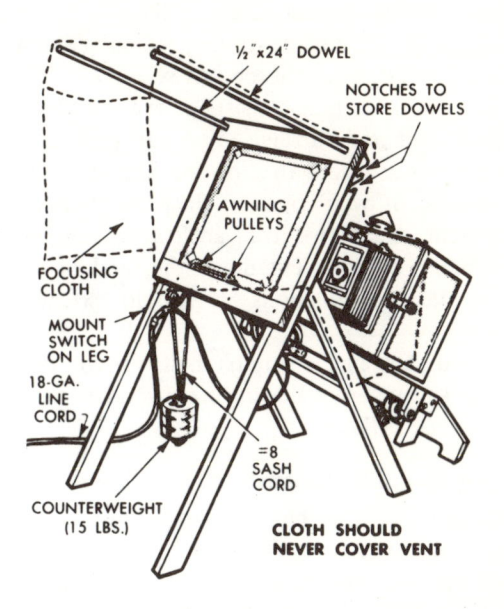

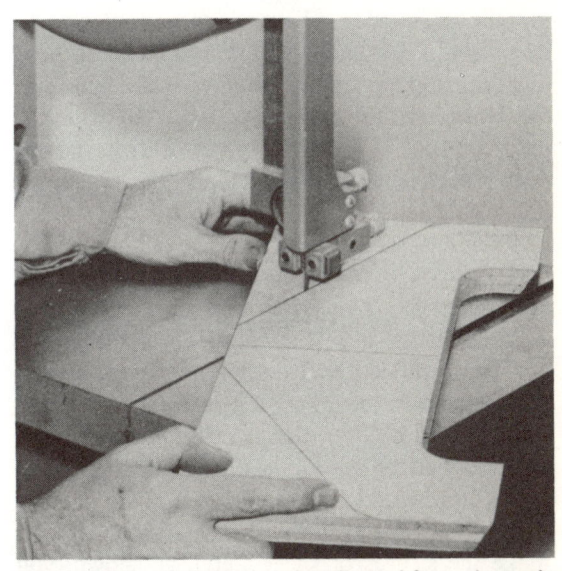

The foot of the slide frame is bandsawed from plywood, and the saw table tilted for a 60-deg. bevel at the base. The dowel-supported cover, shown in the drawing above, permits use of unit in a lighted room

focal length and an aperture of F:8 or larger can be used, if you already own one. If you must buy a lens, Edmund Scientific Co., of Barrington, N.J., offers a war-surplus 6-in. F:3.5 Metrogon lens (Catalog No. 60,305). Mounted in a specially-machined barrel, the lens has a square-field angle of 66 deg. that will cover 12 x 12-in. copy at 2x magnification, or an even larger area at reduction sizes. For less money, they offer the same lens in its original mounting, which can be used with a little adaptation.

The easel-projector consists of two parts: the main frame and the sliding lamphouse. Build the easel first, using stock 1 x 3 oak or other hardwood. The tracing frame can either be glued up with doweled corners, as detailed, or cut from a single sheet of ¾-in. birch plywood, with an opening ¼ in. smaller on all sides than the glass. Frame this opening with battens to form a well for the ¼-in.-thick polished plate glass to nest in. Fasten the glass in place with a washer at each corner, held by a small wood screw. Don't tighten these washers against the glass—they should turn freely.

Next, construct the slide unit and attach it to the rear face of the easel with No. 8 1½-in. flathead wood screws. Make certain the units are at exact right angles. Then attach the H-shaped leg unit.

For top performance of the V-belt drive, install

2735

tracing projector

tracing projector, continued

bronze bushings in the bearing blocks. Mount the upper pulley first, with V-belt installed. Assemble the rear bearing unit around the V-belt, then stretch the belt taut and C-clamp the rear bearing blocks to the slide while driving retaining screws. This insures tightness of the drive belt.

The projector unit consists of the lamphouse, bellows unit and carriage. You can pick up an old bellows at a camera shop for next to nothing —holes in it won't matter since it needn't be light-tight. A bellows from an 8 x 10 camera is preferable: it won't cut down the field of view when making reductions. It should extend at least 12 in.

If you can't find a suitable bellows, you could improvise one from nesting hardwood boxes or sheet-metal cylinders.

cut window in front panel

Cut a window in the front lamphouse panel to accept the rear frame (camera box) of the bellows. In the pilot model, this box-window is 10-in. square, but no height is given on the plans for the 8-in.-wide plywood spacer blocks to which the box is screwed, top and bottom; these must correspond to the window size. Note that the blocks are set back from the front panel to pass the socket wires. (If your bellows has no box, attach it to the front face of the lamphouse.)

The reflectors—which can be aluminum or tin-can stock—butt against the camera box and are tacked along the side edge only. Wire four porcelain lamp sockets in parallel, bring the wires out the lower lefthand corner at the front, and attach them to an on-off toggle switch mounted on the front leg. To dissipate the heat from the four 60-watt bulbs, air is drawn through holes in the bottom and exhausted through the double-sleeve ventilator at the top. If you don't want to make the sleeves of sheet metal, as shown, you could use different-size tin cans.

Since the projector rides at an angle of 30 deg., you'll need a clamp to keep the copy panel from slipping backward, and a guide rod so the lens standard won't sag. The clamp is quickly cut and bent from aluminum. For the lens-standard support, pass a metal rod (threaded at one end) through the front of the lamphouse and the bellows box support inside. A nut outside and another inside hold it firmly; you can glue on an extra plywood block, as shown, if you wish to increase the anchoring thickness. You'll have to drill a small block of aluminum (or other metal) to serve as a siding lock.

You need some kind of track for the lens standard to slide on—unless, of course, you're already working with a complete bellows unit. You could either make a wooden track, or buy the 12-in. T-slot slide shown, mounting it with screws to the lamphouse carriage. It's Edmund Scientific's No. 40,891.

On the easel shown, three 5-lb. barbell weights serve as counterbalance. A compound pulley system is used (even though it requires double the weight) because the weight-drop distance is shorter than the lamphouse-travel distance. The compound system drops the weight only 6 in. for every foot of projector travel.

To save time in future operation, index the machine so you'll be able to set it quickly for the magnification or reduction desired, then bring the image to sharp focus from the front of the screen by cranking the projector up or down the slide. The following table, calculated for a 6-in.-focal-length lens, gives you basic settings. Both lens-to-screen and lens-to-copy distances are measured from the *center* of the lens system to the front surface of whichever panel is involved.

Lens-to-Screen Distance	Lens-to-Copy Distance	Magnification
36″	7.2″	5x
24″	8″	3x
18″	9″	2x
12″	12″	same size
9″	18″	1/2x
8″	24″	1/3x

Start with the bellows fully retracted against the lamphouse and the copy panel set for about 3x enlargement. Scribe two short vertical ink lines 1 in. apart in the center of a sheet of white paper and fasten it to the copy panel with masking tape. Focus this image on a sheet of tracing paper taped to the screen. Adjust the copy panel and focus until the inch-marks space out to exactly 3 in. on the screen. Scribe a pencil mark across the bottom copy-panel slide where it emerges from the back of the lamphouse. Using this as "home position" for the copy, try the lens at various extensions, marking the front slide at 2x, 1x (same size) and ½x. To set up for ⅓x, slide the copy panel all the way to the rear of the lamphouse and extend the bellows nearly as far as it will go forward. To index for 4, 5 and 5½ magnifications, back the lens to zero position against the lamphouse.

See also: drafting equipment; ellipsograph.

trailers

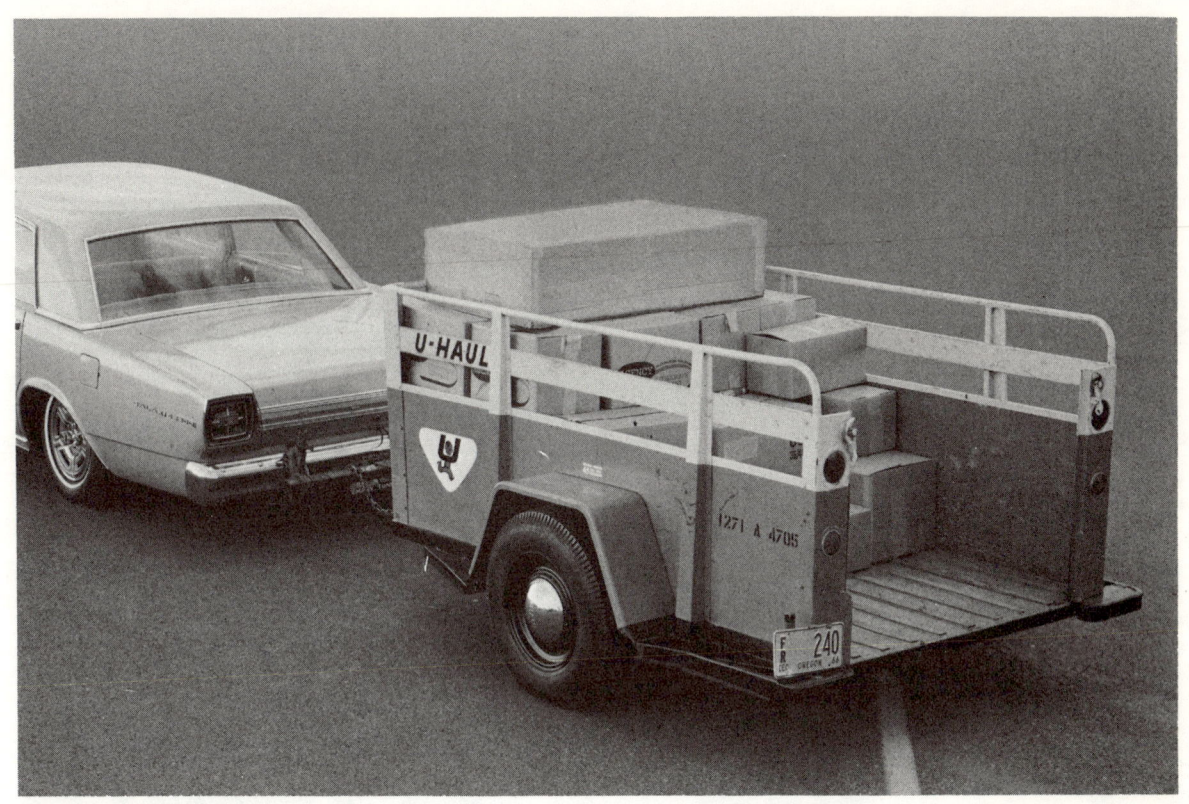

This typical utility trailer is correctly loaded, with the weight over the axle and forward

Service your trailer before you go

BY MORTON J. SCHULTZ

Utility trailers are popular. People are buying and renting a lot of them. Here's how to have a trouble-free trip with a trailer in tow

■ SAY "TRAILER" TO SOMEONE and guess what image that word evokes. Most people immediately think of a travel trailer or a mobile home. Right? Yet many Americans own smaller trailers. Millions own boat trailers, for instance. Other millions own campers. And great numbers also own utility trailers—those all-purpose towbehinds that are so handy for moving furniture, equipment and materials.

These trailers are popping up on American highways in increasing numbers. They are more common than motorscooters in some localities. Yet many owners of new utility trailers aren't aware of how and when they should be serviced.

These small trailers deserve the same kind of care and coddling as their larger, more luxurious cousins: particularly periodic maintenance of tires, wheels, wheel bearings, lights and the braking system (if there is one).

Needless to say, a trailer poses fewer maintenance problems than the car that pulls it. Still, like a car, a trailer must be regularly serviced if optimum performance and safety standards are to be maintained. Best of all, servicing a trailer—unlike tackling many automotive repairs—is something anybody with a rudimentary knowledge of mechanics can do.

Tire care. It doesn't require extrasensory perception to know when a tire—any tire—needs replacing. If either (or any) of your trailer tires

2737

trailers

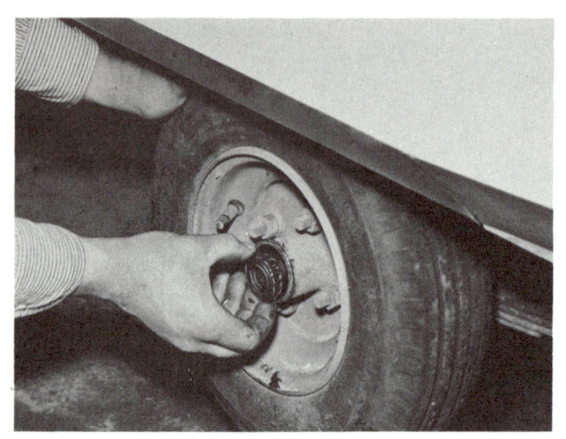

To service the bearings, remove the dust cap, cotter pin adjusting nut and then the wheel. Then pull the bearing from the spindle and go to work

Use a drift to knock out the inner bearing. The races of bad bearings also should be knocked out and replaced immediately with new, well-greased races

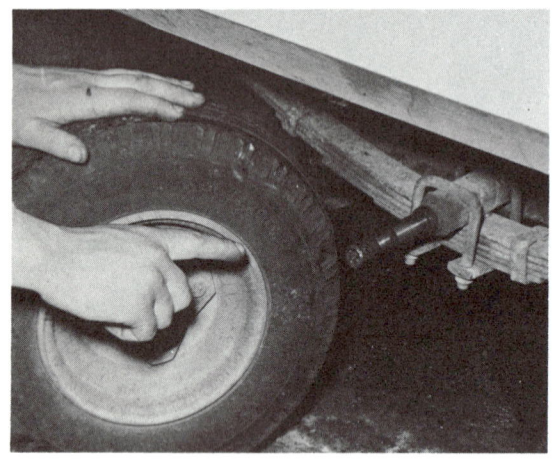

"Look, ma, no brakes!" A hazard that many who pull a trailer for the first time are not aware of is the absence of brakes on the unit behind them. Beware!

This trailer has brakes—a practical inertia-type system. To check out its wheel cylinders for leaking fluids, pull away the rubber as shown above

trailer servicing, continued

are badly worn or cut, replace them with new ones.

Bear this in mind too: trailer tires *rot* faster than they wear out, because a trailer is often left "lying fallow" for long periods of time. If it's left on the greasy floor of a garage, tire deterioration will be accelerated. Gradual tire deflation will speed the process.

When a trailer is to be parked for a long time, park it on an oil-free surface, then jack it up (or put it on blocks) so that the tires *just touch* the ground or floor. Somehow, this slight contact with the parking surface seems to retard deterioration of the tire rubber.

Trailer tires must be inflated properly to insure safe trailering. So note this: the pressures in trailer tires must be *much higher* than the pressures you'd use in an automobile tire of comparable size.

For example, what's the normal inflation for a 6.70-15, 2-ply car tire—26 lbs.? Maybe you go as high as 30 lbs., but no more. If you have 6.70-15 tires on your trailer, you should inflate them to *55 lbs.* to insure safe towing.

The need for higher air pressure in trailer tires is fairly obvious. There is generally more weight *concentrated* on trailer tires than there is, proportionately, on a car's tires. Higher pressures help support that weight and keep the trailer on an even keel. Too-low tire pressure can result in side-to-side trailer sway that could

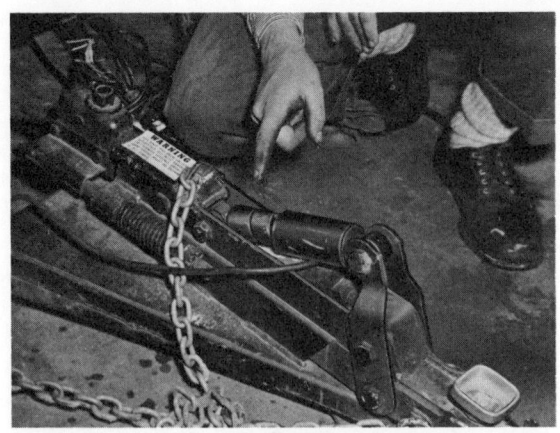

The front end of an inertia-brake system on a trailer drawbar consists of a master cylinder, springs, a shock absorber. Before trailering, check them

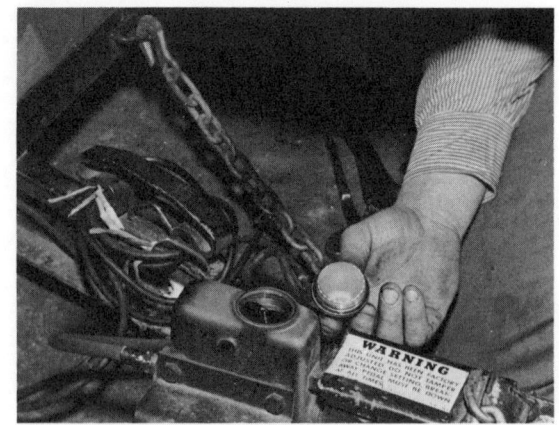

Before hooking up a trailer and pulling it on the highway, take a look into the master cylinder to check the fluid level. Watch for leaks

When you're inspecting your trailer, check brake linings with a lining gauge. Replace linings if they are less than 1/16 in. thick

How are the brake drums? If they are only slightly damaged, they can be turned and made to work like new, but replace badly scored drums and be safe

become violent—and dangerous—at high speeds.

TABLE II (page 2741) gives the recommended pressures for various sizes of trailer tires. Check it against the tire pressure you are currently using. The inflations suggested in TABLE II should be maintained whether the trailer is loaded or empty.

Check inflation when tires are cold, and deflate overinflated tires *only* when they are cold —never when they're hot. A tire increases its pressure as it runs and in that way protects itself against heat. So don't destroy that protection.

Wheel balance. If you've ever ridden in a car that had a wheel out of balance, you probably have noticed how it affects the stability of the vehicle and its riding comfort. There is no question about it. It does. But if a trailer wheel goes out of balance, the rig will actually hop, especially if it's empty or lightly loaded.

Trailer wheels go out of balance statically, causing the trailer to vibrate vertically. Static rebalancing of trailer wheels is done in exactly the same manner as it is for automobile wheels. A trailer wheel should be rebalanced whenever you replace one tire with another.

Wheel bearings. Under ordinary circumstances, wheel bearings should be serviced once a year. However, if you have a boat trailer which is often rolled into the water—especially salt water—these bearings should be serviced every few weeks during the boating season.

A technique for lubricating trailer wheel bearings without having to pull the wheels is to have

trailers

Use a trouble light to check the lighting system. Hook it to the car and touch the prod to the trailer. If the tester lights, you have a bad ground

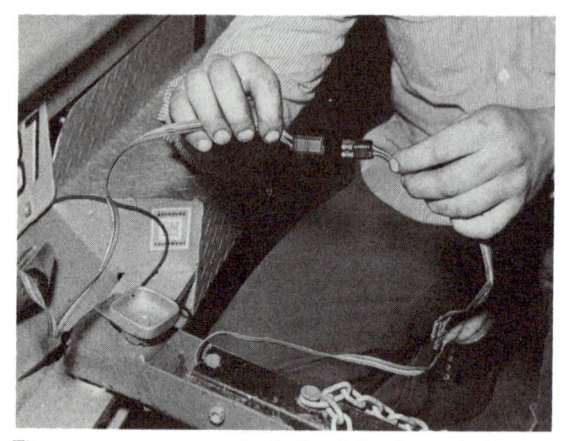

The current necessary for trailer lights is carried from the car to the trailer lights through a simple set of male and female connectors

off the nut to the next notch, then insert the cotter pin.

Springs. Make sure the springs are tight and have no broken leaves. Push the trailer from side to side. If a spring is bad and needs to be replaced, you'll notice an unusual amount of "play" as the trailer is swayed. By the way, this is one trailer repair job that can be a knuckle-buster, especially if the bad spring has become "frozen" at its connections. You might be smart letting a pro tackle the replacement.

Brake system. Most boat and utility trailers, being relatively small, do not have those self-contained braking systems called *inertia brakes*. These small rigs rely on the braking power of the towing vehicle to stop them. However, some trailers do have these systems which tie into the towing vehicle through the ball hitch. It works like this:

As the towing vehicle slows, the inertial force of the trailer exerts pressure against the ball. This in turn forces the fluid in a master cylinder through the brake lines and thence to the wheels where conventional hydraulic principles serve to brake the trailer by activating brake shoes on the wheels.

A trailer's braking system presents a fair number of parts to check on. These include:

• The master cylinder (for fluid level and leaks).
• Shock absorbers and coil springs (for adequacy of tension).
• Wheel cylinders (for leaks).
• Brake linings (for wear).
• Brake drums (for damage, such as scoring).

Inspection and maintenance of the brake system should be done once a year. Do it at the same time you pull the wheels to check the bearings.

trailer servicing, continued

a grease fitting tapped into each hub. Then you can grease the bearings with a hand gun whenever they need it.

Worn or damaged wheel bearings in your trailer will cause it to track poorly and sway from side to side like a drunken camel. When they get *really* bad they can even shear off a wheel.

To get at wheel bearings for inspection or servicing is a fairly simple job, as can be seen in the photographs at bottom of page 2738. In adjusting the bearings after they've been serviced, run up the adjusting nut until the wheel's tight, then check for end play. If there *is* play, turn the nut tighter. When end play is eliminated, back

don't forget the lights

A trailer will have three or four wires leading to it from the car. One wire will go to the trailer's taillights, and two to the (turning) signal lights. There may be a fourth wire for the ground, though in some trailers the ground is established by metal-to-metal contact of ball to hitch.

Trailer lights fail for any of three reasons: a bad ground, burned-out bulbs or worn wiring.

You can check the condition of the ground with a test lamp. Hook one wire of the lamp to the tow vehicle's bumper, then touch the prod to trailer metal. If the test lamp lights, you have a bad ground.

PROPER LOAD DISTRIBUTION
FOR A UTILITY TRAILER

TABLE I. Maximum Controllable Speeds

Trailer Size	Open Rig	Closed Rig
4' x 6' single axle	65 mph	65 mph
4' x 7' single axle	60 mph	60 mph
5' x 8' single axle	60 mph	55 mph
6' x 8' single axle	55 mph	50 mph
5' x 10' single axle	50 mph	45 mph
5' x 12' tandem axle	45 mph	45 mph
6' x 14' tandem axle	45 mph	45 mph

In the case of a trailer grounded through the ball, the poor ground is probably due to corrosion or dirt around the trailer's ball-and-socket hitch. Clean these connectors, using an abrasive if necessary.

If there's a ground wire, remove it at the ground connection and make sure the connector and ground-wire terminal are free of corrosion and dirt. Then reconnect it and try again. If the ground still proves faulty, replace the wire.

Trailer wires are generally supplied in harness form; thus, to replace one you must replace all. One end of the harness hooks into the car's lighting system; the other is connected to the trailer by means of a connector plug.

When towing a trailer at night, the importance of reliable, working taillights cannot be overemphasized. Always check them before you pull out onto the road. Also, carry a spare bulb or two and a couple of spare fuses—just in case.

Loading and towing. A trailer must be loaded so there's a 60-to-40 weight ratio between front and back. In other words, 60 percent of the load must be concentrated at the front of the trailer so it bears on the rear of the tow car.

If the load is centered over the trailer wheels or is concentrated in the rear, the trailer will tend to whip from side to side, especially when towed at high speeds.

For any trailer-towing car there is a speed beyond which the driver will be unable to control the vehicles. This limit is known as the maximum controllable speed (see TABLE I). For everybody's sake—your own included—*don't exceed this speed*.

Remember, too, that no matter what the maximum controllable speed happens to be for your rig, the *legal speed* for a car with trailer is *the same as the posted speed limit for trucks*.

Finally, be sure your own car is in top condition before you put it to work hauling a trailer. It just wouldn't make much sense to tow a conditioned trailer behind an unconditioned car.

See also: camping; mowers; pickup camper; shelters.

TABLE II. Tire Information for Utility Trailers

Tire Size	Ply Rating	Maximum Trailer* Load	Inflation
4.80/4.00-8	2	380 lbs.	30 lbs.
	4	600 lbs.	65 lbs.
4.80/4.00-12	4	790 lbs.	65 lbs.
5.70/5.00-8	4	710 lbs.	50 lbs.
	6	900 lbs.	75 lbs.
	8	1030 lbs.	95 lbs.
5.30/4.50-12	4	915 lbs.	55 lbs.
6.90/6.00-9	4	850 lbs.	40 lbs.
	6	1080 lbs.	60 lbs.
	8	1275 lbs.	80 lbs.
	10	1450 lbs.	100 lbs.
6.00-12	4	1010 lbs.	40 lbs.
	6	1290 lbs.	60 lbs.

*This figure is the maximum load that can safely be placed on each tire. Double maximum trailer load for a 2-wheeled trailer; quadruple it for a 4-wheeled trailer.

trailers

Roadside chuck wagon

BY WALTER H. GERBER

Trail along this compact kitchen
that has a lot of storage space
and plenty of other goodies for
family campers

■ OURS IS A traveling family. We don't wait for our normal two-week vacation. We use those long, holiday weekends to go exploring on the open roads. All of us are converts to the idea that the real way to relax and have fun is to pile in the family car and leave behind the clutter of urban civilization, even for a day or two.

But there were problems involved in our early travel days. We've solved most of them with the trailer pictured and described in detail on the following pages. It provides us with a hot-meal kitchen at the flick of a wrist. There are built-in storage compartments that let us stock up with several days' provisions (including an icebox for perishables). We can keep dress clothes handy and wrinkleless, and get at our sleeping gear without unpacking anything else. Although we intended it for a small light car, the trailer is designed to take the travail out of travel whatever size car you drive. We even built in a hi-fi speaker for music while we dine. Since long-distance travel keeps your battery charged, it's safe to tie this speaker into a car radio—though, for a better selection of good music, we carry a tape-recorder in the car which runs off its own battery.

There's no fuss involved in setting up the kitchen; lifting up and swinging back the hinged leaf opens up the stove pit and creates a work counter with two handy drawers for utensils and paper plates. For cleaning with one wipe of a moist cloth, I covered the work face of this leaf with plastic laminate. You can also plastic-coat the stove platform. The detail on page 2747 shows how you bring the stove up to working height (our two-burner uses LP gas). When the folding legs are tapped out from under it—by inserting fingers through the grip slots—the platform drops into the pit, leaving plenty of space around it to pack pots and pans.

To keep the closed drawer leaf from flying up when you sail over a bump, you can tie it down with slide-bolts or turn buttons—although if you lash items to the railed-in deck, this will probably

REFUSE HERE

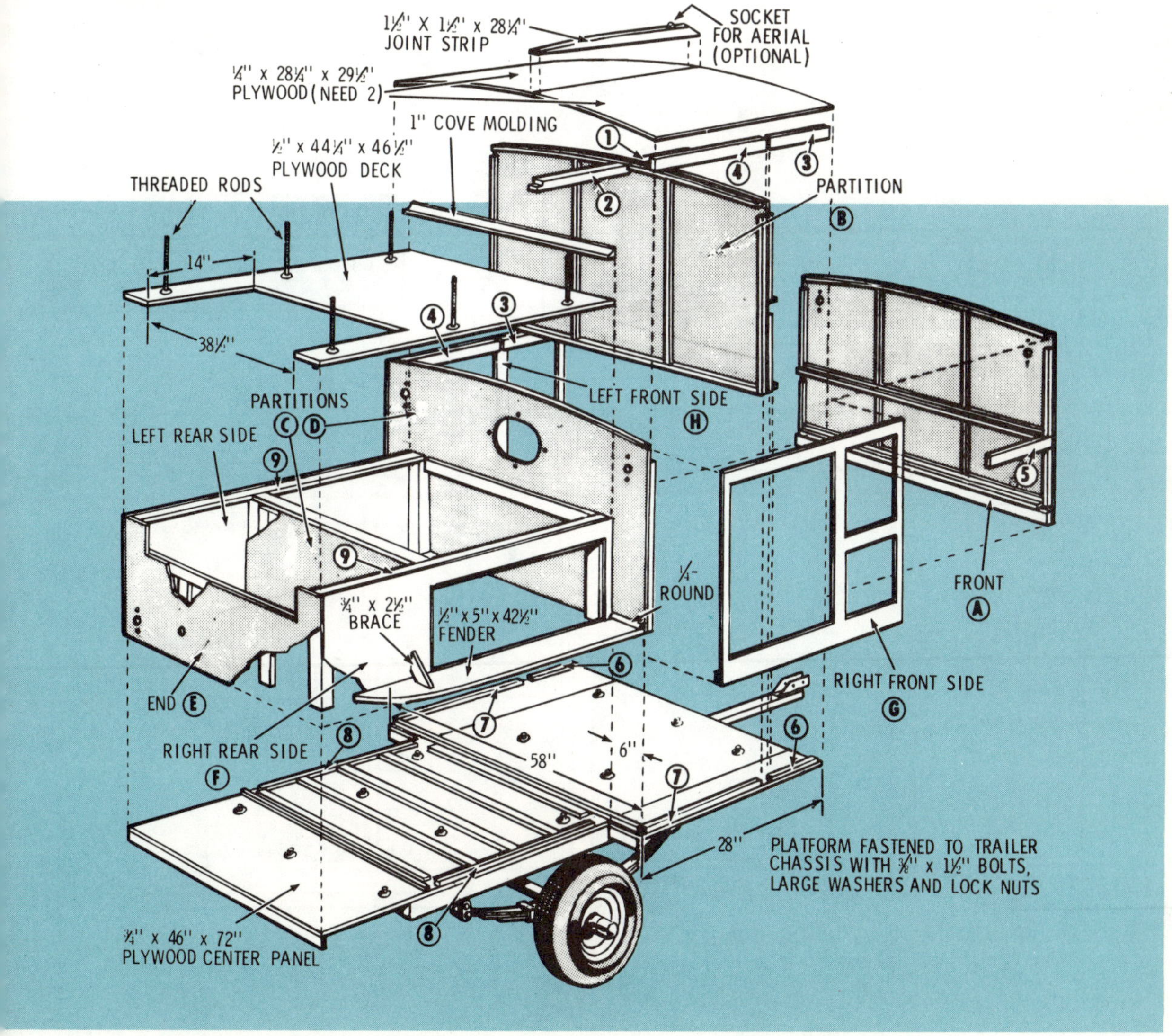
1½" X 1½" x 28¼"
JOINT STRIP
SOCKET
FOR AERIAL
(OPTIONAL)
¼" x 28¼" x 29½"
PLYWOOD (NEED 2)
1" COVE MOLDING
½" x 44¼" x 46½"
PLYWOOD DECK
THREADED RODS
14"
38½"
PARTITION
B
PARTITIONS
C D
LEFT REAR SIDE
LEFT FRONT SIDE
H
¼-
ROUND
FRONT
A
¾" x 2½"
BRACE
½" x 5" x 42½"
FENDER
END E
RIGHT FRONT SIDE
G
RIGHT REAR SIDE
F
58"
6"
28"
PLATFORM FASTENED TO TRAILER
CHASSIS WITH ⅜" x 1½" BOLTS,
LARGE WASHERS AND LOCK NUTS
¾" x 46" x 72"
PLYWOOD CENTER PANEL

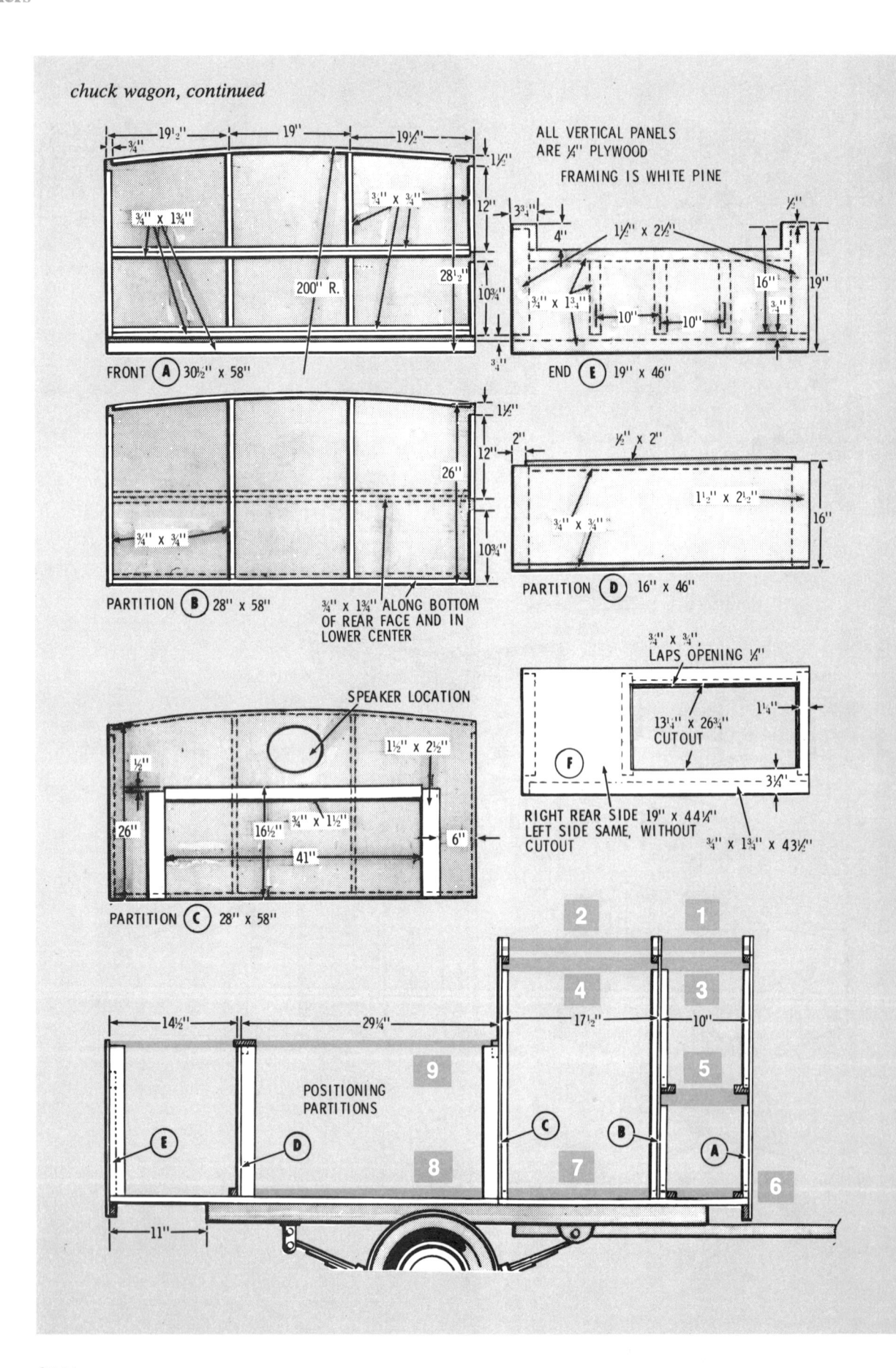

trailers

chuck wagon, continued

ALL VERTICAL PANELS ARE ¼" PLYWOOD
FRAMING IS WHITE PINE

FRONT **A** 30½" x 58"

END **E** 19" x 46"

PARTITION **B** 28" x 58"
¾" x 1¾" ALONG BOTTOM OF REAR FACE AND IN LOWER CENTER

PARTITION **D** 16" x 46"

SPEAKER LOCATION

PARTITION **C** 28" x 58"

F
RIGHT REAR SIDE 19" x 44¼"
LEFT SIDE SAME, WITHOUT CUTOUT
13¼" x 26¾" CUTOUT
¾" x ¾", LAPS OPENING ¼"
¾" x 1¾" x 43½"

POSITIONING PARTITIONS

2744

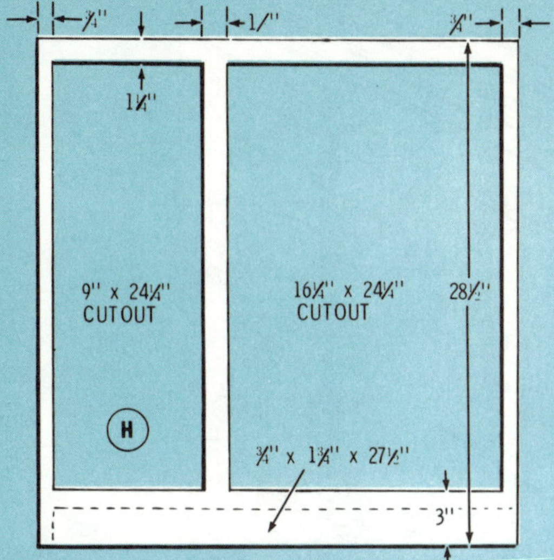
¾"
1½"
¾"
1¼"
9" x 24¼"
CUTOUT
16¼" x 24¼"
CUTOUT
28½"
H
¾" x 1¾" x 27½"
3"

FRONT SIDES - BOTH 28¼" x 28½"

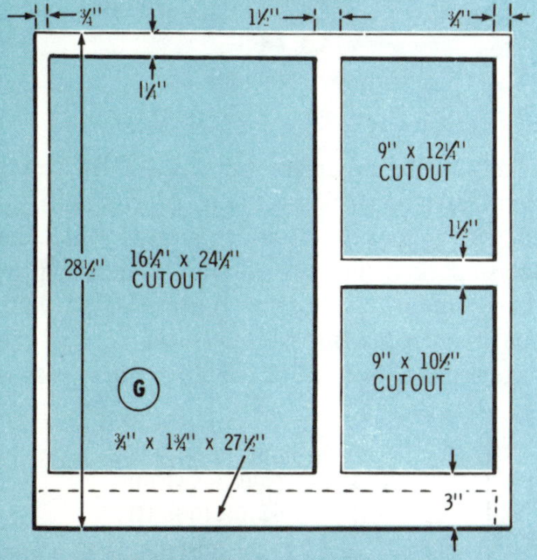
¾"
1½"
¾"
1¼"
9" x 12¼"
CUTOUT
1½"
28½"
16¼" x 24¼"
CUTOUT
9" x 10½"
CUTOUT
G
¾" x 1¾" x 27½"
3"

LATERAL FRAMING

Key	Need	Size (White pine)
1	1	1½" x 1½" x 10"
2	1	1½" x 1½" x 17½"
3	2	¾" x 1¾" x 10"
4	2	¾" x 1¾" x 17½"
5	2	¾" x 1¾" x 10"
6	2	½" x ¾" x 8½"
7	2	¾" x ¾" x 16"
8	1	¾" x ¾" x 26¼"
9	2	½" x 2" x 44"

The front partitions are anchored to the bed through framing feet (above); add lateral bracing, and then fix in side panels with screws and glue (below). The rear deck laps verticals and ties together assembly

The drawer leaf swings back from the stove pit and is held level by its own thickness. The water-cooler bay (below) is screwed to the front. The drop door rests on the tongue to form a shelf for setting a glass or pan under the water spigot

trailers

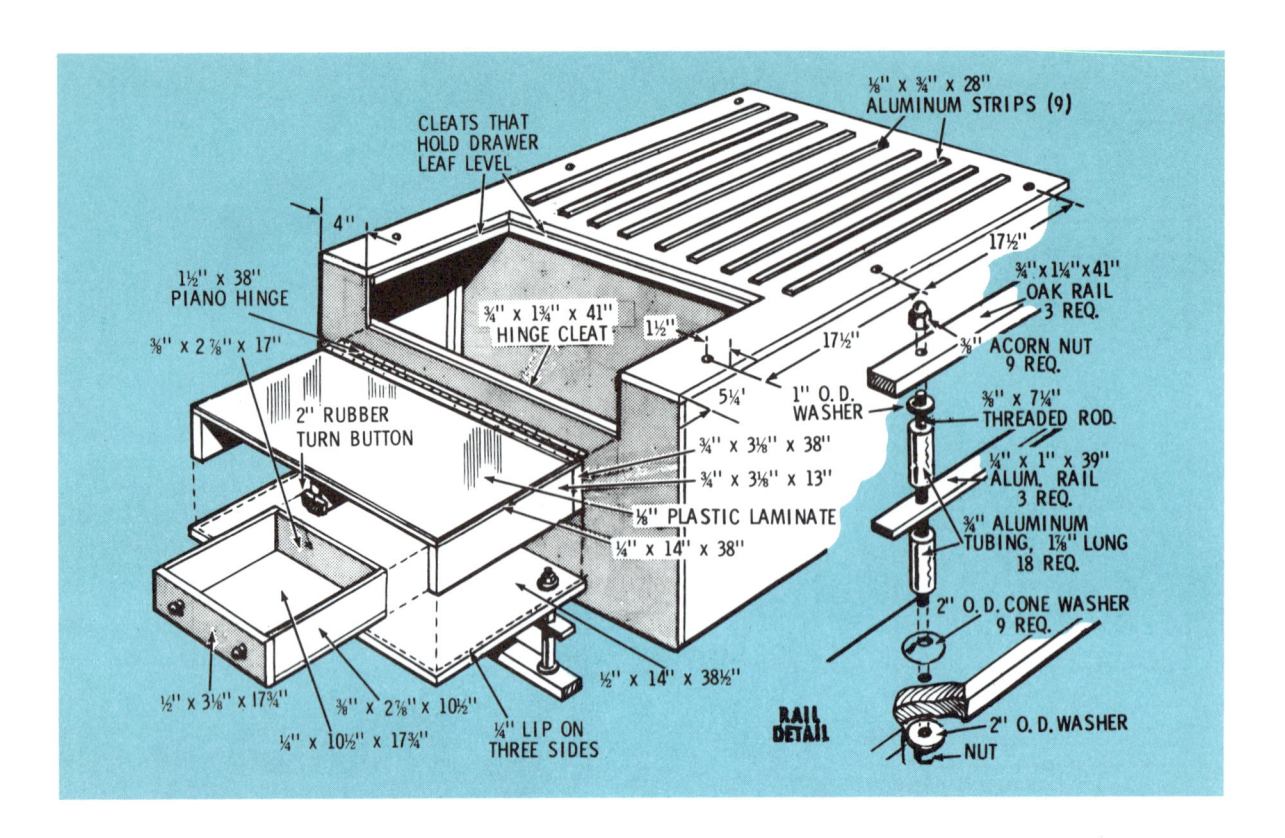

chuck wagon, continued

anchor the leaf. We usually tie down several folding chairs there. In a pinch, the leaf is large enough to serve as a snack counter for several people, and the chairs provide comfortable seating.

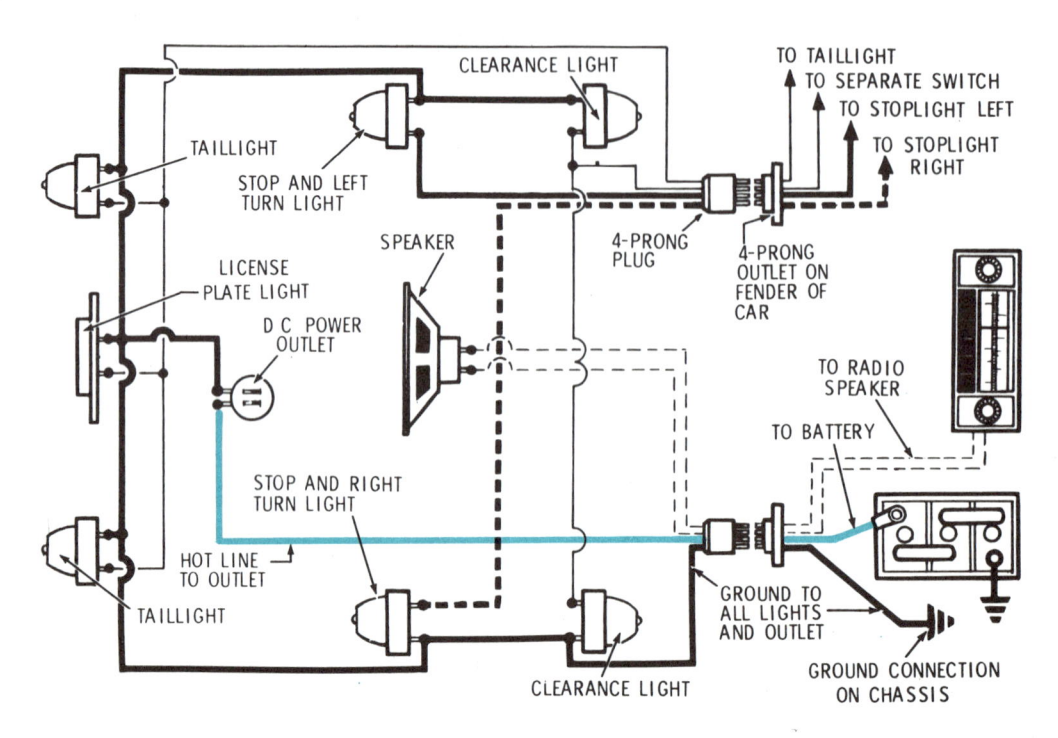

Access to the other compartment is by means of ½-in. plywood doors—each, of course, provided with a lock to discourage theft when the trailer is parked unattended. In the details provided, there are no lateral partitions, so each compartment runs full width. In the case of the luggage section, in front of the stove pit, access is from one side only. The slats on the floor are to provide clearance of the bolt heads, and to protect the plywood from wear when sliding heavy luggage, boxes—or even your spare tire—in and out.

In the first (full-height) compartment of the wider front section, the right door opens onto a 25-lb. commercial top-icer held in place by heavy foam-rubber pads at the sides. The left door gives access to the wardrobe closet, where jackets and dresses are on hangers hooked over a clothes rod that bridges the partitions. The stacked front compartments are accessible through two right-hand doors and a single full-height door on the left side. These compartments can be altered to suit whatever you wish to carry in them. And if you don't require a center shelf, you can simplify the framing of panels A and B and use a single door on each side.

The two-wheel chassis is a ready-made half-tonner, bought from Sears, complete with tires. The 6-ft. bed is cut from a single 4 x 8 panel of ¾-in. plywood. Trim 2 ft. off its length and 2 in. off its width to make the center panel, then edge-join two 6 x 28-in. wings to this to form a blunt T with a crosspiece 58 in. wide. Bolt this bed to the chassis securely, using large washers between the top face of the plywood and the nuts.

All vertical panels—plus the roof—are ¼-in. plywood; the deck is ½-in. plywood. Use good-grade exterior type throughout. The framing is mostly white pine 1 x 1s, which actually measure ¾ in. square. *All* dimensions on the plan are actual sizes.

Assemble all parts with waterproof glue and flathead screws, countersinking the heads. Plug all screw holes and cracks with spackling compound. When attaching the fenders, be sure there's a minimum 2-in. clearance above the tires.

To protect all outside corners, I capped them with trunk-type metal corners. For a finish, I used marine primer and enamel on the exposed surfaces, but applied aluminum paint to the chassis, under the carriage and kitchen pit. A tough outdoor varnish is all that's needed on the inside of the other compartments.

My wiring diagram is shown on page 2746 as a suggestion. The two lower taillights, the amber clearance lights (toward the car), and the license-plate light are burning whenever the car's headlights are on. The upper taillights come on only when the brake pedal or turn-signal is operated. I used 1956 Impala style lights. The heavy black line is the ground wire to all lights and to a utility outlet mounted in the stove pit. The green wire is a direct line to that outlet from the 6 or 12-volt auto battery. The light line to the clearance lights can be hooked into the car's taillight, but I made them independent of the car lights for use in city traffic or rain.

All the wires are brought together in one place, to an 8-pole strip of binding posts. From here, two 4-wire cables run through the trailer drawbar, emerging near the hitch, where they connect to two 4-prong connectors mounted on the bumper.

My chuck wagon's been road tested thoroughly at speeds up to 70 mph. It tracks obediently, hugging the road without sway. And you can be sure it's always ready to follow us into the open spaces any time there's a couple days off. Maybe we'll see you there.

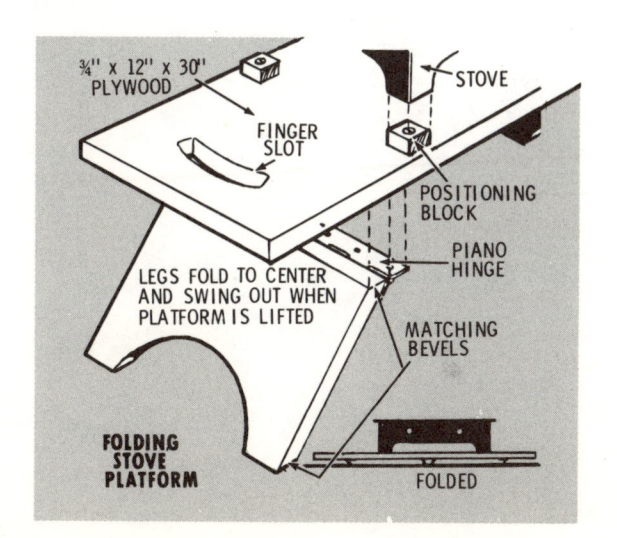

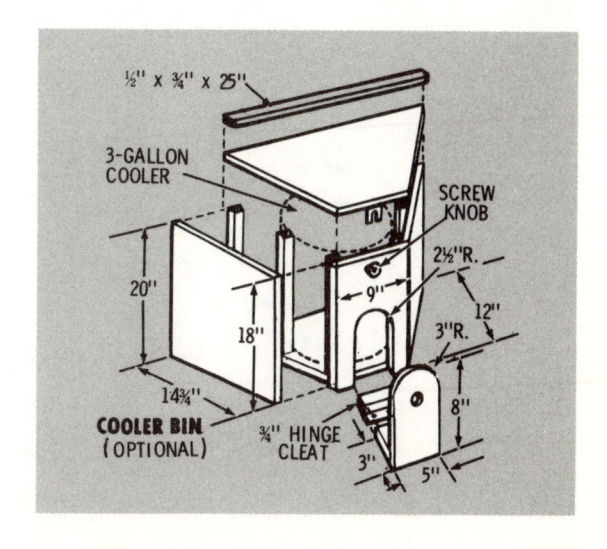

trailers

No-sweat hauling of heavy, bulky items is yours when you hitch this wagon to your yard tractor

Handy trailer for yard tracs

BY HANK ADAMS

A little wagon building
    gives you big load-hauling
capacity to save time
    and your back
        in yard work

■ IF YOU'VE INVESTED in one of those popular garden tractors or riding mowers, this handy cart will give you extra benefits.

It would cost about three times as much to get similar features in a commercial cart, and you can cut building costs in half if you can swipe a wheel or two from obsolete wheelbarrows.

Built to the dimensions shown on the opposite page, the cart has a heaped capacity of about 7½ cu. ft., or roughly 1000 lbs. of dirt or stone. With the stake sides in place, it will haul a huge pile of leaves, grass clippings or trash. It takes 5½-7 hp to haul half-ton loads, so if your power unit has less, you'll either have to make a smaller trailer or be careful how you load this one.

The body is ¾-in. exterior plywood, assembled

It beats a wheelbarrow! For this job, the tailgate comes off and lets you dump loads from the seat

2749

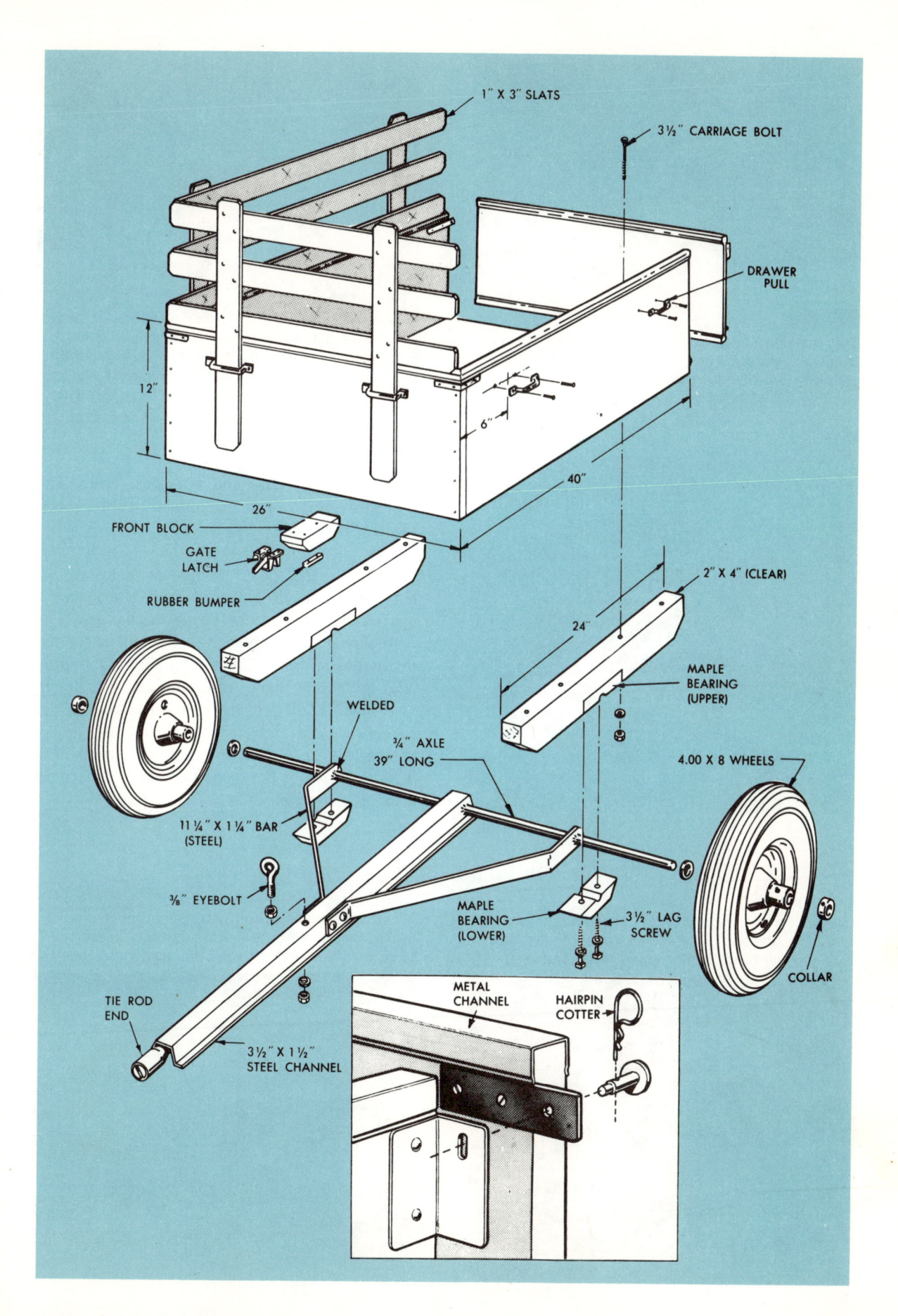

trailers

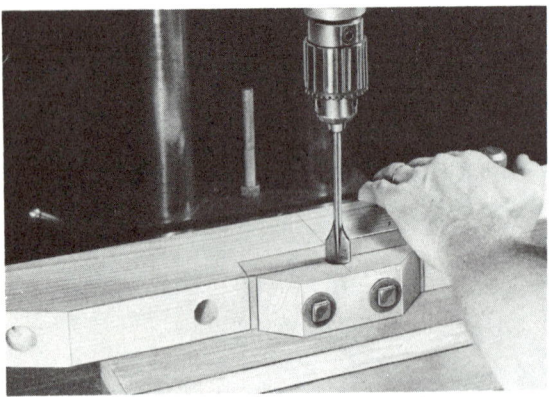

Drill the axle hole after gluing the upper bearing block into the beam and fastening the lower bearing to it with lagbolts. Use joint line to center bit

To assure a square assembly, weld the axle to the drawbar unit and fasten it to beams before you drill ¼-in. holes into the trailer bed for carriage bolts

yard-trac trailer, continued

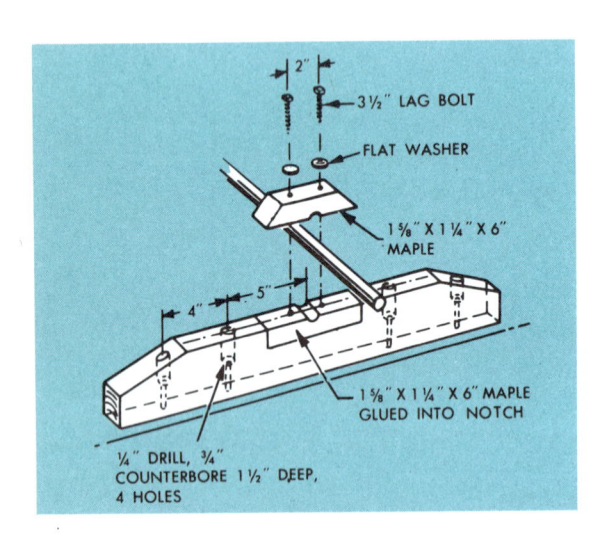

with screw-type nails and waterproof glue. The top edges are capped for durability—the metal raceway used for certain wiring will fit over ¾-in. panels.

Centering the body over the axle makes dumping easier, but a balanced load tends to lift against the hitch. It's best to locate the axle 2 or 3 in. behind the center; this also increases the dump angle. Before mounting the axle, apply stick graphite to the bearing surfaces.

A steering tie rod and ball joint from an old car provide a universal hitch. In the model shown, the tip of the tie rod is welded inside a drawbar made of hat-section channel. This could also be U-channel, or even 1½-in. pipe.

No accidental dumps when you install a gate latch under the trailer bed to engage an eyebolt in the drawbar. Bumper block, behind latch, keeps bed level

Mount the slide bolts horizontally at lower corners of the tailgate. When the gate is pivoted up and back, extended bolts on sides' top edges hold gate

clever ideas

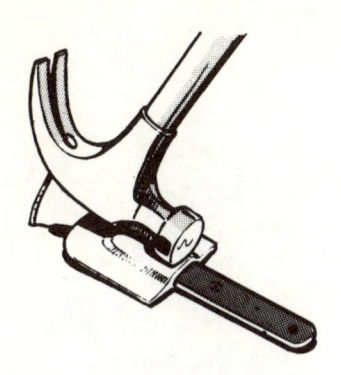

A plate scraper makes a perfect rubber cushion for protecting a wood surface when removing a nail with a claw hammer. Slip it under the hammer head so that the thickest part acts as a pad.

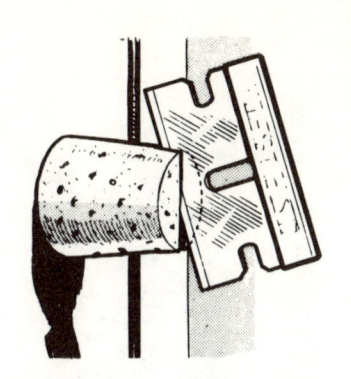

This handy holder for a single-edge razor blade can easily be made by cutting a deep notch in one end of a large cork, then gluing the cork to a shop wall, or a cabinet door.

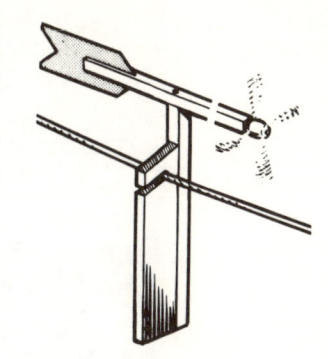

Hook a toy windmill over a clothesline if there is no other suitable support available. Nail the staff to a deeply notched board and the weight will hold the mill upright.

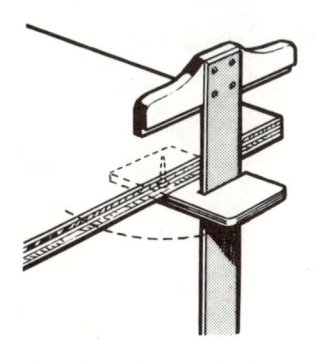

A slotted turnbutton for holding a T-square is a useful addition to any drawing board. Make it from a 3 x 6-in. piece of ¼-in. plywood and mount it tight enough to hold in either position.

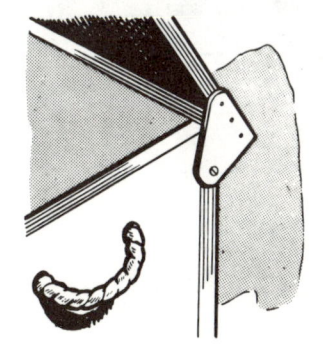

Plywood triangles make fine hinge substitutes for use on a toy chest. Drill a pivot-screw hole in one corner and drive nails through the opposite edge into the chest cover.

Maintain that chisel edge on your paintbrushes by clamping the bristles in a large paper clip, as shown. This will also provide a hanger for suspending the brushes from hooks or nails.

A long-lasting acid brush for use in soldering jobs can be made by slitting the chisel end of a slip-on pencil eraser to form acid-holding "bristles." (Rubber is almost acid-proof.)

To remove a tight ring, wrap the finger with string to compress the knuckle, then push the free end of the string under the ring and unwind it so that the ring is pushed off the finger.

Small paste brushes used with library paste are easy to misplace. To make a holder for such a brush, simply drive a brad into the shelf where the paste is kept and slip the handle over it.

train, children's

Back-yard railroad

BY W. CLYDE LAMMEY

This interior view of the cab shows the brake and throttle levers. Actually the engine has only one speed. The throttle is a forward and reverse switch

■ ROBERT WOOLSON, Chicago TV advertising man, could easily qualify as the little old toymaker, but to him designing and building playthings for children is little more than just a fascinating hobby.

To his growing list of popular back-yard toys, he now adds this delightful replica of an old-time steam locomotive—the most realistic thing on rails for small-fry engineers.

The smoke from its milk-strainer stack is no

trammel, elliptic: see ellipsograph
trampoline: see tumbler
transistor breadboard: see electronics
transistor broadcaster: see transmitter, FM
transistor checker: see electronics

2752

BELL HANGER, ¾" PLYWOOD

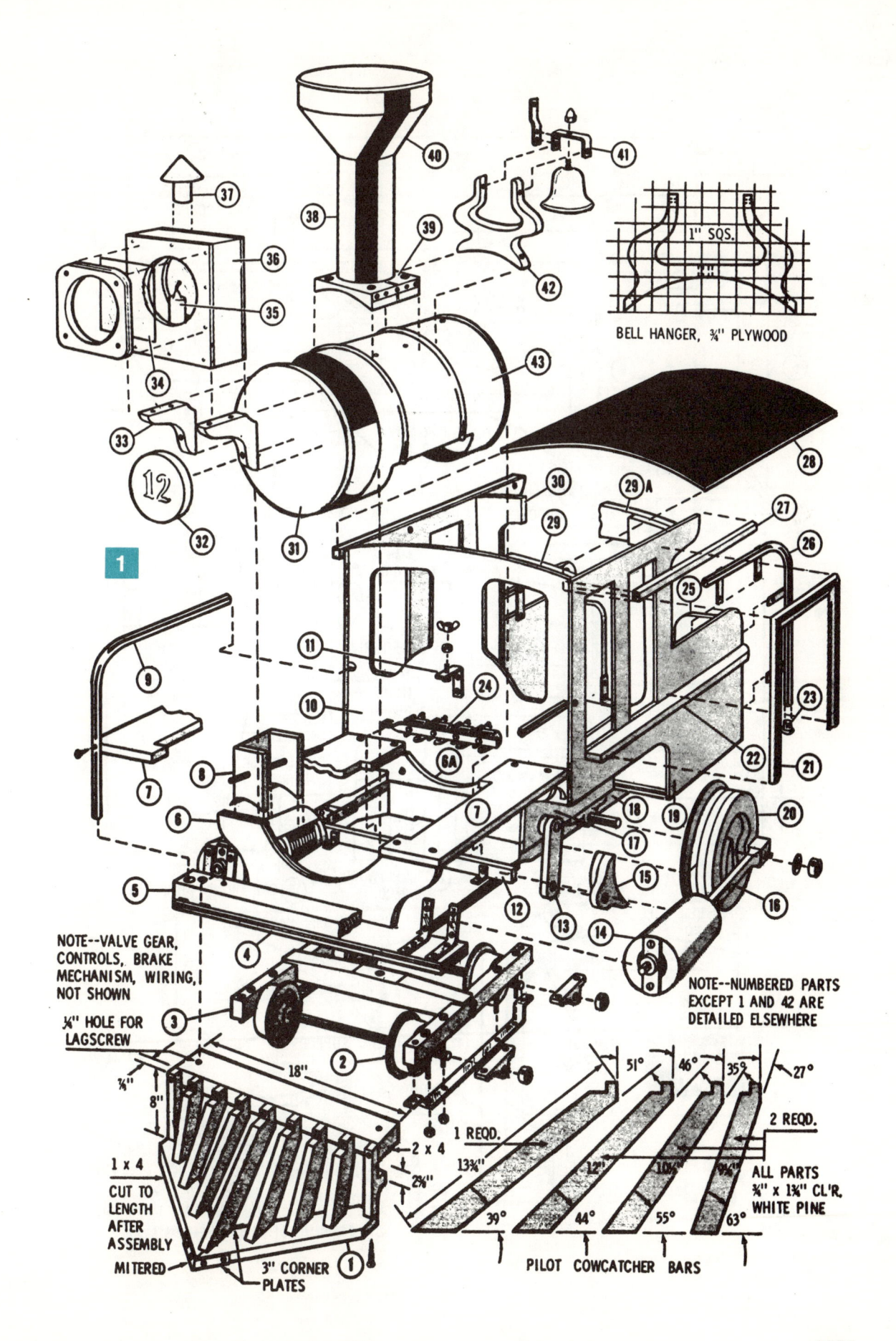

NOTE--VALVE GEAR, CONTROLS, BRAKE MECHANISM, WIRING, NOT SHOWN

¼" HOLE FOR LAGSCREW

1 x 4 CUT TO LENGTH AFTER ASSEMBLY MITERED

3" CORNER PLATES

2 x 4

NOTE--NUMBERED PARTS EXCEPT 1 AND 42 ARE DETAILED ELSEWHERE

PILOT COWCATCHER BARS

1 REQD.
2 REQD.
ALL PARTS ¾" x 1¾" CL'R. WHITE PINE

2753

train, children's

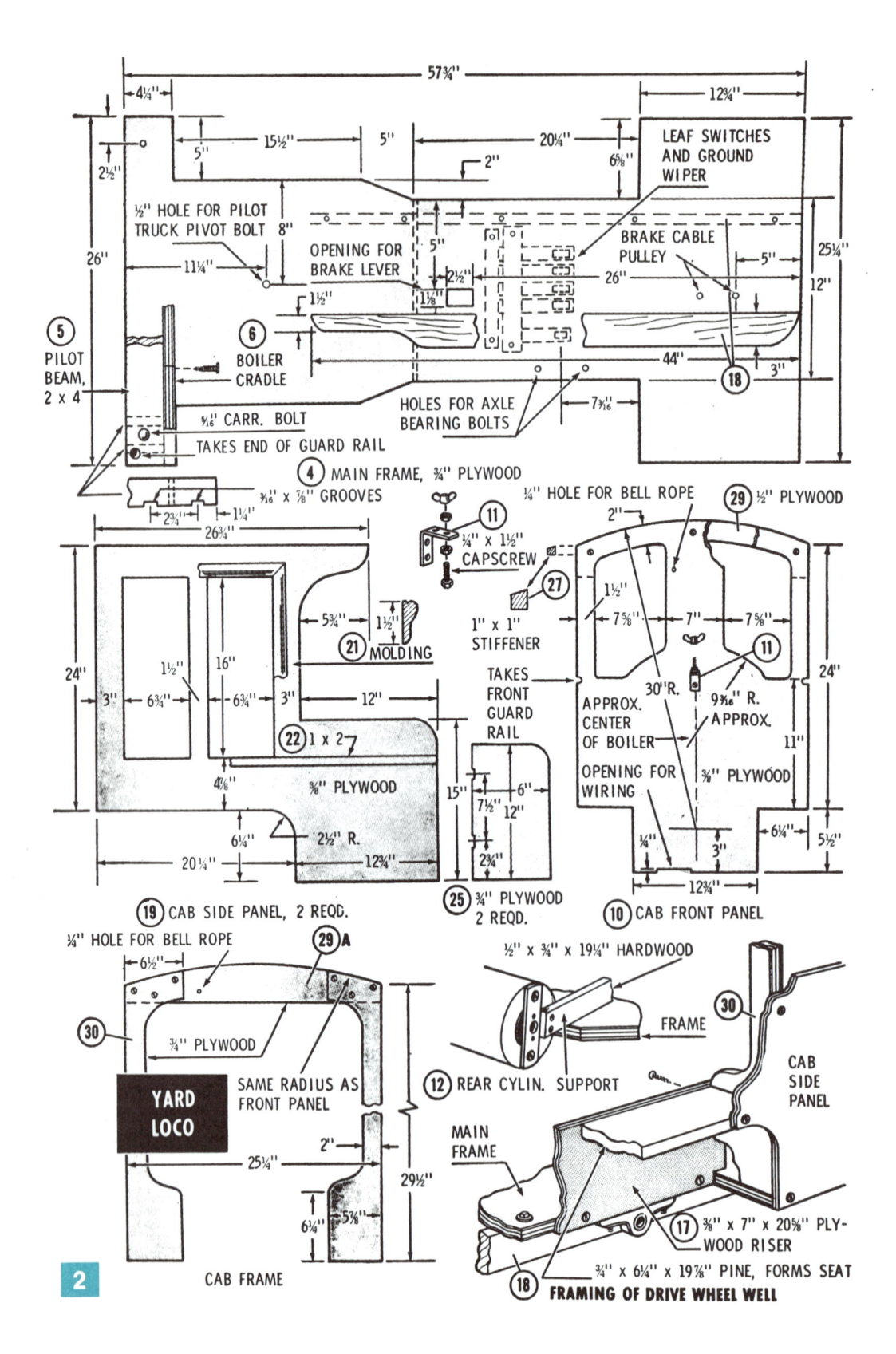

back-yard railroad, continued

tip-off as to what makes it start, stop and reverse, or what keeps it chugging along on its 1 x 2 track at a merry 5 miles per, with all the flair of the real thing; the push-pull pistons operate the drive-wheels in true engine fashion, but they're not powered by steam. The secret?—a couple of king-size solenoids which are energized by two auto batteries hooked in tandem and hidden under the hinged oil-drum boiler. As for safety, there's a handbrake that will stop the engine in less than a half turn of a wheel.

Dad, of course, is in for some fun too in building it and he can get a good idea of the basic construction from the exploded view in Fig. 1. You can pick up everything you'll need—except the electricals and a few odds and ends—from your local hardware and lumber dealers. The first step is to cut out the frame from a piece of plywood and this should be no problem as you'll see from Fig. 2. Only the through holes and an opening are shown; the holes you will later drill for screws are not shown, as it's best to locate these at the time of placement of the parts. Notice that there are two stiffeners, or stretchers, under the frame, the rough location of one shown by dotted lines. These parts should be cut from hardwood.

Ready for painting, here is what your locomotive will look like in the raw. The final step in construction is attaching the cowcatcher

Before attaching them, locate the pillow-block bearings for the driver axle and bolt temporarily in place so that you can locate the holes in the stretchers for the axle.

Next step is building the pilot truck, Fig. 3. Note first the construction of the flanged wheels. Each wheel consists of a V-pulley, two plywood

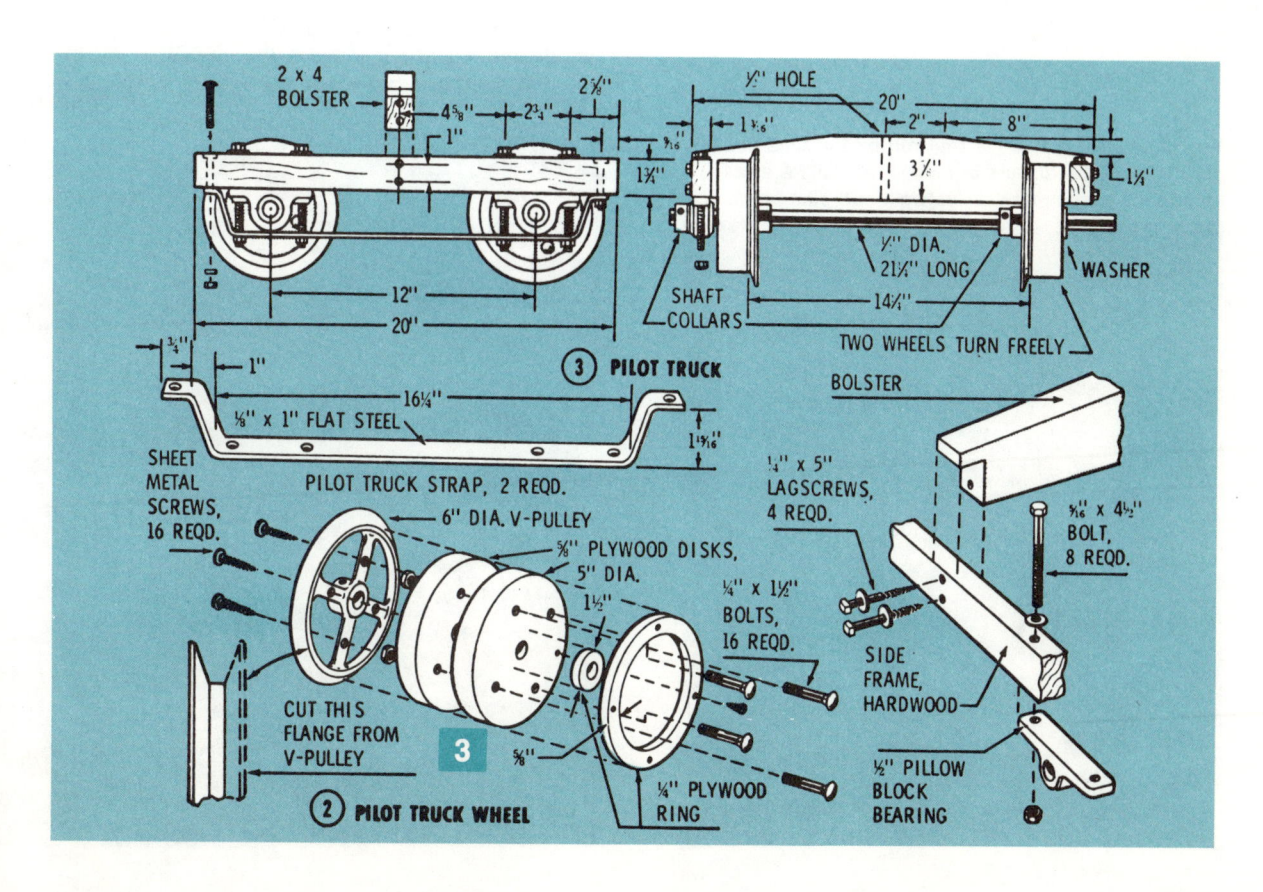

2755

train, children's

back-yard railroad, continued

Two truck wheels are collared on the axles so they can turn freely to reduce rolling friction and eliminate drag on curves. Allow a slight endplay

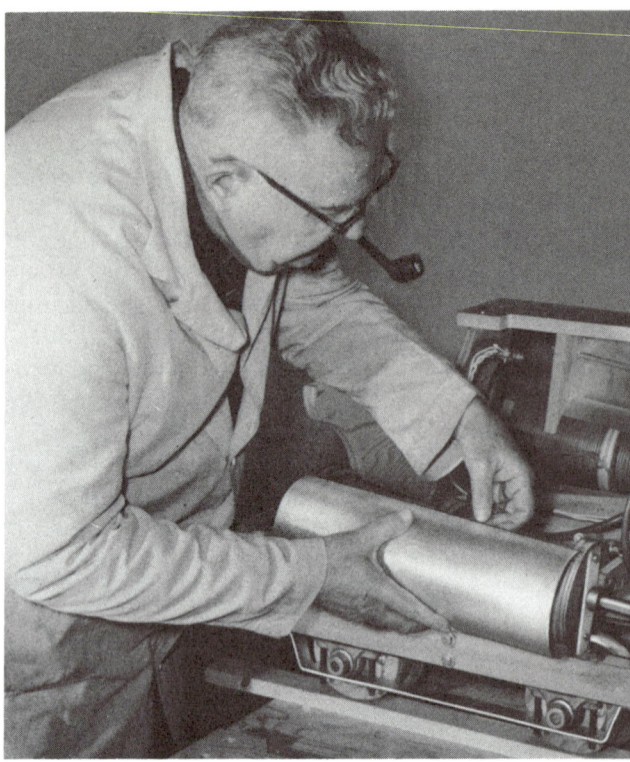

Cylinder covers are light sheet metal rolled to provide a friction fit over the coil ends and separators. Dummy steam chests hold the covers in place

The preassembled parts should be trial-fitted before final placement. The steam chest attaches only to the catwalk and must be prefitted before assembly

You're nearly ready for a trial run by the time you've put the front guard rails in place. The rails are fastened at three points: cab, catwalk and pilot beam

2756

disks and a plywood ring assembled with bolts and screws. Cut one flange off the V-pulley, assemble the sandwich—and there you are—a perfect, flanged rail wheel approximately 5 in. in diameter. Of course, the parts must be made with care so that you obtain a true running wheel. Although the diameter of the disks is given as 5 in. (the usual diameter of a 6-in. V-pulley at the bottom of the V-groove), it's a good idea to check this diameter before cutting the disks, as there may be some variation. The truck frame construction is simply a matter of cutting the parts accurately. But note the 2¾-in. spacing of the bearing holes. This dimension may vary, so check up before you drill the holes for the bearing bolts in both the frame pieces and the straps. Note also that two wheels are collared on the axles so that they can turn freely in rounding a curve.

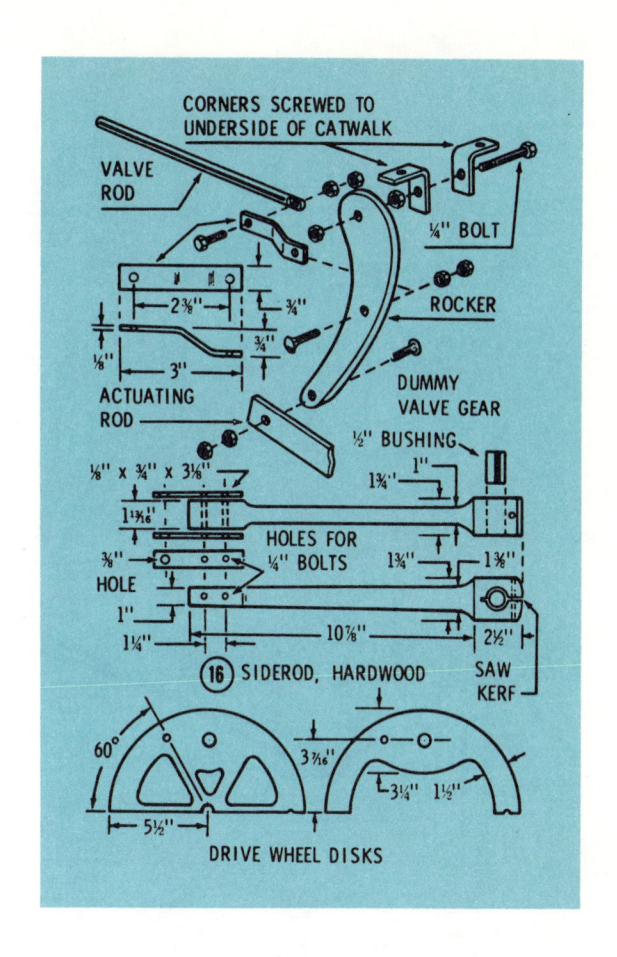

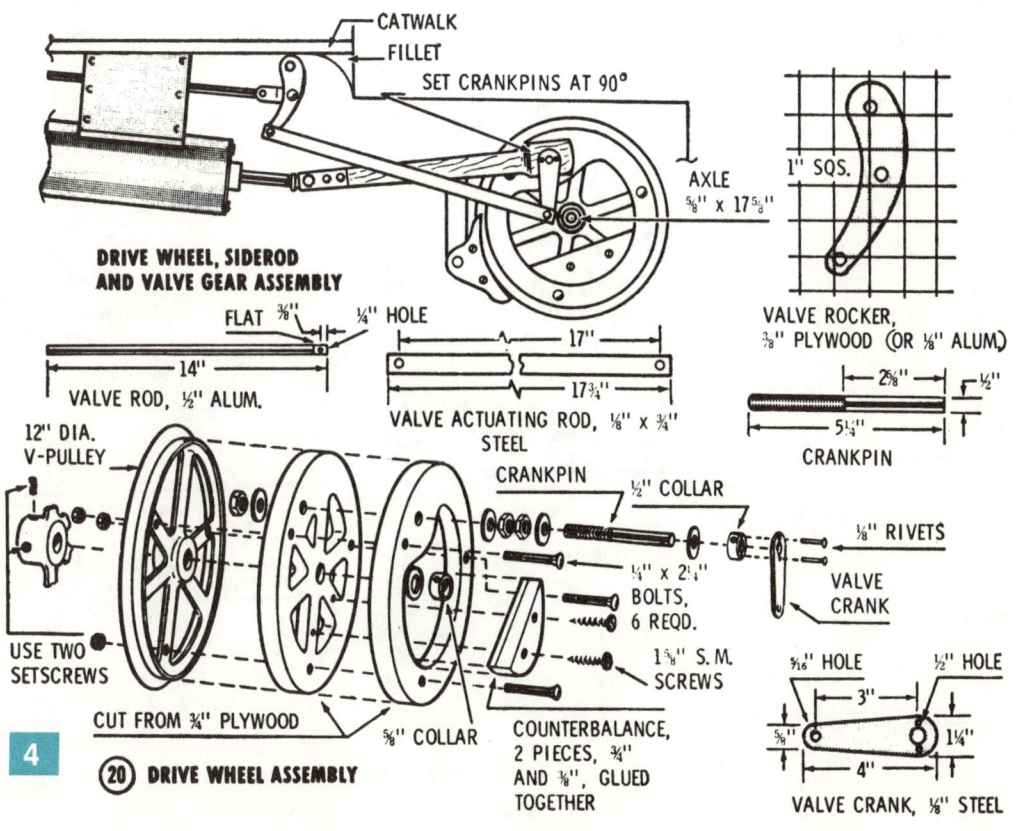

The drivers, Fig. 4, are made in much the same way, except that each wheel is spoked and fitted with a dummy counterbalance. Make sure that you drill the holes for the axles and crankpins (or siderod pins) on 3⁷⁄₁₆-in. centers to give a stroke of just 6⅞ in. Also, before assembling

train, children's

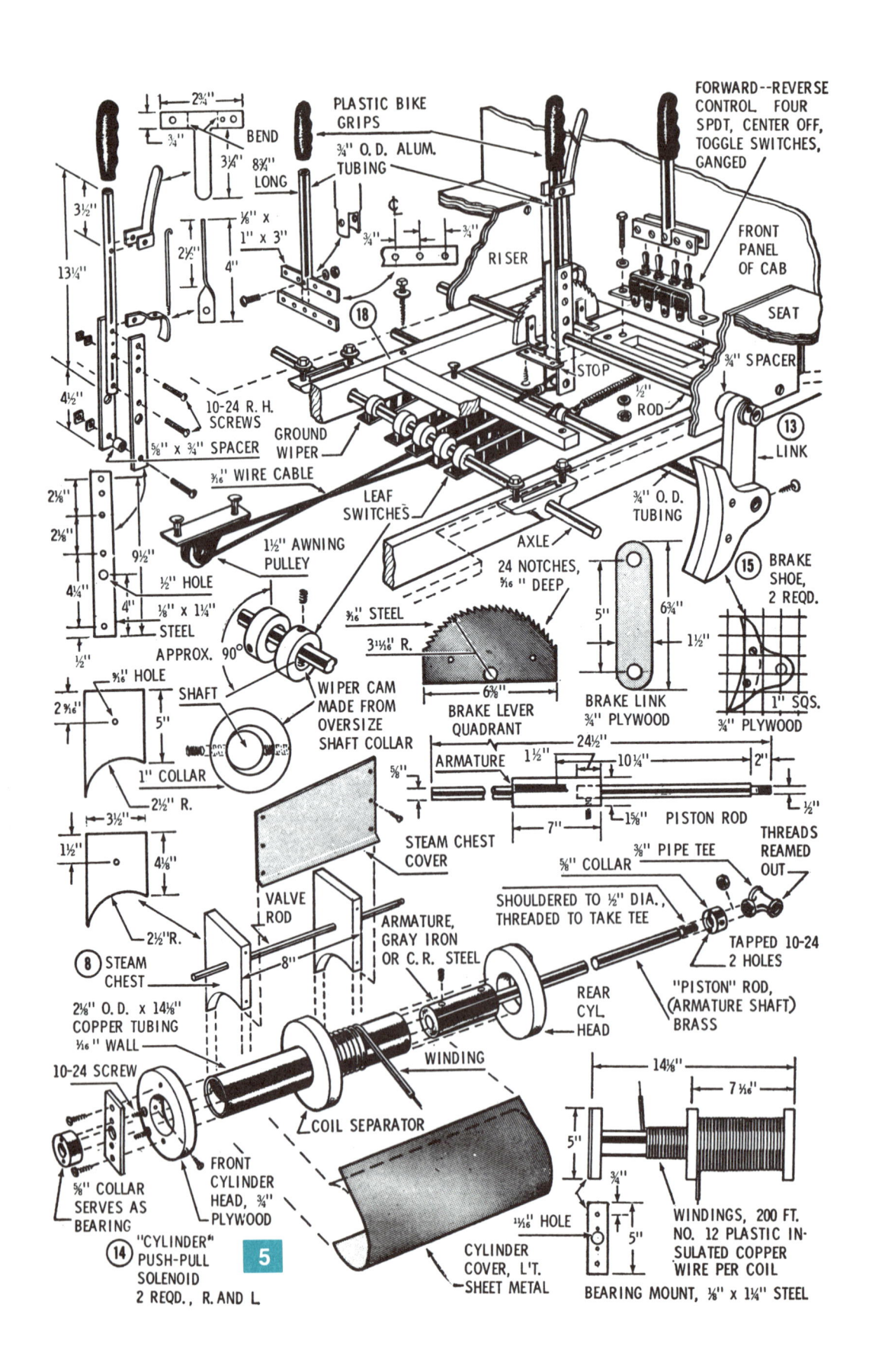

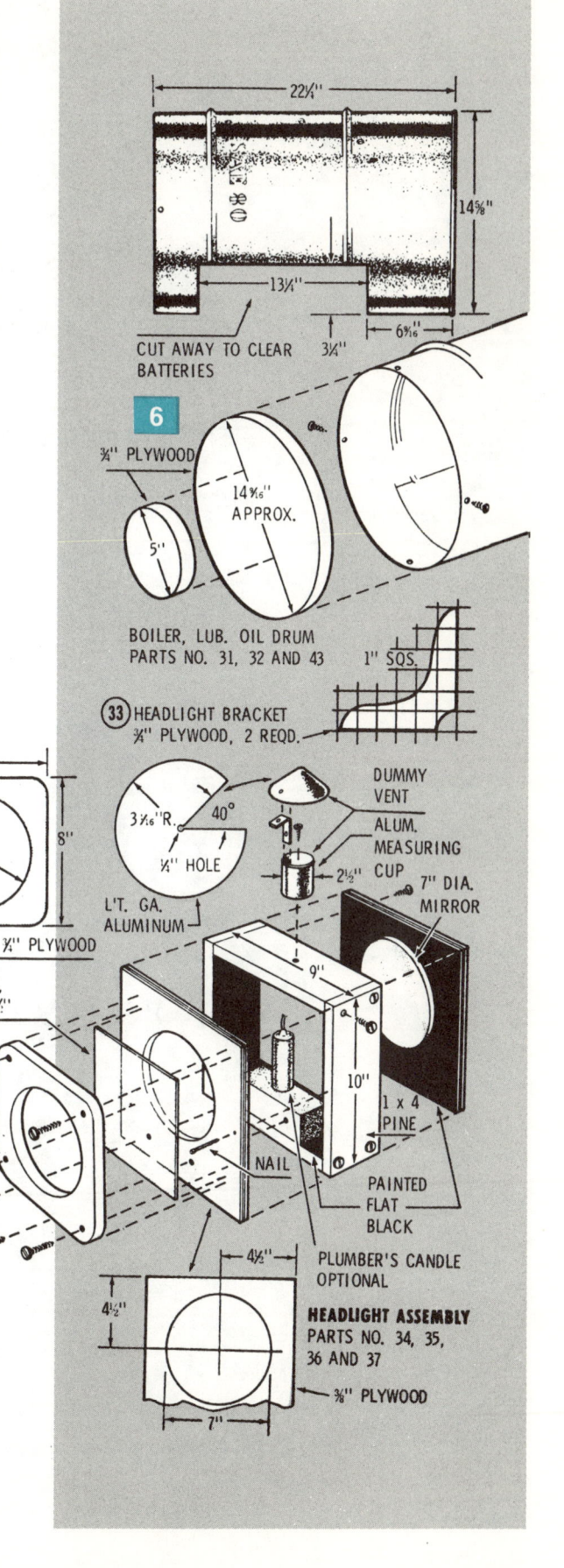

each wheel, drill and tap the hub of each V-pulley to take a second setscrew as indicated. When assembling on the axle, spot-drill the latter for the points of the setscrews and turn the screws up tightly. This will prevent the wheels from shifting on the axle when in operation and throwing the crankpins off the 90-deg. position. It is not necessary to turn the wheels to size. Just use care in bandsawing them round.

Note especially the assembly of the crankpin in Fig. 4 and the method of riveting the valve crank to the collar, which serves the twofold purpose of holding the big end of the siderod in place and of anchoring the valve crank in the proper position on the pin. Use care in drilling the holes for the rivets in both the valve crank and collar to get them in register, then countersink the holes so the upset ends of the rivets won't protrude.

Fig. 4 also details the dummy valve parts and the siderods and while these may be made at this stage, they are not assembled until later on in the construction. The valve rocker was originally

train, children's

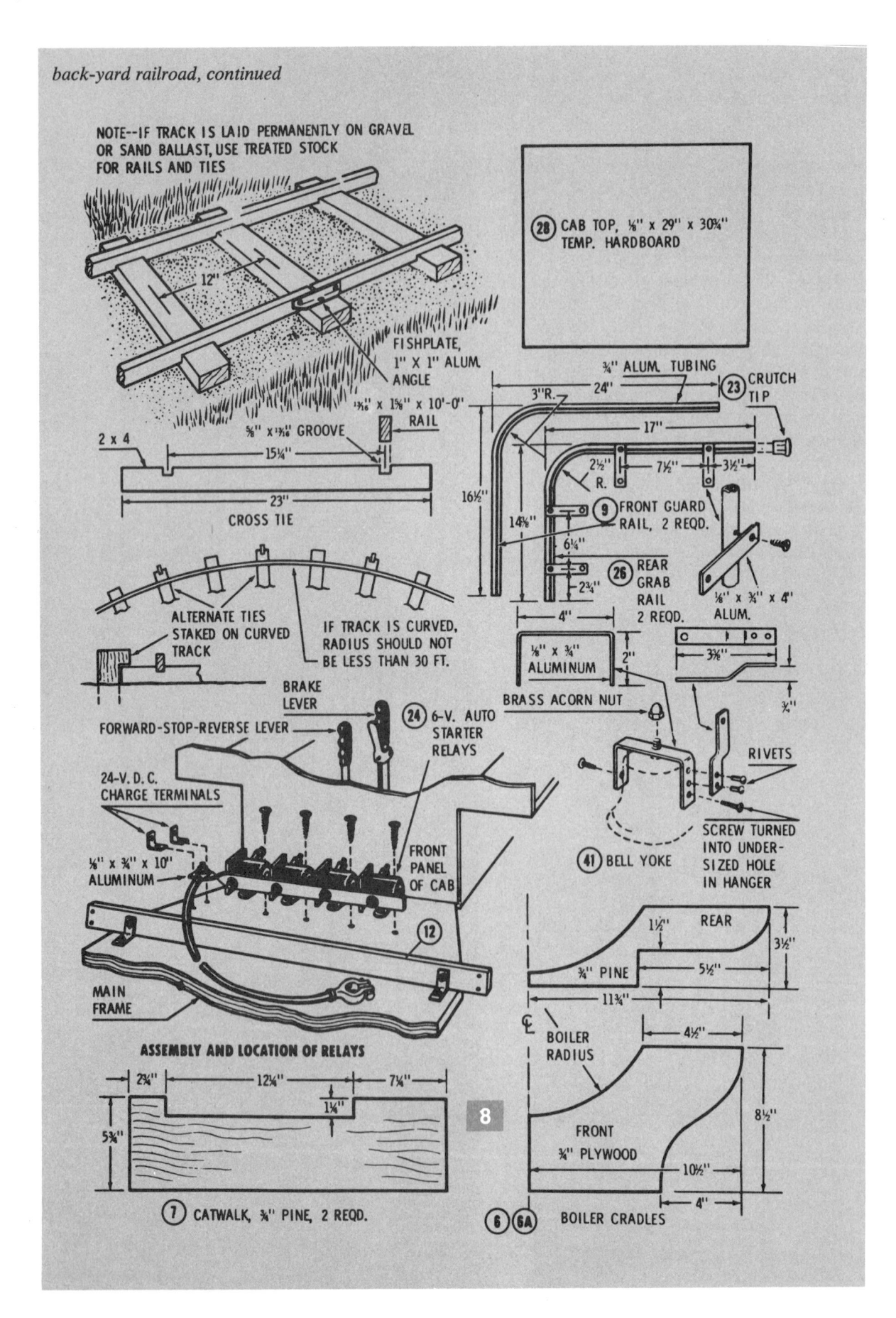

back-yard railroad, continued

NOTE--IF TRACK IS LAID PERMANENTLY ON GRAVEL OR SAND BALLAST, USE TREATED STOCK FOR RAILS AND TIES

12"

FISHPLATE, 1" X 1" ALUM. ANGLE

(28) CAB TOP, ⅛" x 29" x 30¾" TEMP. HARDBOARD

¹³⁄₁₆" x 1⅝" x 10'-0" RAIL

2 x 4

⅝" x ¹³⁄₁₆" GROOVE

15¼"

23"

CROSS TIE

¾" ALUM. TUBING

24"

3" R.

17"

2½" R.

7½"

3½"

(23) CRUTCH TIP

16½"

14⅜"

(9) FRONT GUARD RAIL, 2 REQD.

6¼"

2¾"

4"

(26) REAR GRAB RAIL 2 REQD.

⅛" x ¾" x 4" ALUM.

ALTERNATE TIES STAKED ON CURVED TRACK

IF TRACK IS CURVED, RADIUS SHOULD NOT BE LESS THAN 30 FT.

⅛" x ¾" ALUMINUM

2"

BRASS ACORN NUT

3⅜"

¾"

BRAKE LEVER

FORWARD-STOP-REVERSE LEVER

(24) 6-V. AUTO STARTER RELAYS

RIVETS

24-V. D.C. CHARGE TERMINALS

⅛" x ¾" x 10" ALUMINUM

FRONT PANEL OF CAB

(12)

MAIN FRAME

(41) BELL YOKE

SCREW TURNED INTO UNDER-SIZED HOLE IN HANGER

ASSEMBLY AND LOCATION OF RELAYS

2¾"   12¼"   7¼"

1¼"

5¾"

8

(7) CATWALK, ¾" PINE, 2 REQD.

REAR

1½"

3½"

¾" PINE

5½"

11¾"

₵ BOILER RADIUS

4½"

FRONT ¾" PLYWOOD

8½"

10½"

4"

(6)(6A) BOILER CRADLES

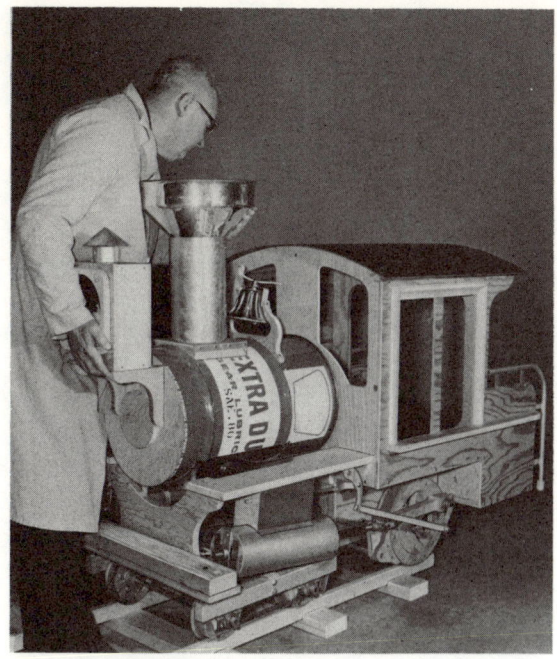

With its headlight, stack and bell in place, the boiler must be prefitted to determine the placement of the clamping bolt which is attached to the cab's front

A roof finishes the cab. Note the beveled strip along each side of the cab. It serves as a stiffener and as an anchor strip for roof screws

made from plywood but you can also make it of aluminum or ¼-in. hardboard. Use straight grained hardwood for the siderods and fit the big ends with an oilless bushing as indicated. To hold the bushing in place and prevent chance splitting of the big end of the rod, saw-kerf the end and drill for a small bolt or rivet as detailed. Plywood parts for the cab, front and side panels and the cab frame member may be cut at this time but shouldn't be completely assembled until the

Removal of the parts after trial fitting makes the wiring job easier. Here the cab side, catwalk, rail and steam chest have been taken off

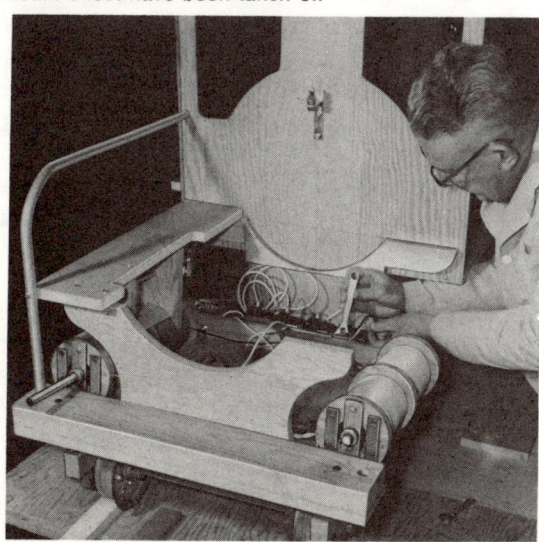

Here is the engine, boiler off, but ready for a trial. Batteries are in place. Coat all wood with a suitable plywood sealer before the final painting

train, children's

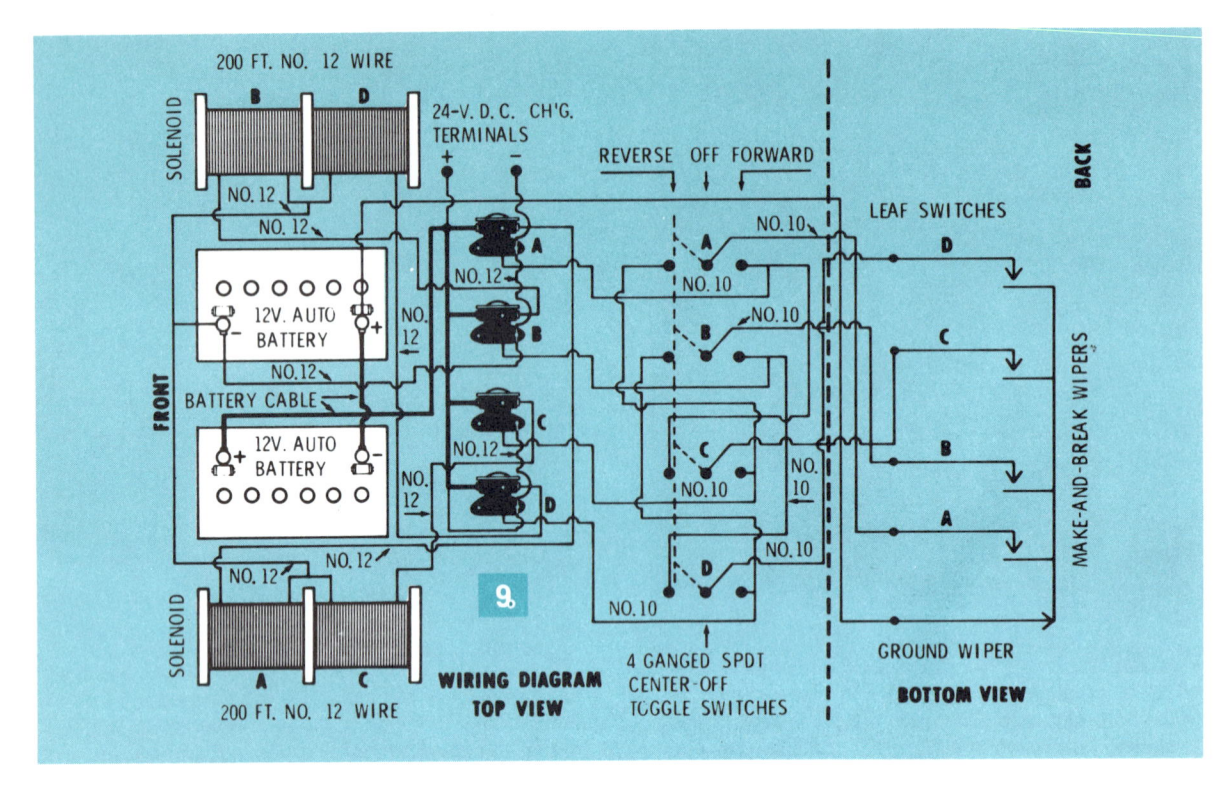

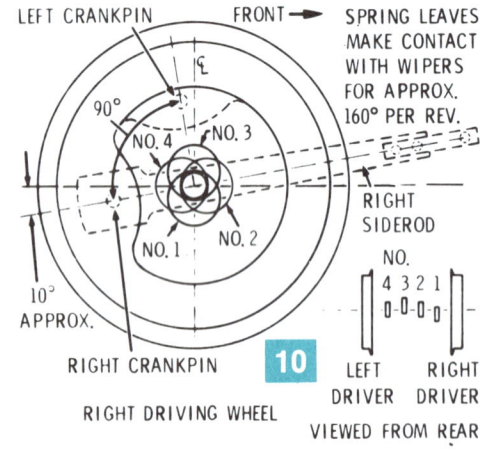

back-yard railroad, continued

cylinders (solenoids) and other electricals are installed, since placement and attachment of the latter is made easier when the frame is clear. Note in the lower right-hand detail in Fig. 2 the framing of the drive wheel well. The riser and seat serve as anchor parts for the cab panels and frame members.

When joining parts wood-to-wood or metal-to-wood, use sheet-metal screws with binder heads. These turn in easily and hold more securely in fir plywood. The binder heads also make a neat assembly job and are especially attractive as fasteners wherever visible.

Now that you have the pilot truck, drive wheels and frame ready for assembly, you're ready to tackle the cylinders (solenoids) and the control assemblies. Note first in Fig. 1 that the front ends of the cylinders are held in place by pairs of 4-in. inside steel corners and that the rear ends are supported by a cross member, Part No. 12 in Figs. 1 and 2. Assembly of the cylinders (solenoids) is shown in the lower details, Fig. 5, and assembly of the controls in the upper details. Be especially careful when winding the solenoid coils to get the same amount of wire on each and to end up with a neat, level winding.

There should be 100 ft. of wire on each coil—or a total of 200 ft. for each pair. Note that the engine requires two pairs of coils to make the two solenoids.

The armature is end-drilled to take the ends of the two-piece piston rods, which are held in place with headless setscrews. Top ends of the setscrews must be flush or just below the surface of the armature when turned in. Spot holes near the ends of the rods to take the setscrews. Ordinary shaft collars serve as bearings, and these must be positioned so that the armature will center in the copper core.

Before the cylinders are mounted, turn the frame upside down and place the main axle, starting it through one bearing and a stretcher, then placing the five wiper cams on the axle before sliding it through the second bearing to its final position. Next, fit the risers (upper details in Fig. 5) and locate and drill holes for the rod carrying the brake lever and brake links. The rod should center over the opening for the lever. Then make the lever as detailed and the quadrant, which can be made from flat steel as indicated or ¼-in. hardboard. Make the links and spacers. Assemble all the parts as indicated, but don't add the brake shoes until later.

Center the four wipers on the axle, spacing about 2 in. apart, center to center; then cut leaves from ⅛ to 1¼-in. copper to about 7-in. lengths and screw to a strip of hardwood, spacing them so they center under the wipers when you bolt the strip to the frame. Position the ground wiper, which is a ⅝-in. shaft collar, then screw a second strip to the bottom of the frame as shown, to carry the ground-wiper leaf, which is 1 in. shorter than the first four. Drill holes through the four leaves and into the second strip for screws, one in each leaf. These provide an adjustment for setting the leaves for proper make-and-break contact. Set the four wiper cams at approximately 90-deg. intervals, beginning with No. 1 as in Fig. 10 at the left. The ground wiper makes continuous contact. The leaf should be fastened with two screws to prevent it from shifting.

plywood brake shoes

This done, place the drivers in position on the axle and make the brake shoes. The latter are two thicknesses of ¾-in. plywood, shaped and joined with two screws as in the crosshatched detail. A screen door spring attached to the brake shaft and to the frame maintains a constant tension on the linkage, keeping the brake shoes clear of the drivers when the brake is released. Then gang the four single-pole, double-throw, center-off toggle switches and mounting as indicated. Make and attach the lever, or "throttle," which throws all four switches simultaneously. Finally, mount the pilot truck, placing a washer between the bolster and the bottom of the frame and two nuts on the bolt.

Turn the assembly right side up and you're ready to mount the cab, boiler cradles, catwalks, the guard and grab rails; then make and fit boiler, stack, headlight, bell and cowcatcher. Begin this stage by cutting and fitting the seats, attaching these to the risers. Then screw the cab front panel to the seat end, fit and screw the cab frame in place and add the sides.

Boiler cradles and catwalks are detailed in Fig. 8, but before you place the catwalks, make and fit the boiler, stack and headlight as in Figs. 6 and 7. These parts are improvised from a lubricating oil drum for the boiler, Fig. 6; a milk strainer and short length of furnace smoke pipe for the stack; and a round mirror, a measuring cup and an enclosed box for the headlight, Fig. 7. The cut end of the lube drum is closed with a disk of plywood. A smaller disk of plywood is screwed to the large disk to serve as a number plate, Fig. 1.

final assembly

Use house numerals for the numbering, which can be any combination that suits your fancy. Make the bell hanger, Fig. 1, and assemble the stack with its clamp in place before drilling the mounting holes in the boiler. Then use the clamp and the hanger as locating patterns. Construction of the headlight is clearly shown in Figs. 6 and 7. The boiler is held in place by a clamping bolt and wingnut, the bolt attached to a corner iron, Part No. 11, Figs. 1 and 2. Drill a slightly oversize hole for the bolt near the rear end of the boiler. Assemble the catwalks, dummy steam chest and valve gear, add the rails front and back and the bunker ends, Parts No. 25, Figs. 1 and 2, and then finish up with the cab roof and the cowcatcher, made as in Fig. 1. This readies the job for wiring, which includes installation of the 6-volt relays, Figs. 1 and 8.

The electrical system is 24-volt d.c. but is set up to provide 12 volts to actuate the 6-volt autostarter relays. Experimentation may be necessary to determine exact positioning of the wiper cams on the axle to give the correct "make-dwell-break" sequence for maximum power impulses to the solenoids. Note that No. 10 and 12 wire is used throughout the system. Be sure before trial that all connections are tight and that wipers are locked on the axle.

Trackage can be almost anything desired within the limits of the space available—straight or curved, straight across or lengthwise to the yard, or perhaps a large oval. Curves should not be less than 30 ft. radius. If trackage is laid more or less permanently on ballast, the rail ends may be joined with fishplates as in Fig. 8. Otherwise, just press rail ends into the grooves in the crossties, alternating the butt joints of the rails.

See also: cars, sidewalk; ferris wheel; merry-go-round; parade floats.

transistor radios

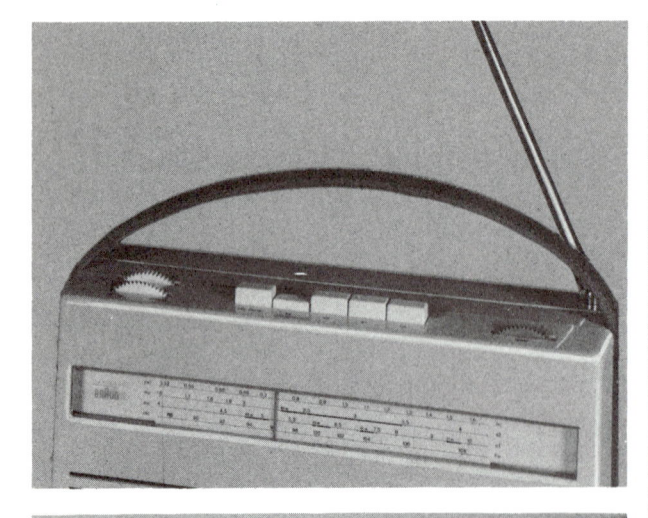

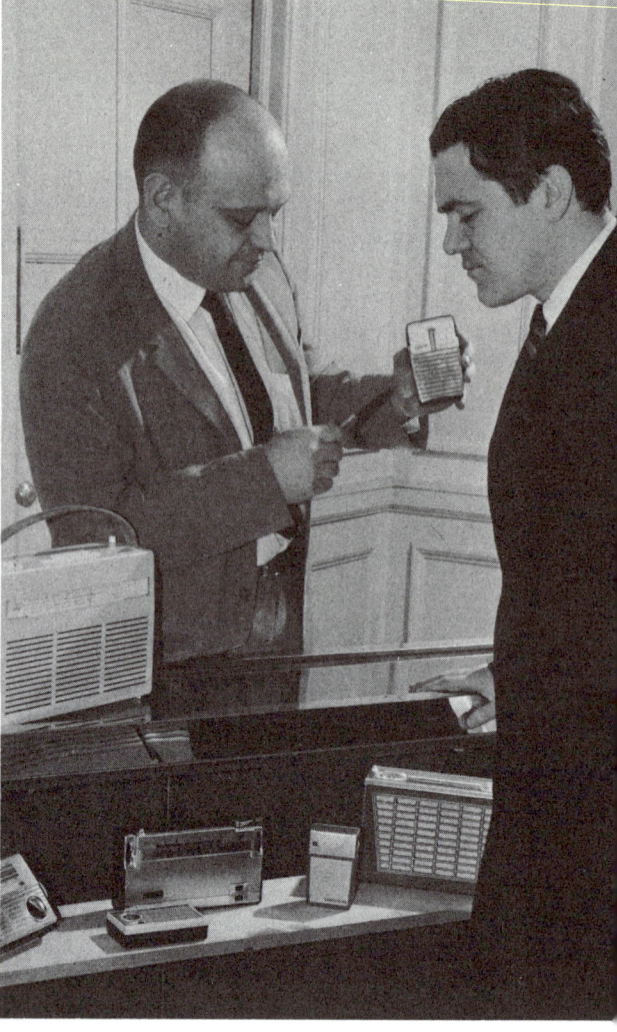

Tilting antenna is an important feature on an AM-FM unit to insure proper alignment (top left). Raise set from counter, squeeze lightly and shake (above, left). Set should perform well without interruption. This one's battery contacts cut out when squeezed, contacted again when released. Sound may increase or decrease when set is grasped by hand (above, right). Raising set away from the counter should not cause any additional alterations in the set's volume or its sensitivity, however

How to buy a good transistor radio

BY BYRON G. WELS

SIMPLE TESTS AND INSPECTIONS you can perform in the store will tell you a lot about any transistor radio you want to buy.

And the way in which the salesman demonstrates radios for you may tell you even more. As the test shoppers found, there are tricks used by some radio salesmen which can make any transistor radio sound better—or worse—than it actually is. Salesmen may "push" a particular set for a variety of reasons. Most will do it openly in their sales pitch; a few will use unethical methods.

One store had a $1.98 transistor radio prominently displayed in the window. The test shoppers asked the salesman to show it. As he

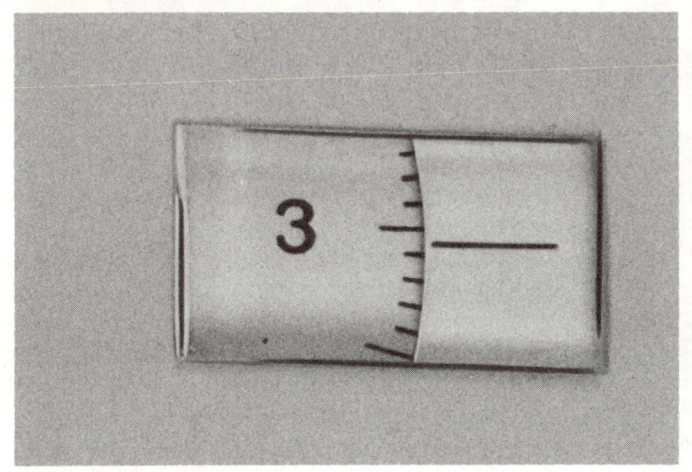

Grille size does not always indicate size of speaker (top). This speaker is larger than most, but be alert for similar grilles which mask tiny, inadequate speakers. Try reading the dial. The radio at the left uses an easy-to-read scale while the unit on the right is harder to reset to the same position. Check also for vernier action. Larger sets have a lighted dial. Don't expect this on pocket-size sets, but look for easy reading in dim light

removed it from the shelf in its glass display case, he switched on a fluorescent light inside the display case. Then he set the radio on the glass counter and turned it on.

The static crackle from the little set was painful—as it would have been from any radio placed that close to an operating fluorescent light.

The test shoppers asked to hear another set which didn't have so much static. The salesman smiled obligingly and brought out a more expensive set. But before he turned it on, he carefully switched off the fluorescent light. The more expensive radio sounded fine—and had practically no static.

The moral? Listen to a radio set away from any nearby fluorescent lights which are operating.

In another store, the test shoppers were shown a small transistor set which, from their knowledge of radio, seemed to be performing miracles in terms of sensitivity and selectivity. On close examination, the display case was found to have a length of wire coiled round and round under its metal edge. Such a remote antenna or signal sucker would have made almost any radio sound good.

The moral? Move any set you want to listen to away from the store counter.

Here's another trick tried in one large and impressive-looking store. When asked to show an AM-FM radio, the clerk brought out two com-

2765

transistor radios

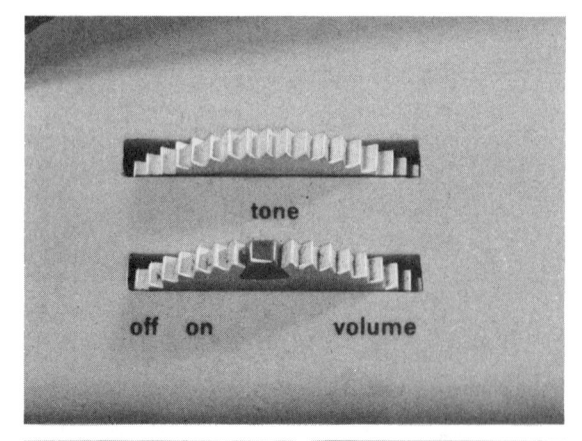

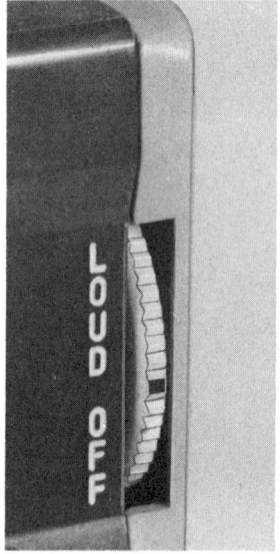

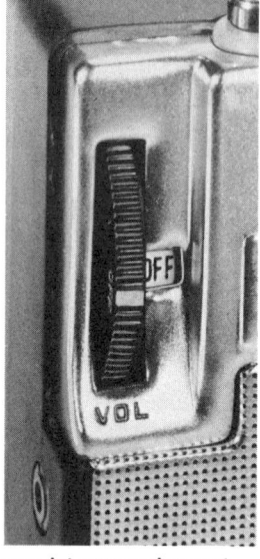

Tone control (top) is almost mandatory requirement on an FM unit. Good OFF indicator (bottom) will save battery replacement. Radio at left simply clicks off or on; no additional information is provided other than relative position of the black dot on the control (it's OFF here!) Unit at right provides window which reads OFF when the unit is off, and red color fills the window when the set is left on. Brush set against the side of your coat to see whether the set will turn on accidentally when you put it in your pocket

have them transferred from one set to another.

These are, unfortunately, some of the tricks of the sales trade. Here are other important performance points you can check right in the store:

To compare the sensitivity of several radios, tune them all to the same *weakest* station the best set will receive. A good set will pick up weak stations; a poor one will not receive them, no matter what the volume setting.

Next, tune to weak stations and rotate the set. Should fading occur, the set lacks good AVC (automatic volume control). Don't fall for sales talk about "directional antennas." You aren't buying a direction finder in this case and, if you were, you would want a far more accurate one than you can obtain in a low-cost transistor radio.

Check for distortion at high volume levels, a sign of an underrated speaker. The sound should always be clear, crisp and not garbled.

On AM-FM units, check for distortion as before, but switch to FM and listen for a telltale howl or squeal (feedback) or a steady pop-pop-pop- ("motor-boating"). These are signs of either faulty components or wiring.

Some sets use the "S"-taper volume control, which provides an impressive blast of volume with just a slight turn of the control knob. From there on, volume increases very little. It's easier to live with a set that gives you a steady volume increase over the full range of control.

For station pinpointing, the tuning dial should be easy to read and the tuning control should be a vernier type. This simply means that one full

To change the batteries in this set, you need to use a screwdriver to remove the back. Some parents prefer this to prevent "exploring," but if there are no kids in the house, look for more convenience

petitive brands whose prices were very close. Yet one sounded far superior to the other, for reasons which the test shoppers couldn't determine. They identified themselves to the clerk, told him the reason for their visit, and asked him to explain the difference in performance. After asking a promise not to use his name, he explained that the store had overstocked on the set that sounded so good. He received a bonus for each one he sold. So he made sure that fresh batteries were placed in the "bonus" brand every day. He didn't worry quite so much about the other set.

The moral? Make sure the batteries in sets you listen to are new; if they are the same type,

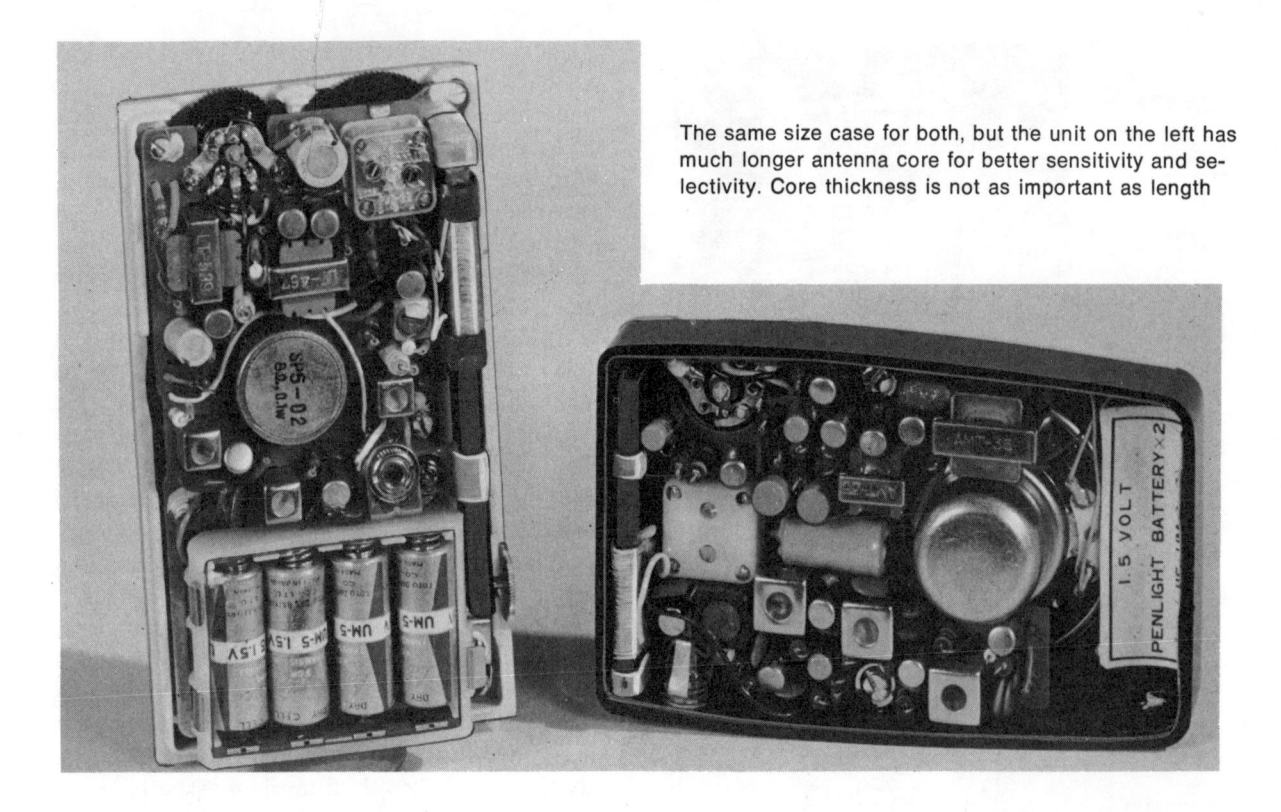

The same size case for both, but the unit on the left has much longer antenna core for better sensitivity and selectivity. Core thickness is not as important as length

turn of the knob does *not* equal a full rotation of the dial scale.

The number of transistors is not nearly as important as the grade of transistors used. Thus some 5-transistor sets could conceivably outperform some 9-transistor sets. Since there is no way for you to tell in the store how good the transistors are, listen to the set instead of counting the number of transistors.

A coin will turn the screw to remove the back for battery replacement with this set. The screw is captive and stays with the cover. Always check that lips of both halves of set meet correctly when closing

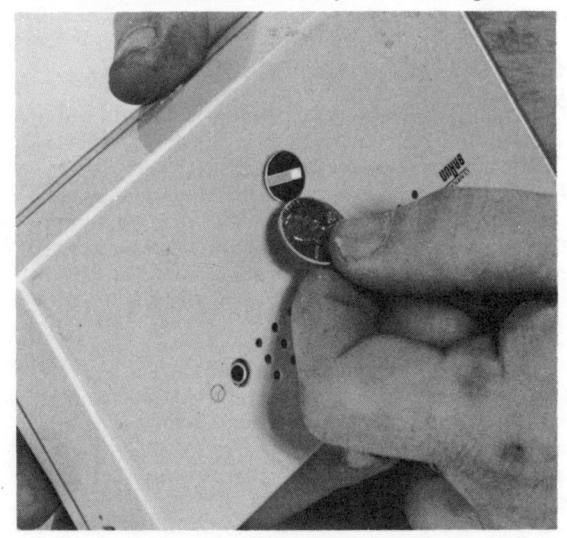

Busy salesmen may be reluctant to show you how to open the back of a small radio, but it is usually an easy job and you *are* entitled to know how to change batteries!

The battery compartment inside should be of

Intermediate-frequency transformers are in shielded cans. Larger ones, on the left, are easier to set accurately and, therefore, usually perform far better with much less trouble. On cheaper units, it's often less expensive to replace the set than repair or adjust

2767

transistor radios

an acid-resisting material and the battery polarity should be clearly marked. It should be easy to remove and replace the batteries.

Mercury batteries will last two to three times longer than pen-light cells of the same voltage and size, but cost four to five times more.

Look at the ferrite antenna inside the case. While a short, thick core is better than a short thin core, neither is as good as a long core.

If the set has a short-wave, marine or FM band, it needs an external antenna which can be tilted directionally to insure good reception.

Ask the salesman to show you the specifications sheet on any radio you want to buy. Check the model number on it with the number of the radio you are examining. The table tells the important points to look for and what they mean in terms of performance.

Although you can buy transistor radios built into desk sets, bottles or even clocks and in a wide variety of shapes and sizes, the basic tests are valid for any type. You can't, of course, put a big AM-FM short-wave unit in your pockets. By the same token, hi-fi music may be hi but it won't be very fi coming through the little 2-in. speaker in a shirt-pocket radio.

Consider the extras that can influence the price, such things as a leather carrying case, earphone, or a.c. adapter.

Some sets provide facility for plugging the antenna from a car radio into the portable set, an additional feature that can increase listening pleasure. The important thing to remember when shopping is to make sure the basic performance of the set is satisfactory.

See also: battery chargers; electronics; radio repair, AM; radios, auto.

Batteries should be easy to reach and easy to change. The compartment should be acidproof to protect circuit in case of battery leak. Markings (top) prevent incorrect installation

---

WHAT THE SPECIFICATIONS SHEET TELLS YOU

CIRCUIT: This tells the number of transistors and other semiconductors and what their function in the circuit is. "Superheterodyne" circuits generally provide better selectivity and sensitivity than "TRF" or "regenerative" circuits. Superhet circuits use IF (intermediate frequency) and converter stages, and the more IF stages, the greater the selectivity.

TUNING RANGE: 550 to 1600 kilocycles (kc) is the AM broadcast range; if you want to receive a full range of stations, your set should cover this band. The FM range is 88 to 108 megacycles (mc). Short-wave bands may include any frequencies from 1.6 mc to 30 mc. Frequencies below 550 kc are for marine radio and weather.

OUTPUT: Output power is stated in milliwatts and usually two figures are supplied. One is called "undistorted" and the other "maximum." The higher these ratings are, the better. The greater the percentage difference between the two, the safer the undistorted rating will be. For example, 280 mw (undistorted) and 560 mw (maximum) will give better performance than 70 mw (undistorted) and 100 mw (maximum).

SPEAKER SIZE: The larger the loudspeaker is, the better its bass response will generally be. However, a 4 x 6-in. elliptical speaker should be about as good as a 5-in. round speaker, as it is cone area rather than diameter that is important in determining listening quality.

transistor radios

Build a portable radio in minutes

BY LARRY STECKLER

This 8-transistor portable radio puts out sound through an 8-in. speaker, so you can use it around the house, out in the yard, or at the beach while still getting "big set" sound quality and volume

■ IT'S A TABLE RADIO, a hang-on-the-wall radio, a portable or all 3 at the same time. It has an 8-transistor circuit that delivers 360 milliwatts of audio to an 8-in. speaker. Best of all, *you* can put the whole thing together in about 30 min. and the total cost is less than $20. All you need are ordinary hand tools, a soldering iron and some solder.

You'll have to spend 5 min. or so on preliminaries. First drill ⅜-in. holes for the volume and tuning controls. You can make them come out the front or out the sides or top, whichever you find most convenient. The choice of cabinet is also up to you. You can use the one specified—it is excellent for wall mounting, tabletop use or as a portable—or any other standard wood cabinet in an electronics catalog. For that matter, you can build your own. Just be sure to leave enough

transistor radios

space for the two subchasses and the batteries.

Now mount the speaker, locating it so that the solder lugs are oriented toward the spot you have picked for mounting the amplifier. Fasten it securely in place.

Next mount the volume control. Like the speaker, it should be positioned so its solder lugs point toward the amplifier. Now you're ready for the battery holders. Mount them on the bottom of the cabinet. This takes a little care since the bottom is not always the same. Portable and table models use the wide side of the cabinet as the bottom. Wall mounted units, like the one shown here, use the narrow side of the cabinet as the

Batteries are fitted into place as a last step. The diagram below shows all wiring details. Follow it carefully and your radio will work the first time you turn it on. The four cabinet styles along the left are some of the many possible arrangements you can use. The amplifier and AM tuner are supplied with a wiring diagram which should be followed instead of the one below in case of any differences, such as color of leads

30-min. radio, continued

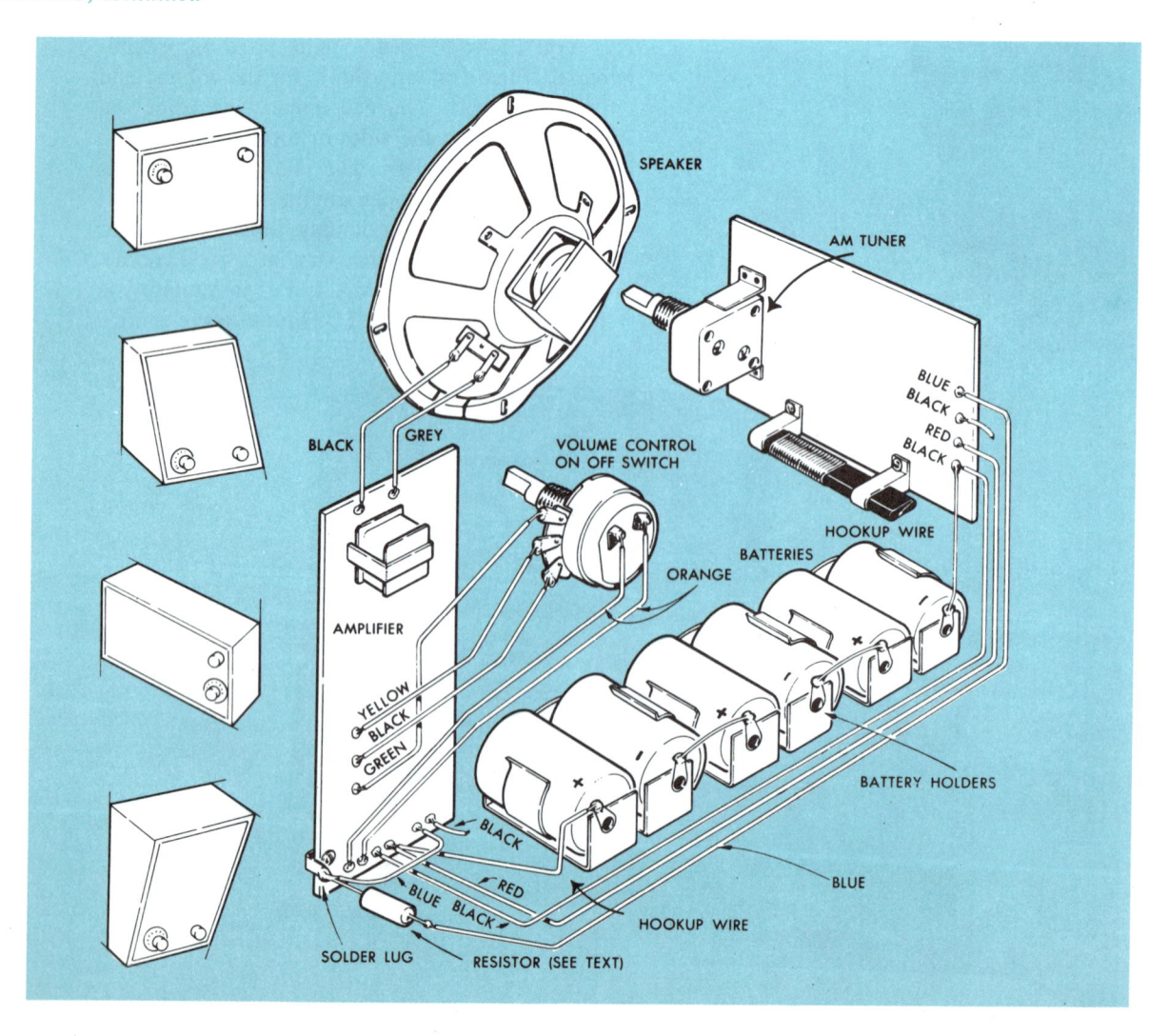

2770

PARTS LIST

AM tuner (Lafayette 99C9040 or equiv.)
  (Lafayette Radio, 111 Jericho Turnpike, Syossett, L.I., N.Y.)
Transistor Amplifier (Lafayette 99C9037 or equiv.)
Speaker, 8-in. (8-ohm voice coil)
Speaker baffle (cabinet) for 8-in. speaker
Volume control and SPST switch (IRC Q13–116 control plus 76–1 switch or equiv.)
3 battery holders (each holder takes two D cells)
6 D cells (for longer life use alkaline or mercury types)
2 knobs, ivory, 1-in. diameter
Plywood back cover (if needed)
Handle (for portable unit)
Closed-circuit miniature phone jack (if desired)
Miniature earpiece (if desired)
Assorted wood screws
Hookup wire (bare)
Solder

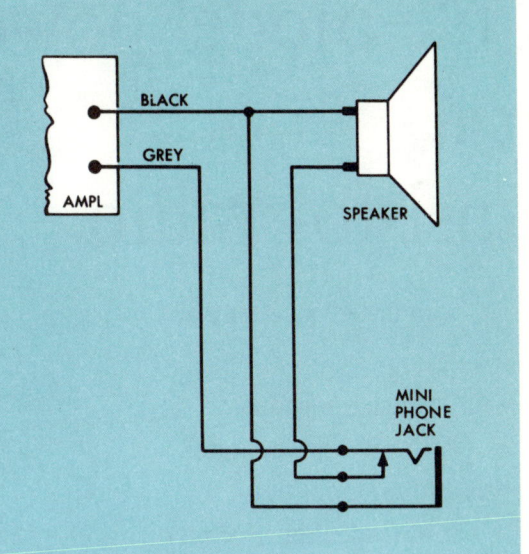

Want to use earphones? Simply change the speaker wiring to conform to this little schematic. Note that you'll have to add a miniature phone jack. The earphones should be rated from 3 to 16 ohms impedance

bottom. To make things easier, wire the battery holders before mounting them. If you don't you may have some trouble getting at their lugs once they are inside the cabinet.

Now the amplifier can be mounted. Use ⅜-in. wood screws, one in each corner. Place small nuts or washers between the amplifier chassis and the cabinet to space the amplifier board off the cabinet itself. Once it's mounted, connect leads to the volume control, batteries and switch.

All that remains is to mount the AM tuner. Before doing so, remove the 4 machine screws that hold the tuning capacitor in place. Then carefully move the capacitor forward over the edge of the printed-circuit board until the rear pair of holes on its mounting bracket line up with the front pair of holes on the board (the holes closest to the edge of the board). Reinsert two of the little screws to hold the capacitor in place and tighten them until the capacitor is firmly set. Do not overtighten or you will strip the threads in the board. This insures that the capacitor shaft will extend through the cabinet.

Remove the knob from the tuning capacitor and mount the tuner in the cabinet, using ¼-in. wood screws. If any mounting lugs extend be-yond the rear edge of the cabinet, cut off the projections.

Now wire the tuner into the circuit following the illustrations carefully. Put the tuning and volume control knobs into place and insert the batteries (be sure to observe correct polarity).

If it's to be a portable, add a handle to the top of the cabinet. If you use the set as a portable or table model, close up the back with a sheet of ¼-in. plywood. If you're going to hang the unit on a wall, let the wall act as the back.

You may find that the set gives you too much gain. It is extremely sensitive, especially if you live fairly close to your favorite stations. If so you'll get too much volume even with the control barely turned up. Simply add a ½-watt resistor between the tuner output and the amplifier input. This resistor is shown in the accompanying diagram, but don't use it unless you must. The correct value will be somewhere between 36,000 and 82,000 ohms, depending on how much you have to cut the volume. Start with the lower value and work up to the one you like.

If you care to add earphones, follow the little schematic and use phones rated from 3 to 16 ohms impedance.

2771

transistor radios

Table-model power for a transistor radio

BY ARTHUR KENNEDY

Give your transistor radio
    the power of a table model
with this add-on amplifier
        and speaker. For picnics and
    the beach, it'll provide the
music you want, or the news

The plug-in connecting cord couples the speaker to the amplifier. Then turn on the power, tune in a station and supply music for a party

■ POCKET-SIZE TRANSISTOR RADIOS are marvelous inventions. Ask any teenager! They are small enough to slip into a coat pocket and they do bring in the stations. But they have one limitation—power. They are fine for personal listening and almost useless for anything else.

A pocket transistor radio just can't be loud. The maximum audio output of the average set is $\frac{1}{5}$ of a watt. For more power and louder sound —table-radio use, patio dance parties, on the beach—an additional outboard speaker with its own self-contained transistor power amplifier is a must.

Here is just such an accessory. A 2-transistor amplifier is built right into the speaker case and delivers up to 10 watts of audio power. The amplifier is driven by the signal from the pocket radio by plugging a modified earphone cord into the radio and speaker.

To make this transistor-radio power booster, start with a Sound Piper Portable Patio Speaker. It is weatherproof, has an aluminum case and is not expensive. Similar units can also be used. But

transmitter, code: see electronics

for simple wiring, a compact speaker that has a metal case is a big help.

Before starting on the amplifier, remove the speaker from the enclosure and put it aside. Drill holes for the power-transistor leads and mount the transistors on the outside back of the metal enclosure with their leads projecting through the holes into the case. Be sure the leads or the clips that will attach to them do not touch the case.

Next mount input and output transformers T1 and T2 to the inside rear of the enclosure. Place a ground lug over one of T1's mounting screws and secure the mounting screw with a locking nut.

As strange as it seems, there is no readily available power-transistor socket. So to make a connection to the base and emitter leads of each transistor you'll have to use clips obtained from a 7-pin miniature tube socket. Use a wafer-type socket and drill out the center rivet. Then separate the plastic halves of the socket and carefully remove four of the tube prong clips. After they

The battery for the outboard amplifier (above, right) slips into a sheet-metal bracket on the rear of the amplifier case. Below, right, the circuit of the 2-transistor booster amplifier is uncomplicated and quick to assemble. It withstands abuse

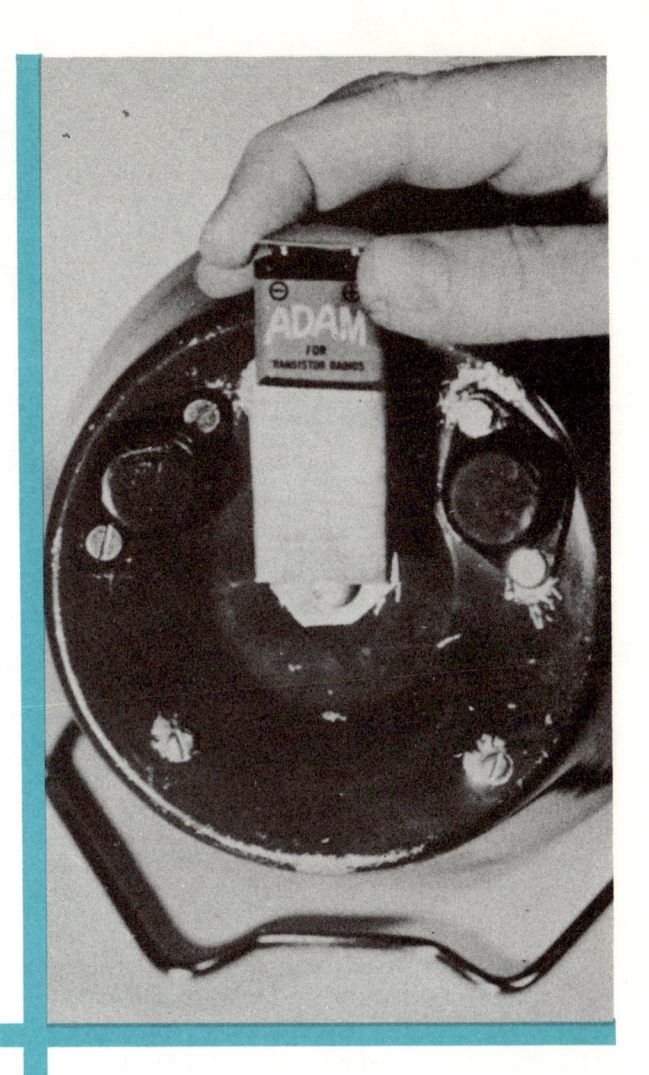

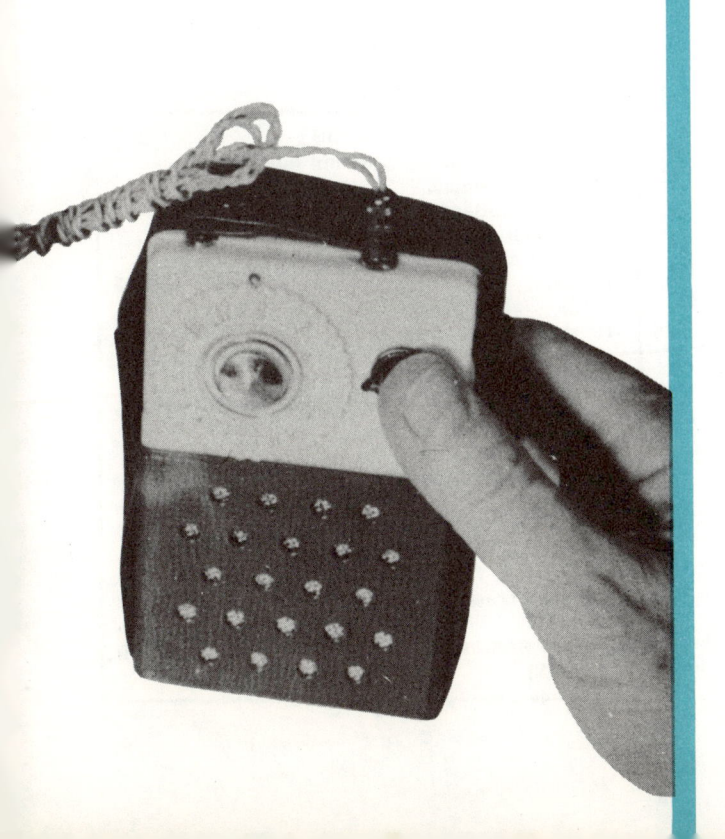

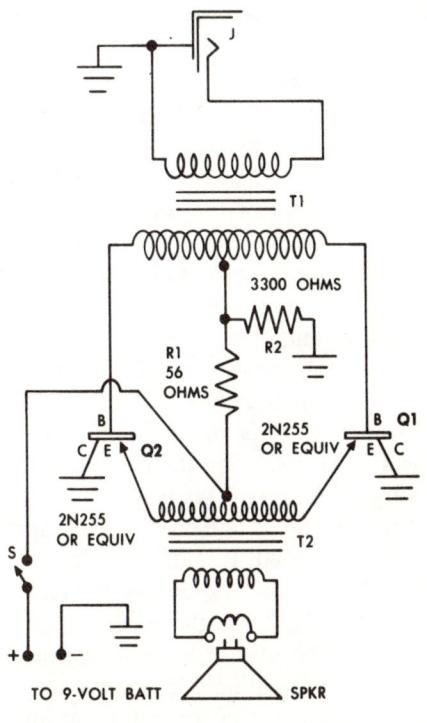

2773

transistor radios

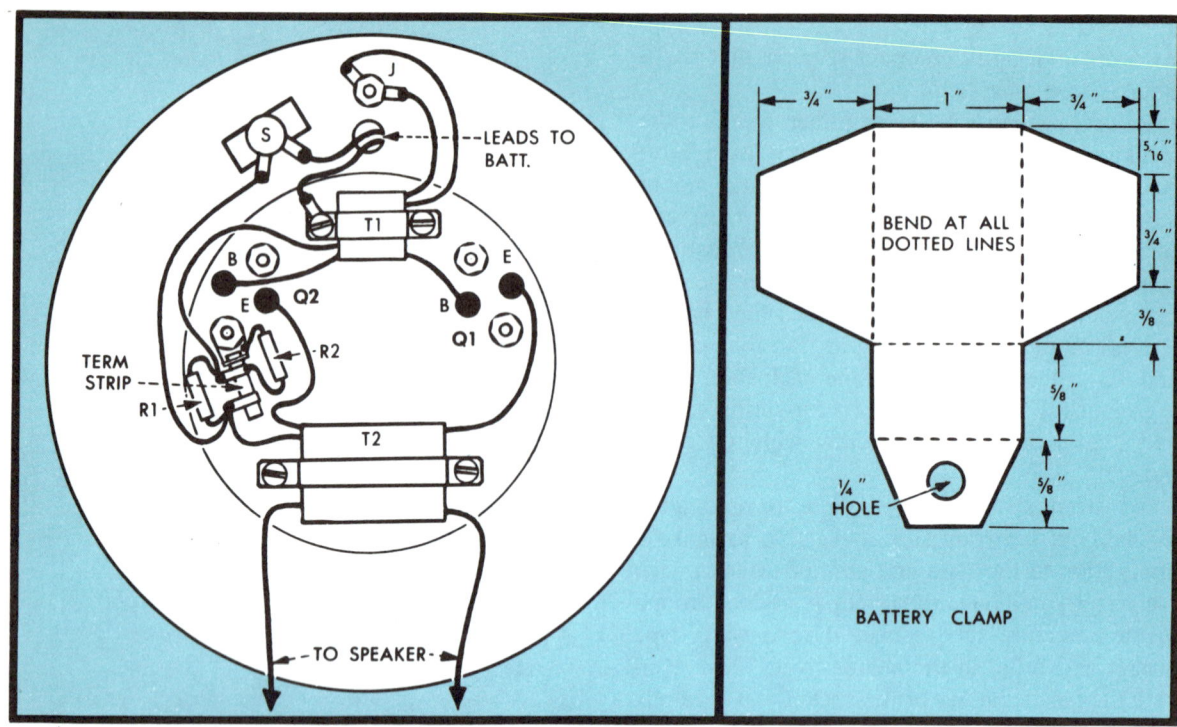

Using the pictorial diagram (left) and the schematic on the previous page, you should have little trouble assembling the amplifier. This is an inside view. Transistors and battery clip are mounted outside the case. At the right is the layout for the battery clip. You'll need a 2 x 2½-in. piece of sheet metal. You might want to add a tripod socket to the speaker housing to keep it off the sand at the beach and up at ear level

are wired into the circuit, push them on over the proper transistor base pins. The transistor collectors are automatically connected when the transistors are fastened down to the metal case—the collectors are connected internally to the transistor cases.

Next mount the toggle switch inside the speaker case, its handle projecting out the top.

Now push the leads from the battery cable through a hole on the case and connect the red lead to one terminal of the toggle switch. Connect the other lead (the black one) to the ground lug on transformer T1's mounting screws. Then, following the schematic and pictorial diagram, finish wiring the amplifier.

The last bit of construction is mechanical—making the clip that holds the battery for the booster amplifier. It is made from a piece of scrap sheet metal following the pattern shown in the drawing at the top of this page.

The finished clip is attached to the speaker when it is reassembled. It is held in place by the same single screw that holds the speaker case together. If you don't use the specified speaker, bolt the clip to the rear of the unit you do use. Self-tapping screws will hold it securely.

To get the signal out of the radio and into the booster amplifier, use the earphone cord that came with your transistor radio. The only change is to remove the earphone and attach in its place a miniature phone plug.

Now use this cord to connect the radio to the booster. Turn on the amplifier and radio, tune in a station and you're in business.

PARTS LIST
Portable Patio Speaker, Sound Piper Model 81PO67 or equiv.
Transistor Battery, 9 volts, Eveready No. 216
Battery clip and cable
Miniature phone jack and plug
Transistor output transformer, Argonne AR-503 (T2)
Transistor output transformer (T1), select secondary impedance to match speaker impedance
Spst toggle switch
Medium power p-n-p transistors, 2N255, 2N301, etc. (Q1, Q2)
Terminal strip, 3-lug
Resistor, carbon, 56 ohms, ¼ watt
Resistor, carbon, 3300 ohms, ¼ watt
Ground lug
Sheet metal, 2 x 2½ inches
Tube socket, 7-pin miniature, wafer type
Machine Screws, ⅜-in. x 8-32 (6) with matching nuts (7)
Machine Screws, ¼-in. x 8-40 (2) with matching nuts (3)

transmitter, FM

Wireless FM mike in a cigarette case

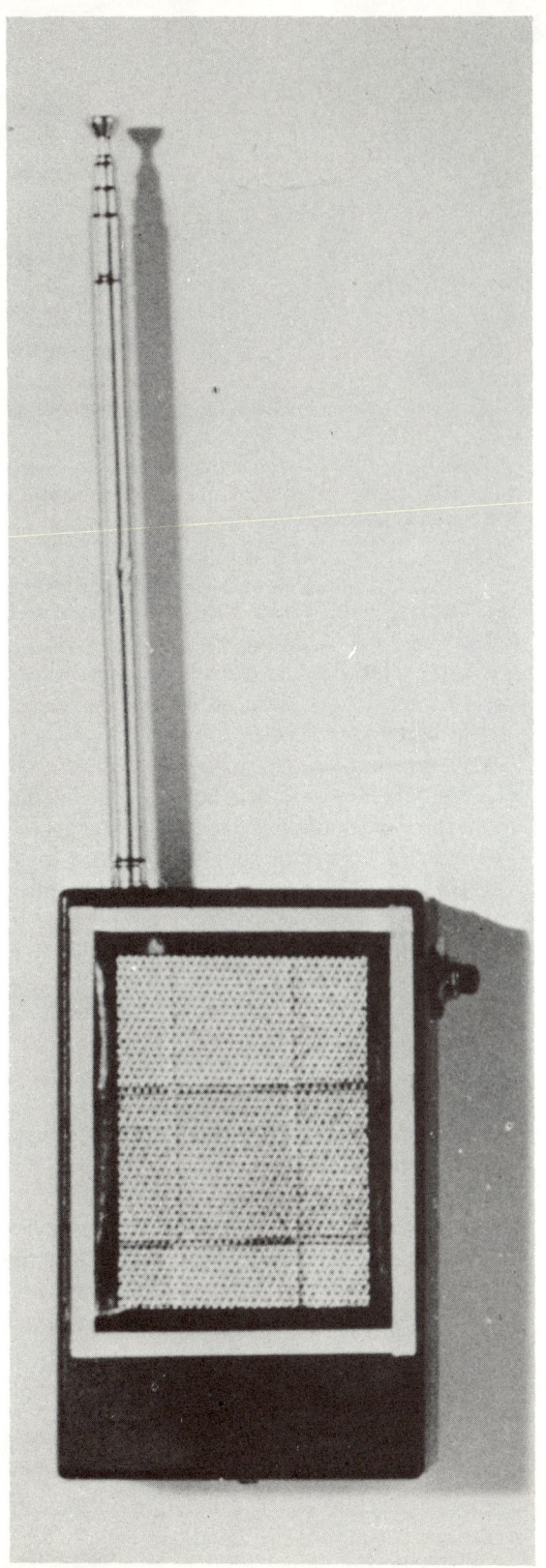

Make your own two-transistor shirt-pocket broadcaster. It will transmit to any nearby FM radio or hi-fi tuner. You can put it together in a single evening. With a maximum range of 200 ft., it will justify its rare need for a fresh battery in fun for all the family

■ IN JUST A FEW HOURS you can assemble this simple FM wireless microphone. It really comes down to a matter of mounting the parts on the circuit board and wiring in the antenna, on-off switch, microphone and battery. The assembly is a cinch and the circuit board makes a mistake extremely unlikely.

This unit is a two-transistor transmitter. The first stage (Q1) is an audio amplifier. Input signals from the microphone are fed to Q1's base through capacitor C1. The amplified audio signal is then fed through capacitor C3 to the base of the FM oscillator transistor, Q2.

Before beginning assembly of your unit, first drill all necessary holes in the circuit board. Use a 1/16-in. drill for the small holes and a 1/8-in. drill for the two large holes for the trimmer capacitor. A 1/4-in. hole will permit adjusting the trimmer capacitor.

Now insert all resistors, capacitors and transistors into the board. Use 1/4-in. lengths of spaghetti over the transistor leads to keep the transistors above the board. Next, solder the tap into place on the coil and mount it on the board. Then insert capacitor C5. Solder all leads carefully.

Connect the battery clip leads; red to hole 4

transmitter, FM

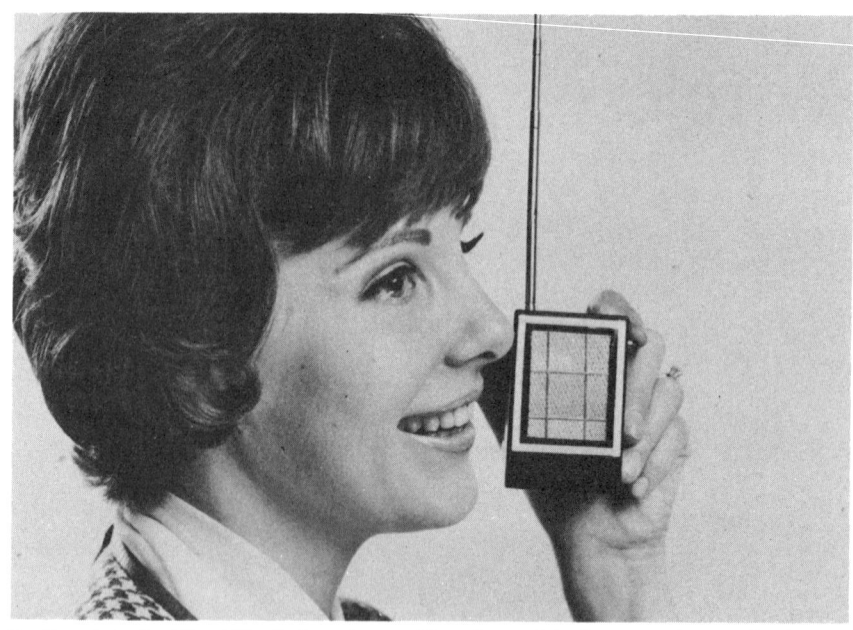

On-the-air test of the FM wireless transmitter shows it to be operating perfectly. Voices are clear and distinct and reception is static-free

Parts List

Resistors:
- R1—62,000 ohms, ¼-w.
- R2—33,000 ohms, ¼-w.
- R3—1,500 ohms, ¼-w.
- R4—3,300 ohms, ¼-w.
- R5—91,000 ohms, ¼-w., 5%
- R6—510 ohms, ¼-w., 5%

Capacitors:
- C1—10 μfd, 12 v. electrolytic
- C2—30 μfd, 10 v., electrolytic
- C3—10 μfd, 12 v., electrolytic
- C4—.001 μfd ceramic
- C5—6-30 pfd trimmer
- C6—5 pfd ceramic
- C7—.001 μfd ceramic
- Q1—HP-100
- Q2—P-404
- Printed circuit board
- Antenna coil—6 turns No. 14 enameled, tap at 1¾ turns
- Mike—crystal
- Ant.—15" 3-pc. collapsible
- Battery—9 v. (Burgess 2U6)
- S1—s.p.s.t. pushbutton (open)
- Case—3⅛ x 2 x 1³⁄₁₆" plastic
- *Complete kit

* Available from Bowman Electronics, 325 North Ave., Garwood, N.J. 07027

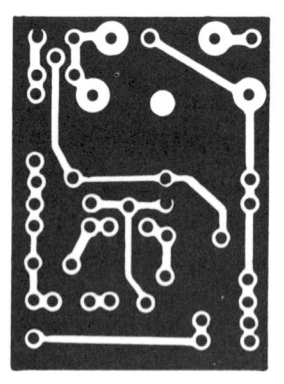

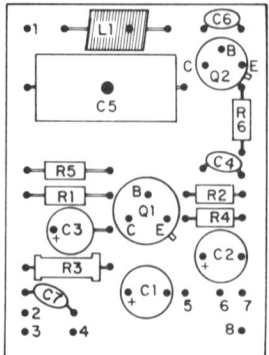

These views of the printed circuit board are actual size. They show the layout for parts placement and wiring. Be sure to follow them exactly and use solder sparingly. Too much solder can cause shorts

and black to hole 3. The microphone leads go to holes 5 and 6; the switch to 7 and 8. Hole 2 is not used. Connect the antenna, mount all the parts in the plastic case, hook up the battery and you're ready to go.

Case preparation. No matter what plastic case you use, you'll have to drill holes for the antenna connector, pushbutton switch and microphone. The antenna connector should be located at the top left rear of the case; a ¼-in. hole is required. On the upper right side make a similar hole for the pushbutton switch.

The microphone can be cemented to the front of the case; if you do this, drill a ¼-in. hole for its leads. For a neater-looking package, cut a hole on the front of the case, equal to the diameter of the mike, and mount it flush. You can dress up the unit with a scrap piece of metal grille obtained from an old transistor radio. You could also use a scrap of metal grille cloth.

Obey FCC rules. It's a good idea to review the regulations of the Federal Communications Commission before tuning and operating your FM wireless microphone. As it is a low-power FM transmitter, it must comply with part 15.205 of FCC rules. This means it can be used only on the portion of the FM band which is clear of broadcast stations. You must not tune the unit to frequencies outside this band (88 to 108 mc.). You must check to see that there are no spurious radiations outside the FM band.

Do this by tuning your TV to channels 6 and

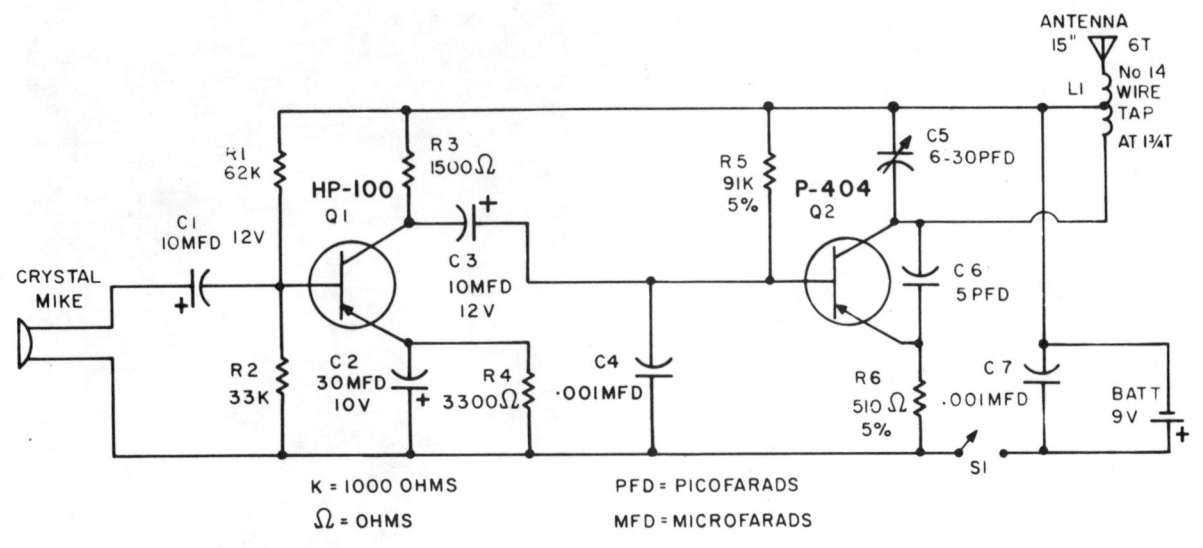

Complete two-transistor circuit of the FM wireless microphone. Do not attempt to alter it in any fashion

7 while operating the transmitter. There should be no interference visible on the screen.

Lastly, the transmitter should be tested by a competent electronic technician. He should determine that the unit meets FCC requirements and give you a written statement to this effect. Attach this certificate to your transmitter.

Tuning and operation. To tune and operate your transmitter, follow these simple instructions:

1. With the antenna in place, open the case to gain access to trimmer capacitor C5. Adjust this capacitor only with an insulated screwdriver. You can reach the adjustment screw through the ¼-in. hole you made in the board for this purpose.

2. Tune a nearby FM receiver to 88 mc. Depress switch S1 on the transmitter. Hold the mike near the receiver speaker and slowly adjust the trimmer capacitor until you hear a whistle or howl from the speaker. This is at the lower end of the FM band.

3. Retune your radio to 108 mc. and repeat step 2. A whistle or howl will be heard, marking the upper end of the FM band. The entire band, you will note, can be tuned with about a half revolution of the adjustment screw. *Caution:* Do not tune the transmitter outside this range—if you do, you are violating the FCC regulations covering the operation of this pocket FM radio.

Now you're ready to use your wireless mike. Tune it to a blank portion of the FM band and put it to work. With the 15-in. antenna specified, the range of this unit will never exceed 200 ft. Any extension of this range is not permitted.

There are countless uses for the wireless FM microphone around the house, once the original novelty of the unit begins to wear off. For example, the mike will keep a watchful ear on a sleeping baby, so be sure to take both the mike and an FM receiver along on your vacation.

With a portable FM receiver, you've got a perfect way of keeping in touch with the house when gardening or just loafing out back. Set the mike near the telephone and the first ring will tell you that you're wanted. If someone's in the house, they can call you quickly and easily if the call's for you.

The kids can use it to put on amateur radio shows and all sorts of guessing games—sounds, voices, imitations—will have added mystery if you place the mike and performers in one room and the receiver and audience in another.

You should find the FM mike fun to build and use as long as you keep the FCC rules governing its use in mind. For more details, write the FCC, Washington, D.C. 20554, and ask for a copy of OCE Bulletins 11 and 12. No. 11 is titled *Does My Transmitter Need a License?* and No. 12, *Operation in the Broadcast Band Without a License.*

These bulletins give completely detailed information on all FCC rules governing the use of low-power, license-free operation of radio transmitters, and you should be thoroughly familiar with them before beginning to operate a transmitter of your own.

See also: electronics; intercoms; transmitter meter.

Pocket CB meter for walkie-talkie

BY HOMER L. DAVIDSON

You can wire a field-strength meter for your walkie-talkies with just a handful of components. It's also a fast way to keep check on the batteries

■ Is YOUR WALKIE-TALKIE really transmitting? How about the batteries? Are they still putting out? Just slip this pocket CB meter over the telescoping antenna and take a signal check.

Only a handful of components is used in constructing the meter. A pickup coil which you wind yourself picks the signal off the walkie-talkie antenna; a fixed crystal diode rectifies the RF signal and the amount of signal is shown on the face of the small, flat-type panel meter. This unit fits over the telescoping antenna of the walkie-talkie.

A 36-in. length of covered No. 22 solid hookup wire is wound around a ⅜-in.-dia. form for the pickup coil. The inside hole of the coil must let the button on the telescoping antenna rod pass through it. You should end up with about 20 turns of wire for the coil. Wind each turn tightly and do not space the windings. After 10 turns, close-wound, double up the last 10 turns in a second layer. Let the wire protrude ½ in. from one end of the coil and 2 in. at the other. The small end will solder directly to one terminal on the small meter, while the longer one will lie

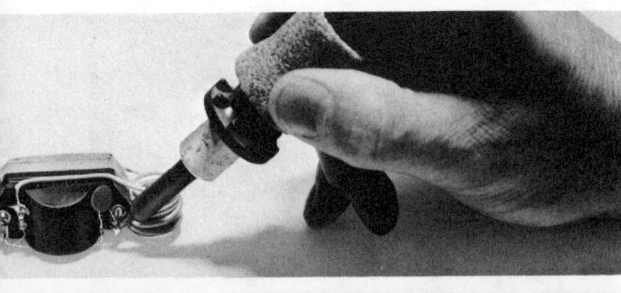

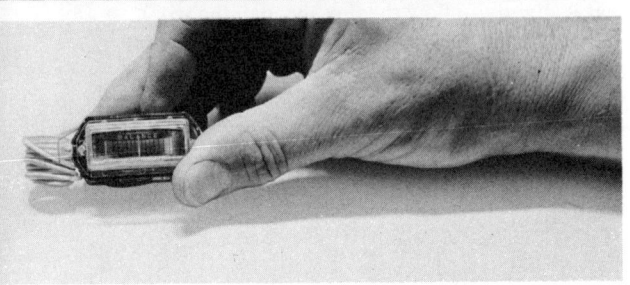

Small pencil soldering iron is suggested for tight wiring around the meter terminals. In the top photo, one lead of C1 and coil L1 are wired to a meter terminal. Diode CR1 on the left is wired between L1 and other terminal. Wired components make a compact package which is housed in a plastic case. Both halves of the case are cut to mount the meter, then drilled to allow the walkie-talkie antenna to go through the pickup coil L1. Polarity of the meter can be ignored when wiring since it is the center-null type and reads in either direction. When completed, the unit is secured to the top of the walkie-talkie; you can use it to keep tabs on battery strength

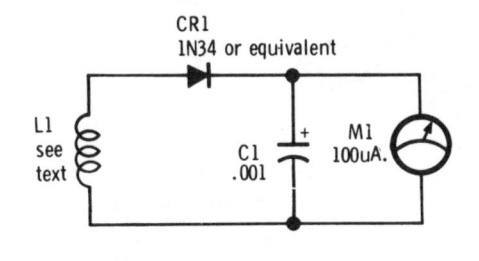

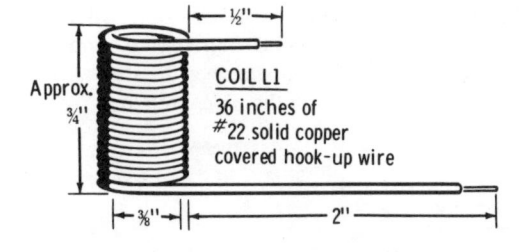

across the top of the meter. Solder the latter end to the crystal diode, CR1. With No. 22 wire coil L1 is self-supporting and will stay in place.

Solder and tie all parts to the small meter. Place the coil tightly against the meter case and solder in place. Keep all parts tightly together to make the meter as compact as possible. Run the leads of C1 across the meter terminals.

Meter polarity connections are not critical. The meter is a center-scale, balanced type so the reading can be pulled to either side of the center scale. It was originally designed for stereo balancing or receiver tuning.

The plastic case came from a discarded phono-cartridge box. Any type box is okay as long as it isn't metal. Cut out a slotted opening in the case for the plastic meter face. Also cut a matching slot in the top lid of the box. Use a hacksaw for the downward and upward cuts. Then take a pocketknife and, with the help of a straightedge, scribe a line across the two cut slots. The plastic cut can now be snapped out cleanly. Drill a ½-in. hole through the top and bottom of the plastic case for the walkie-talkie antenna.

A rubber seal or rubber adhesive sealant can be used to hold the wired components in the case. First line up the pickup coil over the bottom ½-in. hole in the case; then hold the halves of the case together, using plastic cement.

Test your CB meter by placing it over the telescoping antenna of a small 3-transistor walkie-talkie. The one shown here is a Lafayette HA-70A. Turn the receiver switch on and press to talk. The meter hand should move two or three divisions. Larger CB units of greater milliwatt output will make the meter pointer hit the peg. If you will use the meter only for small 3-transistor walkie-talkies and desire a greater reading, add five more turns on coil L1. A greater reading can also be obtained when the antenna is collapsed to about 2 in. All power output from the small transmitter is concentrated in these 2 in. and a higher meter reading is obtained.

You can add a rubber suction cup to the bottom of the pocket meter if you desire to hold it on top of the walkie-talkie for a constant check on output. This also keeps check on your batteries.

PARTS LIST

C1—.001 μf disk capacitor
CR1—1N34, 1N56 or equiv. diode
L1—Pickup coil, 36 in. of covered No. 22 solid hookup wire wound on ⅜-in. diameter form
M1—100 μa balance meter (Lafayette 99C5034 or equiv.)
Misc.—Plastic case, cement, solder

See also: intercoms; transmitter, FM.

clever ideas

Before you cut an opening in a plastered wall for an outlet box, or for some other purpose, tape a small cardboard box to the wall just below the point where the opening is to be made. Use masking tape to hang the box as it will not peel the paint when it is removed. The box will catch the bits of plaster, pieces of lath and most important, that flour-fine plaster dust that is so difficult to get up off the floor. Even the vacuum cleaner won't pick up all of it.

Fine steel wool can serve as a carrier, or bridge, when it is necessary to fill a hole with solder. Use a pinch of wool just large enough to fill the hole loosely, dip it in the liquid (acid) flux and heat it slightly to flow the flux through the wool. Preheat the metal around the hole very nearly to soldering temperature. Then press the wool in place and flow solder over it. As soon as the work cools, file the solder patch flush with the surface. Use of a torch will make this job easier and faster.

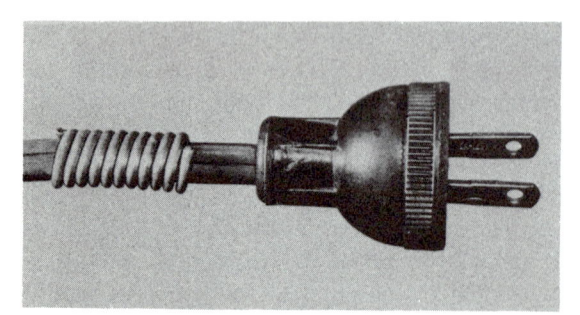

No serious handyman or modeler ever runs out of solder at a critical stage of the project he's working on—or does he? To prevent this ever happening unwind a length of wire solder from that new spool you just bought and rewind it—not too tightly—on the soldering-iron cord. Wound on the cord the extra supply is never in the way and does not interfere with normal use of the iron. Be sure to replace this emergency supply whenever you use it.

You have a set of socket wrenches but obviously you can't use them to tighten that stubborn locknut you see in the photo. It's turned down too far on the stud. You have no open wrench that fits and you can't use the pipe wrench as the alligator jaws will burr the corners of the hex nut, which, in this case is not permissible. What to do? Simple. You just drop the socket down over the stud and onto the nut. Then turn it with the pipe wrench.

2780

Rule-of-three in felling trees

1 Start the wedge cut on the leaning side of the trunk (the tree to fall in this direction). Make the bottom notch-cut first

2 Make the second cut (wedge cut) at about a 35-deg. slant after the first cut is halfway through the trunk

3 To fell the tree, make the back cut just above the bottom of the wedge cut. Then, yell "timber" if you like and back away, fast

■ SO THAT TREE in the backyard has to go to make room for the addition you're building. Before you start sawing check these simple rules:

1. Determine which way the tree will fall. This should be easy. Nearly all trees lean in some direction but how they fall depends on how the felling cuts are made. If your tree leans even slightly toward the house, secure a guy (cable or rope) near the top and have a helper guide the falling tree away from the structure.

2. Use a chain saw, of course; felling with an ax went out long ago. Saw a notch, about waist-high, on the leaning side of the trunk, or in the direction the tree is to be felled. Make the bottom cut first, about halfway through. Make the second notch-cut at an angle of 30-40 deg.

3. To fell the tree make a square-across cut into the trunk opposite the notch and 1 to 2 in. above it. Don't cut all the way to the notch; leave a thin "hinge" to prevent the trunk from twisting. Then trim a wedge from waste wood and tap it into the saw cut. Continue tapping the wedge until the trunk begins to tilt, then back away fast and let gravity take over. Before wedging be sure you've moved the chain saw to a safe distance. Finally, saw the stump off close to the ground. Don't attempt to fell a tree on a windy day.

See also: landscaping; rustic furniture; tree stumps.

tree houses

Every kid should have a tree house

Here are five different designs for tree-level living. And you don't even need a tree to build one

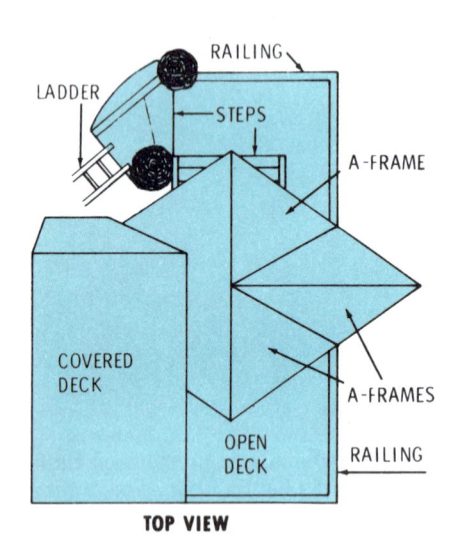

This house of many gables, designed by band leader Fred Waring, has ridges from 3 A-frames set at right angles, as shown in the roof plan at left

■ REMEMBER WHEN YOU were young, when it was great fun to climb up into a tree house? Well, even in this age of outer space, boys get just as big a kick out of living a few feet above the earth. It's an adventure in isolation—a lifting of oneself into a special world where imagination can soar, doesn't have to keep its feet on the ground.

Of course, today's kids are too sophisticated to be content with a rustic platform. They want a perch that *looks* adventurous and inviting. And as far as that goes, you don't want to create an eyesore, either.

So here's a handful of novel designs you can build into any large tree in your yard—it needn't even be a live one. And if you don't *have* a tree, you simply erect a house on poles.

In building either a tree or a pole house, it's a good idea to plan it carefully on paper—perhaps even build a scale model—before attempting to erect the structure. You may also want to check local ordinances to see if any sort of permit is required. Even communities that have such nuisance ordinances are often understandably embarrassed about enforcing them; but if you should build in violation of local codes, you'll be at the mercy of any complaining neighbors. So play it safe.

The design of any tree house is pretty much dictated by the size and shape of the tree it will perch in, so it's impractical to present exact plans, here. But we offer band leader Fred Waring's house, above, for the many ideas it suggests. For example, the jutting roof-peaks that add space to a limited floor plan, and the plastic-rope "nest" at the first level. The A-frame design on page 2783, on the other hand, offers the novel idea of setting a house atop the fork of a dead tree. A hurricane left this trunk standing and, rather than pay the steep cost of having it up-

2782

Diagram labels (top):

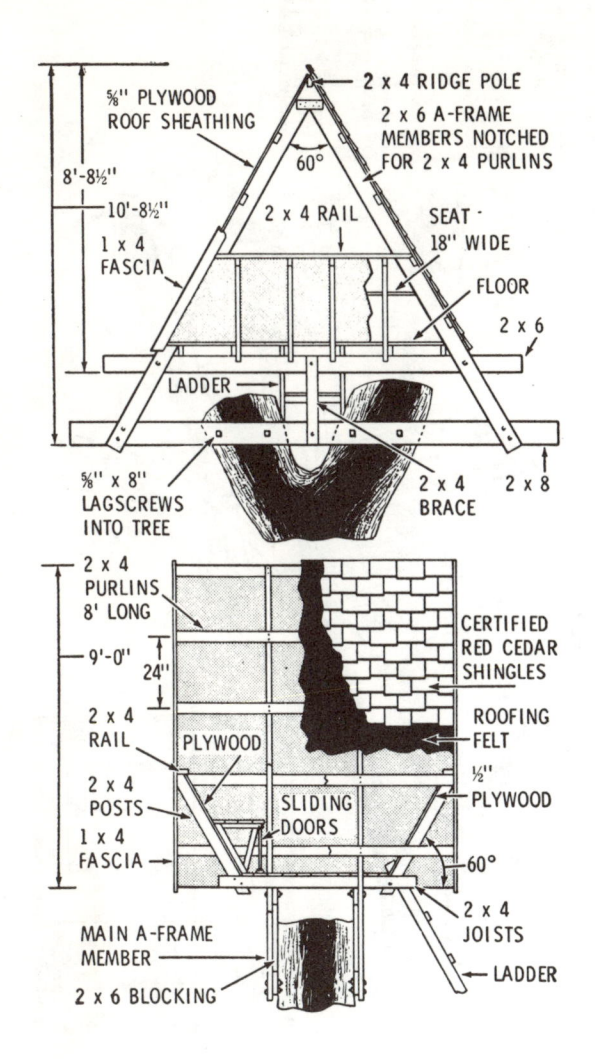

- ⅝" PLYWOOD ROOF SHEATHING
- 2 x 4 RIDGE POLE
- 2 x 6 A-FRAME MEMBERS NOTCHED FOR 2 x 4 PURLINS
- 60°
- 8'-8½"
- 10'-8½"
- 2 x 4 RAIL
- SEAT 18" WIDE
- 1 x 4 FASCIA
- FLOOR
- 2 x 6
- LADDER
- ⅝" x 8" LAGSCREWS INTO TREE
- 2 x 4 BRACE
- 2 x 8

Diagram labels (bottom):

- 2 x 4 PURLINS 8' LONG
- 9'-0"
- 24"
- 2 x 4 RAIL
- 2 x 4 POSTS
- 1 x 4 FASCIA
- PLYWOOD
- SLIDING DOORS
- CERTIFIED RED CEDAR SHINGLES
- ROOFING FELT
- ½" PLYWOOD
- 60°
- 2 x 4 JOISTS
- LADDER
- MAIN A-FRAME MEMBER
- 2 x 6 BLOCKING

Perched on the stump of a dead but solidly rooted tree, this simpler A-frame doesn't have to dodge branches. It was built by Alfred Webber Jr., and sports red-cedar shingles

The ladder on Waring's creation climbs to the far end of the lower deck—at right in this view from the south. The front door is a hinged panel of a short unseen gable, up the steps just right of center

The lowest platform on the gable house is "free form," jutting out between branches. The holes along the edges have rope laced through and up to holes in the floor joists, to form a cage

tree houses

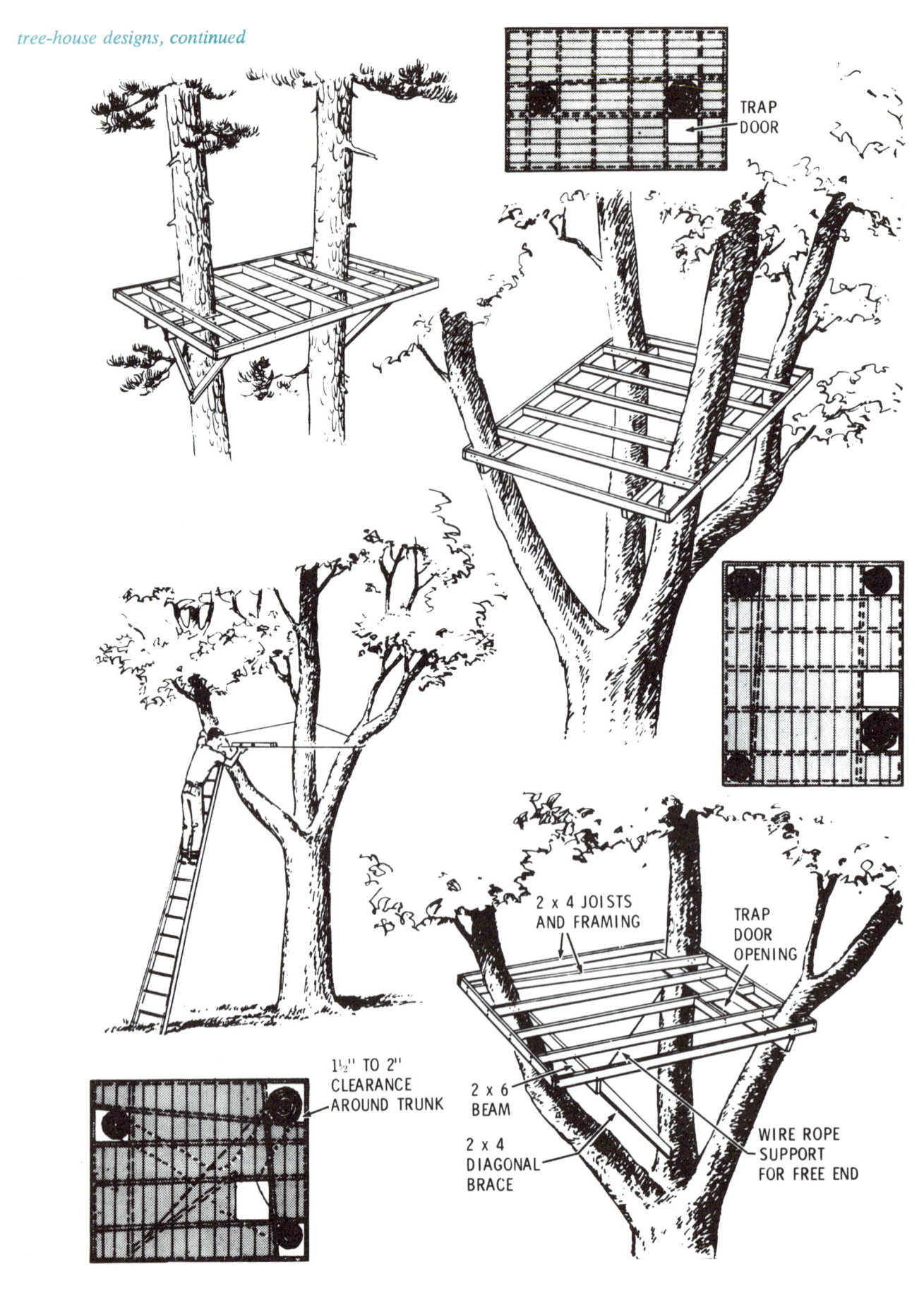

tree-house designs, continued

TRAP DOOR

2 x 4 JOISTS AND FRAMING

TRAP DOOR OPENING

2 x 6 BEAM

2 x 4 DIAGONAL BRACE

WIRE ROPE SUPPORT FOR FREE END

1½" TO 2" CLEARANCE AROUND TRUNK

2784

rooted, the owner salvaged it by perching a clubhouse on top. Again, to *copy* this house, you'd need a tree trunk of similar structure. But you could *adapt* the idea by constructing the A-frame on a platform supported by four poles (see page 2786).

As originally built, the house is framed around two main "A" assemblies which extend down past floor level and bolt to cross beams that are solidly lagscrewed to the tree trunk. The 2 x 6 members of the frames are dadoed on 24-in. centers to let in the 2 x 4 purlins and ridge pole that support the plywood roof panels. The 2 x 4 floor joists rest on two 2 x 6 cross beams which are also bolted to the main A-frames; flooring is applied to within 7½ in. of the ends of these joists. The canted railings across each end of the house are identical except that a doorway is cut in one to receive a hinged panel and the end of a ladder. A bench, with storage below, is built across the opposite end of the house and fitted with sliding doors. Red cedar shingles, laid in a staggered pattern, add to the attractive appearance.

Methods of framing sturdy platforms within various limb arrangements are also detailed. Bridging between two trees (first sketch) is not practical very far from the ground since the trunks will move independently in high wind,

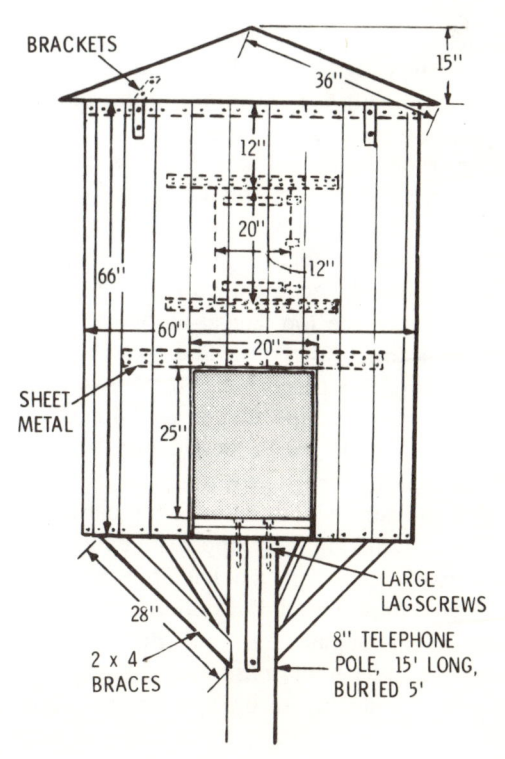

tree houses

tree-house designs, continued

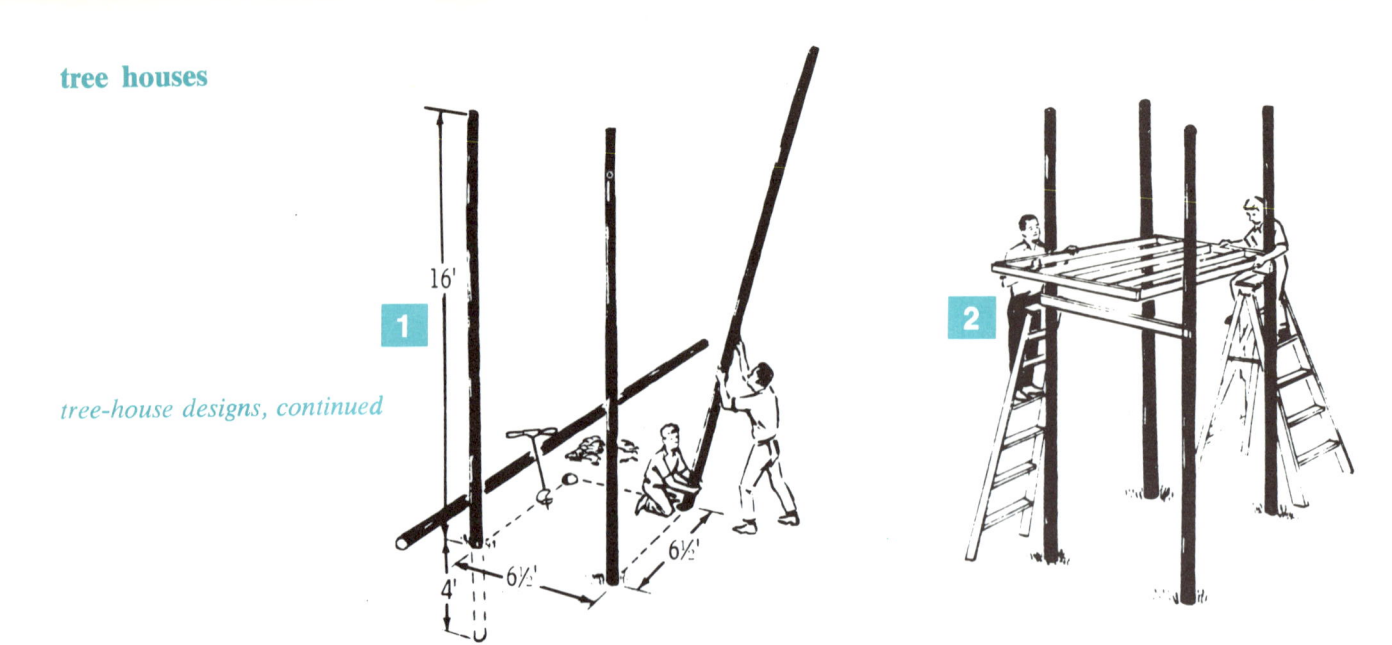

twisting the entire structure. The same goes for working too high above the crotch of the branching trees seen in the other sketches.

Where no suitable tree is available, you can "create" one by planting one or more telephone poles, as for the "silo" house on page 2785, or the platform structure on page 2787. Telephone companies often have discard or surplus poles they'll sell you. They come in various lengths in 2-ft. steps, such as 14, 16, 18 and 20 ft., and are graded by the diameter of the top, such as 4, 5 or 6-in. tops.

Edward R. Robertson, of Advance, N.C., designed and built the "silo" house from a discard pole and an empty cable reel that cost him only $2.00. He cut the pole down to a 15-ft. length and mounted one reel flange on it, bracing it underneath with 2 x 4s. Then he raised the pole and slid it into a 5-ft.-deep hole. After plumbing the pole, he tamped dirt around it.

Construction proceeds like this: you lean a ladder against the edge of the mounted flange and slide the other flange up it as you climb. When the loose flange is aligned on top of the first one, nail three boards, each cut 66 in. long, securely to the edge of the top flange, flush with the top face, projecting downward, and spaced equidistantly around the perimeter of the flanges. Mark the edge of the bottom flange on both sides of each board to determine where they are to be nailed when the top flange is raised.

You will need help to raise the top flange. Start raising it by hiking it up approximately 6 in. at each board, and driving a nail temporarily to hold it as you move around. Continue to raise the flange in this manner until one man can get his shoulders under it and raise it all the way. While he holds it, quickly secure the bottom of each board to the lower flange.

With this done, fill in all around with more boards, add the prefabricated, sheet-metal roof, and secure it in place with 5 angle brackets. Mount the feet of the ladder on bricks and fasten the top of it to the sides of the door opening to bring the top step level with the floor. For the sake of safety, Robertson placed the window high and the doorway low enough, so that not even a small child could tumble out.

Poles for the "Four Poster" shown on these pages should be 5 in. top diameter and 20 ft. long—lodge-pole pine, if available. Lay out the hole spacing and then, using a post-hole digger, dig holes deep enough so the poles will be buried about 5 ft.—or at least 6 in. below the frost line in your area. This will give your pole house a solid foundation, without fear of frost-heaving.

Drop the poles into the ground and back-fill just enough to hold them upright, but not so solidly that they will be hard to shift in their holes. Next level and bolt to the poles the 2 x 4 beams that support the floor at the desired height (about 10 ft. above ground), using ½ x 10-in. bolts.

Build the 2 x 4 floor frame on the ground and then, with the aid of a helper, hoist the frame in place and nail it securely to the poles and beams with 16d nails. Follow this by covering the floor frame with 1 x 8 boards and cut the hole for the trap door and ladder. Now you can back fill solidly around the base of each pole, soaking with a garden hose as you tamp the dirt. Be sure each pole is plumb.

Frame up the walls, railing and finally nail the roof rafters to the poles. Add the roof boards, close in the sidewalls and complete the job by adding roll roofing, starting at the low side and overlapping each strip 6 to 8 in. as you go.

See also: children's furniture; playhouses; rustic furniture; screen house; tea house.

3 **4**

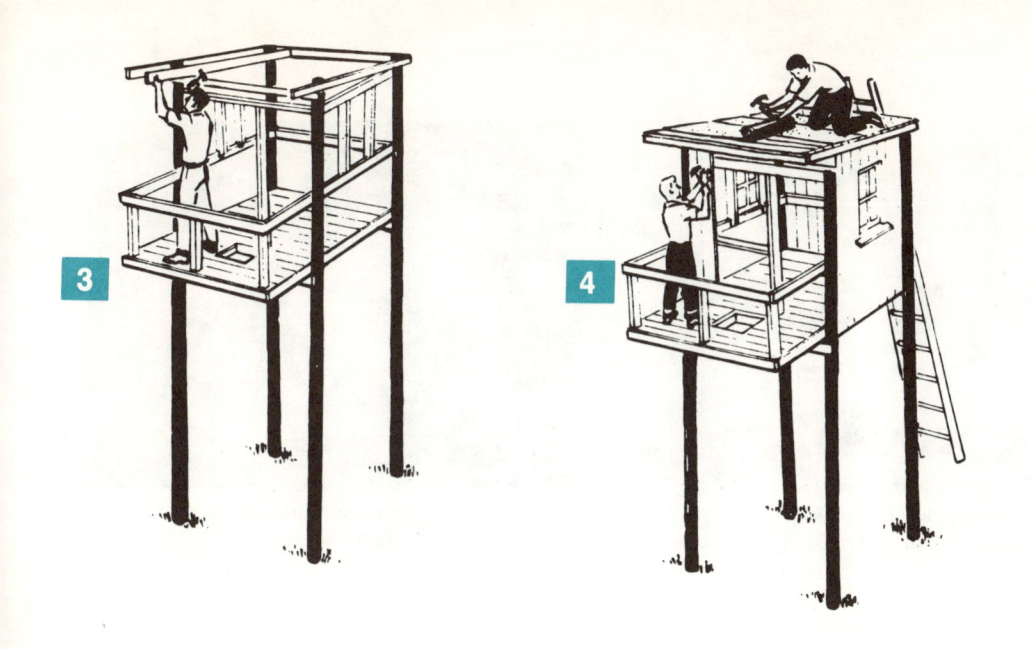

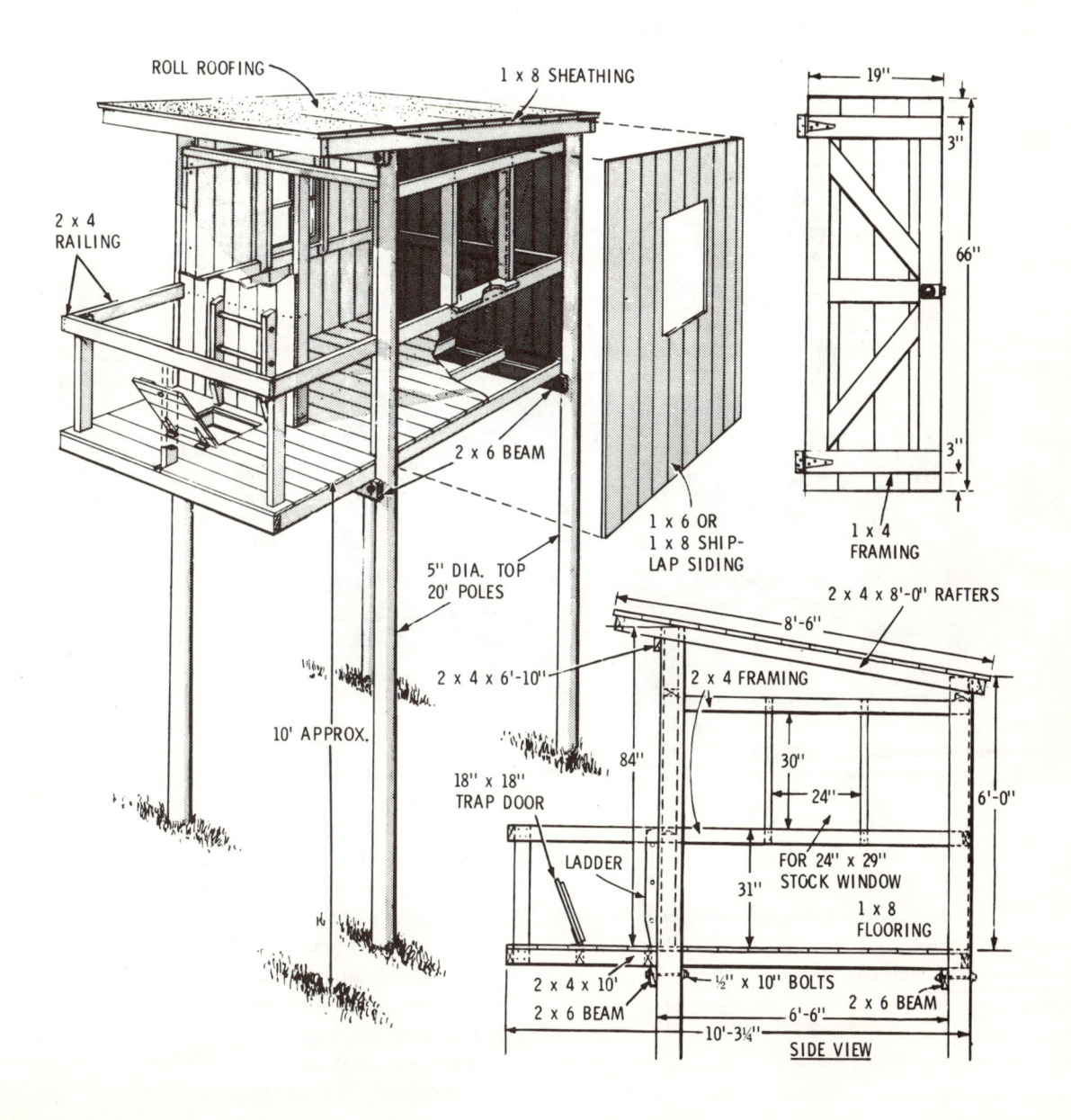

- ROLL ROOFING
- 1 x 8 SHEATHING
- 2 x 4 RAILING
- 2 x 6 BEAM
- 1 x 6 OR 1 x 8 SHIP-LAP SIDING
- 5" DIA. TOP 20' POLES
- 2 x 4 x 6'-10"
- 10' APPROX.
- 18" x 18" TRAP DOOR
- LADDER
- 2 x 4 x 10'
- 2 x 6 BEAM
- ½" x 10" BOLTS
- 2 x 6 BEAM

19"
3"
66"
3"
1 x 4 FRAMING

2 x 4 x 8'-0" RAFTERS
8'-6"
2 x 4 FRAMING
30"
24"
84"
6'-0"
FOR 24" x 29" STOCK WINDOW
31"
1 x 8 FLOORING
6'-6"
10'-3¼"
SIDE VIEW

2787

tree stumps

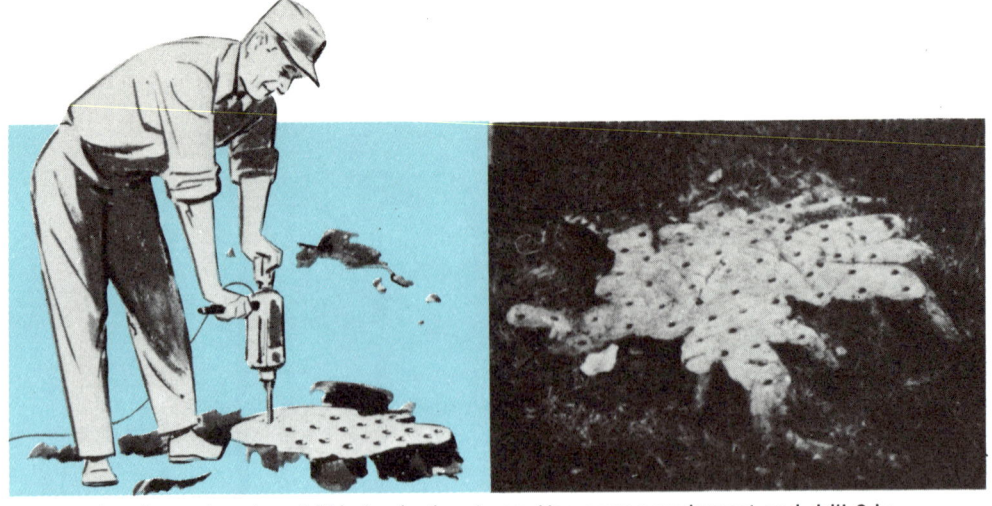

To speed rotting or burning, drill holes in the stump. Use power equipment and drill 6-in. holes about 3 in. apart. Such holes are essential when you plan to use chemicals

Get rid of that tree stump

BY FRED R. JAMES

To rot a stump cut it flush with the ground, cover with a thin layer of soil and water frequently

When burning a stump, check the fire often to make sure it has adequate ventilation and fuel so you keep a hot blaze

After you have drilled a stump and treated it with chemicals protect it from children and pets with a tight waterproof cover. The chemicals are toxic

trestle table: see tables
trickle charger: see battery chargers
tricks, magic: see magic
trimmer, hedge: see garden tools
trim paint: see house paints

■ THE UNFORTUNATE DEATH of thousands of American trees through the ravages of disease during the past few years has brought many property owners face-to-face with the problem of stump removal.

While the removal of the upper portion of a tree is a relatively simple project, getting rid of the stump is something else again. Digging it out by hand is a laborious job. But there are easier ways—at least easier on your back.

Probably the easiest and cheapest method of

To start burning a treated stump, use kindling or charcoal. A steady fire will destroy a stump in one to three weeks

A simple reflector shield made of aluminum foil tacked over a light frame will speed the burning of a stump

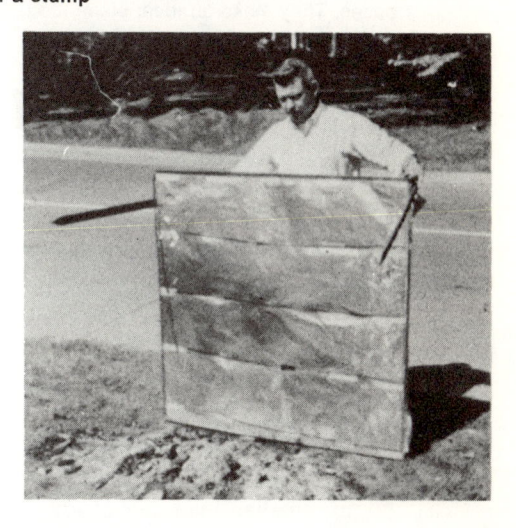

removing a stump is to let it rot in moist soil. If not already done, cut the stump at ground level or slightly below, cover it with soil and keep this soil moist. Decay organisms will rot the wood, and grass can even be planted in this thin layer of soil if you are careful to water it during dry spells. The main shortcoming of this method is that it is extremely slow. However, rotting can be hastened by boring several vertical holes about 6 in. deep in the stump before you bury it.

It's possible to burn out a stump using a fire fed with charcoal, coke or coal. Make a "stove" to hold the fire by removing the bottom and top from a metal container and punching a few 1-in. draft holes near the bottom. A 5-gal. pail makes a good stove for use with most smaller stumps. Place it either on top of the stump or down over it and build the fire. Use kindling wood to start the fire before adding the charcoal, coke or coal. When the fire burns one part of the stump, move it to a new location. For very large stumps, you can make a stove from a 55-gal. drum or an enclosure of bricks.

One of the most promising methods of stump removal is the application of chemicals which filter through the root system and create a condition of maximum combustibility to hasten burning. One efficient chemical is a mixture of 4.5 parts sodium dichromate, 1.5 parts cupric chloride, 1 part lead acetate and 1 part manganese dichloride.

Chemicals to increase flammability should be applied in late spring or early summer. After cutting the stump flush with the ground, bore a pattern of 1-in. vertical holes 6 in. deep at 6-in. intervals. These should extend out to within 2 in. of the bark.

The chemicals come in powder form and must be mixed with water to the consistency of thick molasses. You'll need about 2 lb. of this mixture for a stump 12 in. in diameter, pouring ¼ cup into each hole. Add a few drops of liquid household detergent to increase penetration of the chemical mixture throughout the stump.

After treating the stump, cover it with a protective sheet of plastic or other waterproof material and leave it for two or three months. Begin burning in the late summer or early fall, preferably after a long dry spell, using kindling wood or charcoal to start the fire. Depending on its size, the weather and the thoroughness of chemical penetration, the stump will smoulder for one to three weeks before being reduced to ashes. To hasten burning, place a reflective cover made of aluminum foil on a frame of 1 x 1 lumber over the stump. Be sure that one side of this cover is elevated a foot or so off the ground.

Caution: Because the chemicals recommended are toxic, always wear rubber gloves when handling them. Keep them away from children and pets and avoid getting any on clothing. Flush away leftover chemicals.

See also: landscaping; tree felling.

trinket boxes

Cigar humidors? No. They're antique napkin rings, fitted with lids and bases. They make an ideal stamp box, paperclip cup, or cuff-links holder

Trinket boxes made from napkin rings

■ AT FIRST GLANCE you'd never guess that these beautifully engraved trinket boxes were once napkin rings. These fancy metal bands are seldom seen today—but they can be transformed into useful little boxes and conversation pieces by fitting them with lids and bases of wood, metal or plastic.

To convert the silver ring shown at the left, above, a lid and base were turned from maple disks. A neck ¼ in. thick was turned on the lid, ³⁄₆₄ in. smaller than the inside diameter of the ring. A velvet ribbon glued to this neck gives a smooth working seal. On the base, a neck ⅛ in. thick was turned to give a tight press fit.

The second napkin ring, which is made of brass, was fitted with a brass cap and base. A blank for the top was made by sweat-soldering disks ⅛-in. thick to a mandrel rod (see drawing). Disks were cut with a drill-press circle cutter. After turning, the mandrel was rounded into a knob. The base blank was prepared the same way. However, its mandrel was cut off flush and three ball feet soldered on.

See also: jewelry case; sewing box.

Brass lid, already soldered to the mandrel, is being fitted with ring that extends into napkin ring, machined 0.040 smaller than inside diameter of napkin ring, then soldered into groove turned in lid

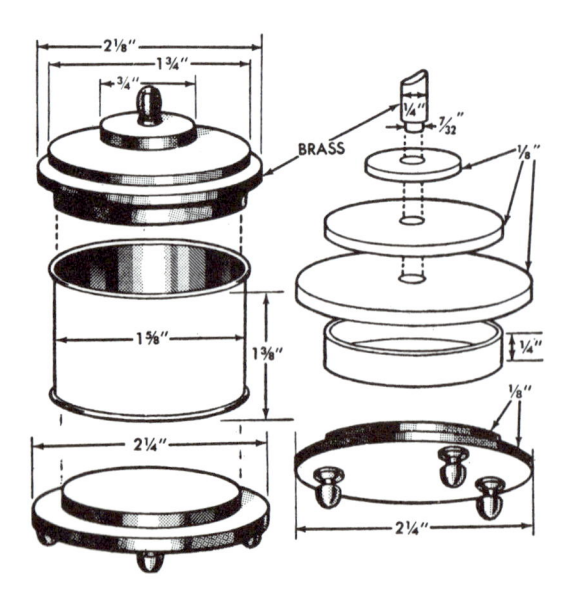

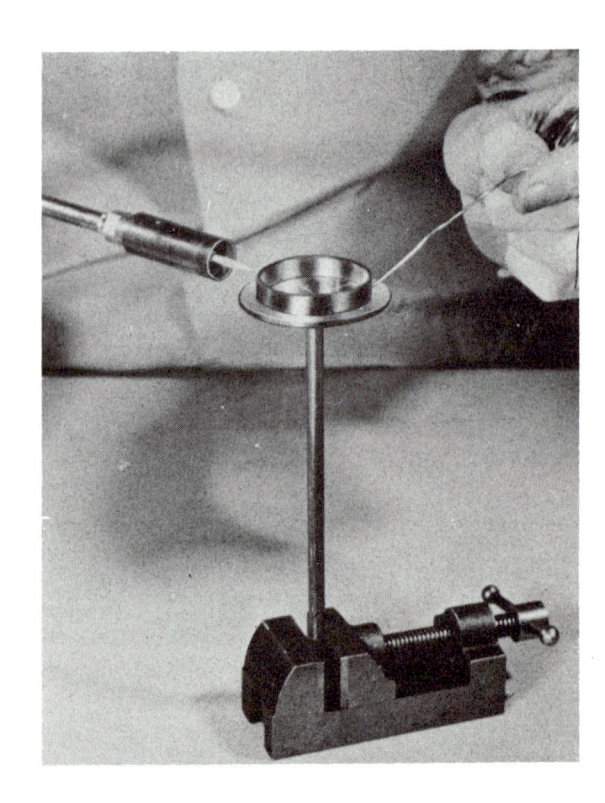

clever ideas

A drip catch eliminates the messy condition that occurs when paint runs down the handle of a brush when in use. Simply tie a cloth around the handle. Put used rags in a metal container until burned.

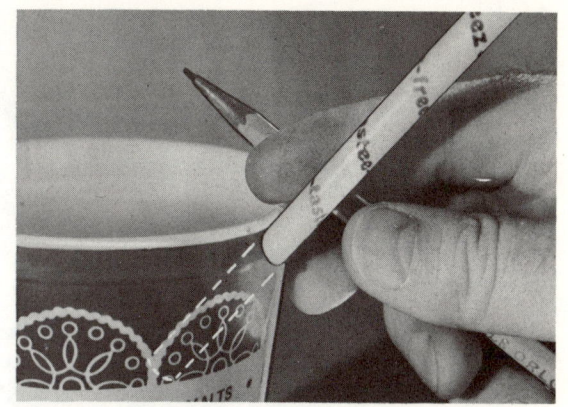

This straw holder for a paper cup can be made by using the point of a pencil to punch a hole under the cup rim. Inserting the straw through the hole will make it easier to manage the cup and straw.

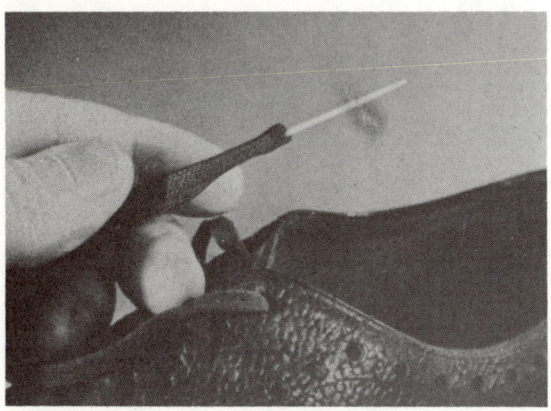

When a metal tip is lost from a shoelace a wooden toothpick makes a quick emergency repair. Dip one end of the toothpick in glue, insert it in the shoelace and then break off the end.

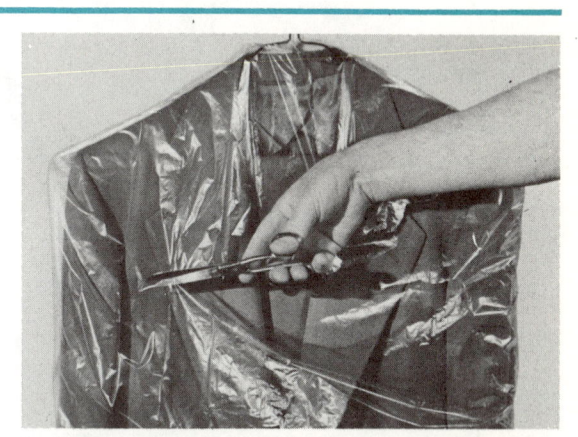

A shoulder shield made from the top third of a drycleaner's plastic bag prevents dust from settling on the garment while hanging in the closet. Tie the bag neck to the hanger for quick removal of the garment.

Water your plants with a dispenser made from an empty bleach jug. Drill small holes in the cap and a larger hole in the top side of the hollow handle. Thumb pressure over the hole creates a vacuum to control flow.

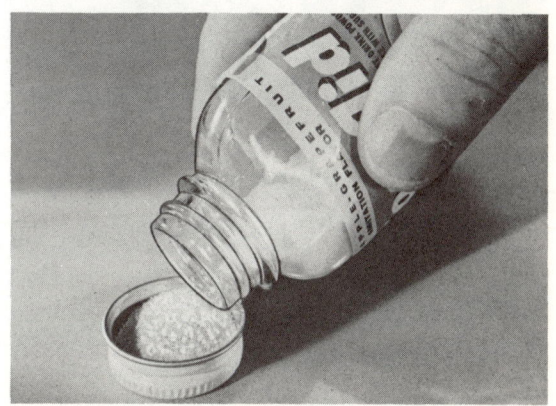

The screw cap of an empty 100-tablet aspirin bottle is the right size for measuring enough flavored powder to make an 8-oz. glass of beverage. Transfer the powder and label from its regular packet to the bottle.

2791

tripods

Dolly-in with a rolling tripod

BY JOHN BURROUGHS

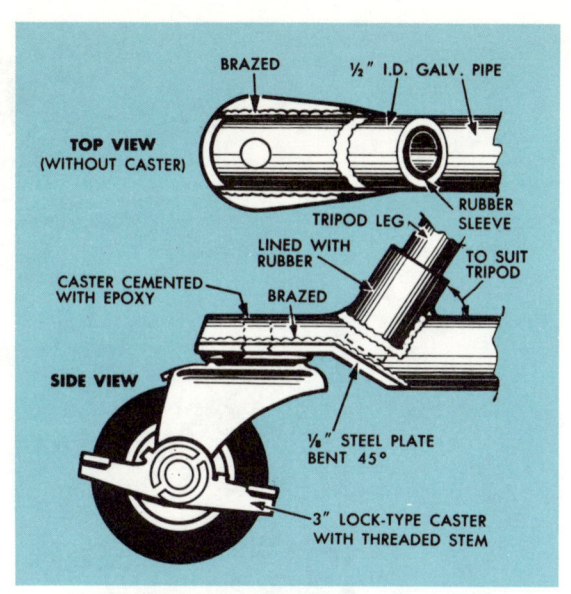

IF TRIPOD HAS RETRACTABLE FEET

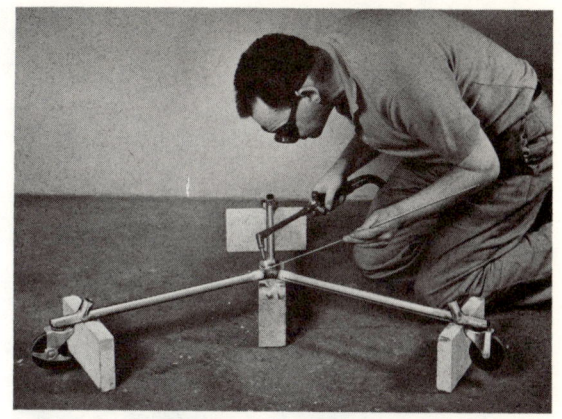

After mitering the legs so they meet at a 120-deg. angle, make sure they are of equal length. Then drill vent holes in each leg and braze the joint

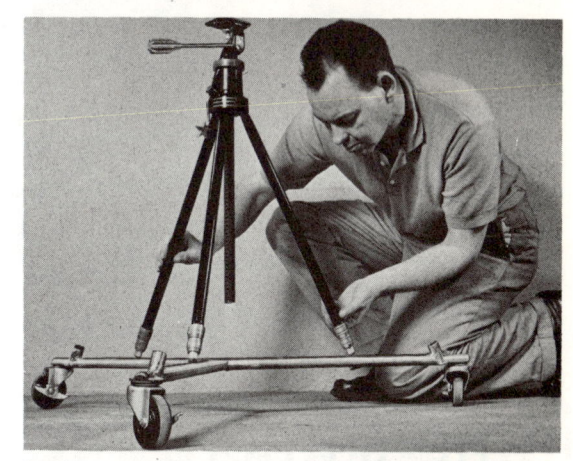

For low-angle shots, a second set of leg sockets is required. The exact location of these is determined by the tripod itself in its fully closed position

Tripod legs have retractable rubber feet fitted into the slotted tabs. If the tripod has threaded ends, drill the tab and secure with a wingnut

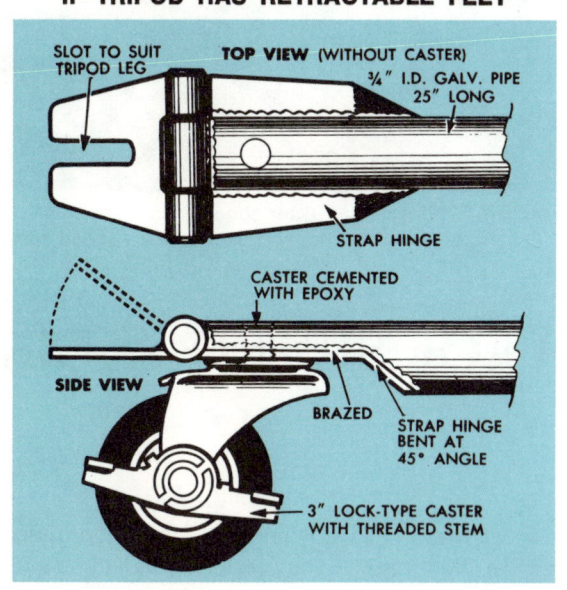

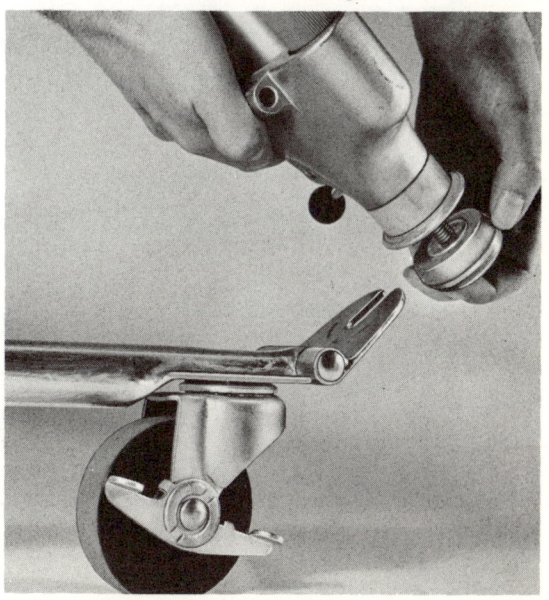

■ TEAM UP YOUR MOVIE CAMERA and tripod with this 3-wheeled dolly and you'll be able to duplicate those dolly-in closeups you've seen in the commercial films. Assemble the dolly by brazing 3 lengths of pipe or tubing to form a "spider" with arms 120 deg. apart. Braze a socket on each arm to take the legs of the tripod or attach a hinge with a slotted leaf to the end of each arm if your tripod has retractable feet. One hinge leaf forms a base for the lock-type caster, the stem of which is held in place with epoxy. In this dolly you sacrifice portability (it does not fold, of course) for steady support and rollability. Use 3-in. washing-machine casters which are available as repair parts for wringer-type washers.

See also: cameras, used; easels, artist's; movies, sound; photography; portrait photography.

tripods

For precision results in stereo photography and close-up work, run your camera on a rail

Stereo is a snap with this sliding camera mount. After shooting the first exposure, simply slide the camera sidewise 2½ in. and then take a second shot

Sliding camera mount for stereo shots

BY WALTER E. BURTON

For close-up work, turn the camera at a 90-deg. angle to the track. A 6-32 bolt at either end of track acts as a stop to limit block travel

■ How MANY TIMES have you fussed and fumed when shooting close-ups because you had no easy way to make minor adjustments in the camera-to-subject distance? This sliding mount is designed specifically for just such photography. There's a fringe benefit too—if you turn the camera so that it is parallel to the track you're able to take stereo photographs of non-moving subjects. All you have to do is make an exposure with the camera positioned at one end of the track. After that, you simply slide the camera sidewards about 2½ in. and take the second picture.

The camera is attached to a block which slides along a T-shaped aluminum track. A suitable length for the track is 6½ in., but if greater travel is needed the length may be increased. An aluminum angle riveted to the center of the track and tapped ¼-20 makes it possible to attach the unit to a standard tripod screw. The aluminum required is available at most hardware stores.

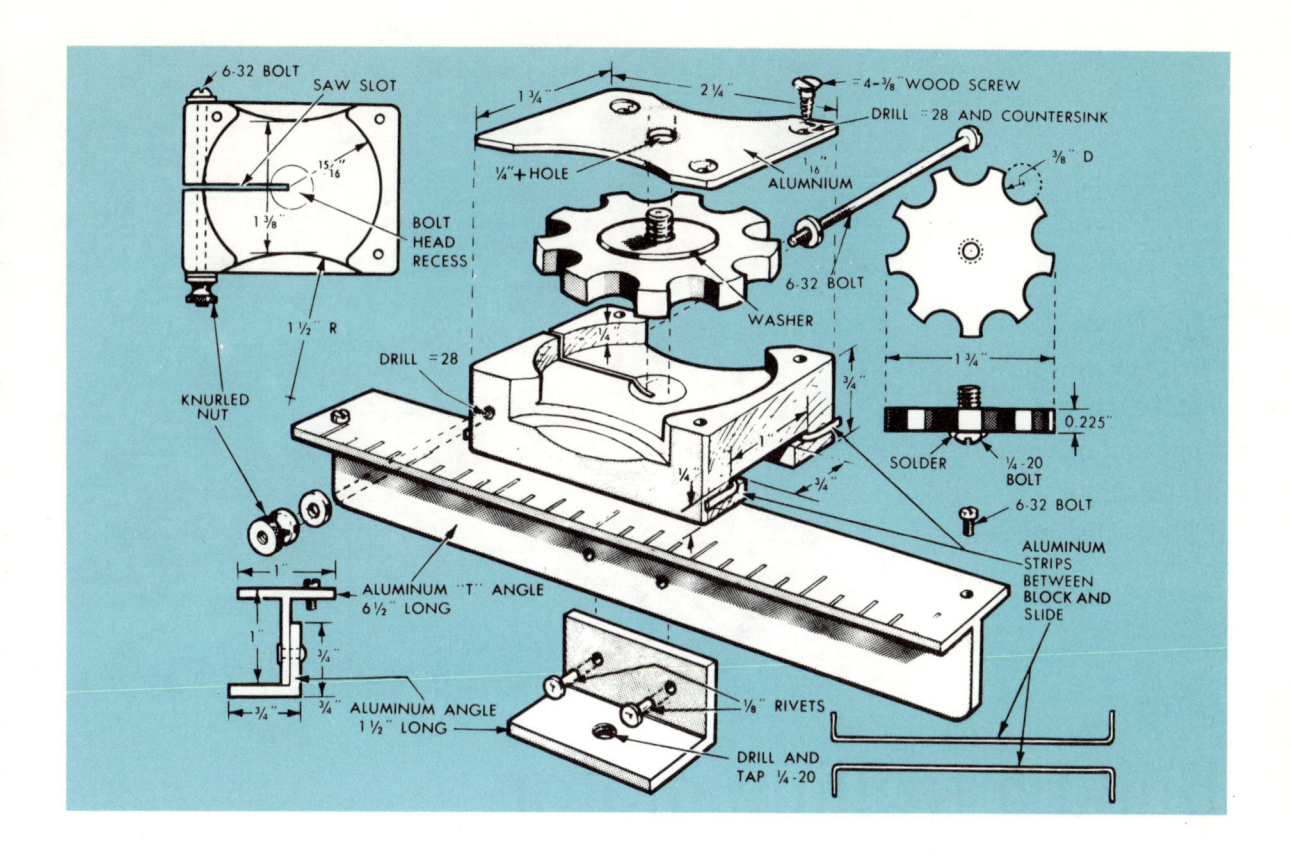

The block has a T-slot cut in the bottom to allow it to slide along the track. A choice of material is possible; either maple or aluminum may be used. If maple is chosen, the slot should be cut parallel to the grain. The top of the block is recessed to accommodate a locking wheel which incorporates a screw to fit the camera's tripod socket. A saw slot extending half the length of the block permits the T-slot to be squeezed together by a 6-32 bolt and knurled nut. This locks the block firmly in position on the track. A flat strip of thin aluminum should be inserted between each edge of the track and the T-slot in the block. These strips serve a double purpose: they reduce play between the block and track and also act as bearing surfaces. Their ends are bent flat against the block so they will slide with it.

For the locking wheel, aluminum or brass is best. The notches are made by drilling ⅜-in. holes around the circumference of a 1¾-in. circle and sawing through the webs that remain between the holes. The wheel is completed by soldering a ¼-20 bolt in a tapped center hole.

An aluminum plate is attached with screws to the top of the block. This plate serves as both a retainer for the locking wheel and as a support area for the camera. Only one screw should be used in the portion of the plate over the split end of the block so that the locking action will not be hampered. As the final step, cut away both the block and the plate so the locking wheel can be manipulated easily with the fingers.

You'll find that this slide is sturdy enough for use with twin-lens reflex cameras. If you anticipate doing stereo photography with it, a scale should be engraved on the track.

A top view of the camera slide, with the aluminum cover plate removed, shows how the block and wheel are assembled

2795

trolling motor

You can make one for
a few dollars, using
a car-heater motor
and a few odds and ends

Build a trolling motor

BY RICHARD HANSON

■ HIGH-POWERED outboard motors are fine for zooming out to your favorite fishing spot, but once there, all those "horses" are not needed for treading slowly (about 2 mph) among lily pads or over other likely lunker hangouts. What you really need is an electric trolling motor like the one pictured in use above. The assembly, detailed on the opposite page, is simplicity itself.

The basic part of the troller is the motor. The unit used in this one is a 1952 Oldsmobile 6-volt heater motor obtained from a wrecking yard. Except for cleaning it and installing new brushes, the motor was used as is. A 12-volt motor may be used, but keep in mind that it will discharge the battery more quickly. If the power lead on the motor you use leaves the housing at the rear end, it must be relocated to a side position in an area that will permit a hole to be drilled through the housing. When doing this, first grind one end of the pipe coupling to fit the housing contour.

Then, position it on the motor and locate the hole so as not to drill into vital motor parts.

Next, the coupling is centered over the hole and welded in place, after which the lead is fished through and solder-connected to the positive lead of the two-wire conductor. Be sure to make the latter long enough to reach from the battery to the lead on the motor. Since the conductor wire is led out through a hole drilled in the handle at the bend, it should be fished through the handle before soldering it to the motor lead. The slit-pipe sleeve below the cotter-pin stop must be slipped on the handle and the stop hole drilled before connecting the leads. If you intend to use the motor on rental boats, it's a good idea to drill several additional holes spaced 1 in. apart to permit raising and lowering the motor to match variable transom heights. Since the motor is not sealed, it should not be used in salt water. Fresh water in the motor will not short it out, but when storing it for a long period, it is advisable to disassemble the motor, clean the parts and coat them lightly with oil.

trophy shelf: see boys' projects
truck, fork lift: see toys
truck, pickup: see pickup camper
t-squares: see drafting equipment

See also: carburetors, outboard; magnetos, outboard; outboard motors, overhauling; outboard motors, repair; outboard motors, storage; outboard motors, used; sparkplugs, marine.

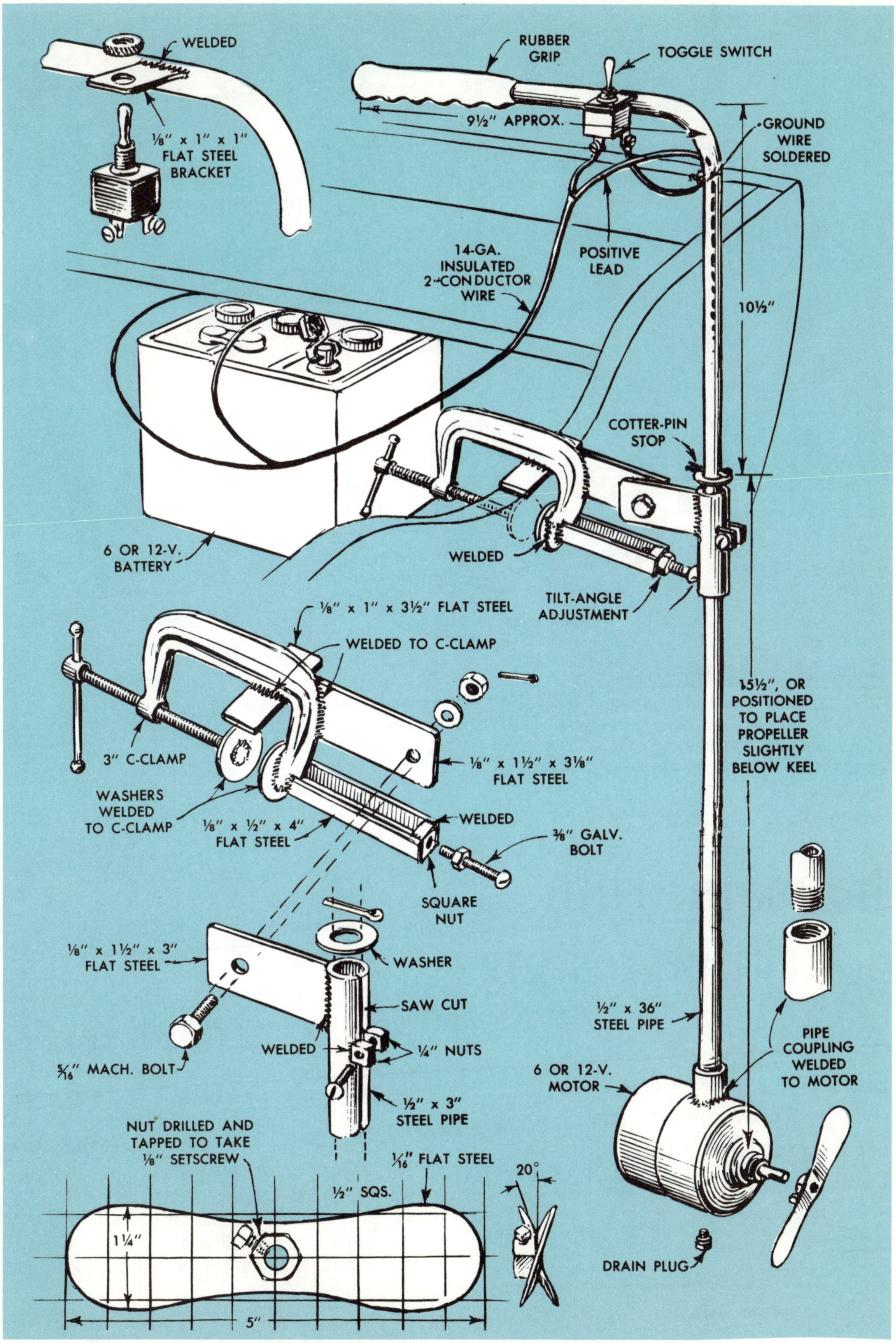
WELDED
1/8" x 1" x 1" FLAT STEEL BRACKET
RUBBER GRIP
TOGGLE SWITCH
9½" APPROX.
GROUND WIRE SOLDERED
14-GA. INSULATED 2-CONDUCTOR WIRE
POSITIVE LEAD
10½"
COTTER-PIN STOP
6 OR 12-V. BATTERY
WELDED
TILT-ANGLE ADJUSTMENT
1/8" x 1" x 3½" FLAT STEEL
WELDED TO C-CLAMP
3" C-CLAMP
WASHERS WELDED TO C-CLAMP
1/8" x 1½" x 3⅛" FLAT STEEL
1/8" x ½" x 4" FLAT STEEL
WELDED
3/8" GALV. BOLT
SQUARE NUT
15½", OR POSITIONED TO PLACE PROPELLER SLIGHTLY BELOW KEEL
1/8" x 1½" x 3" FLAT STEEL
WASHER
SAW CUT
WELDED
¼" NUTS
5/16" MACH. BOLT
½" x 3" STEEL PIPE
½" x 36" STEEL PIPE
PIPE COUPLING WELDED TO MOTOR
6 OR 12-V. MOTOR
NUT DRILLED AND TAPPED TO TAKE 1/8" SETSCREW
1/16" FLAT STEEL
½" SQS.
20°
1¼"
5"
DRAIN PLUG

tubes, television

Double check all control settings before depressing the test button, when you are checking tubes at the do-it-yourself tester. One wrong dial setting can make the machine goof by calling a good tube bad or a bad tube good. If a tube won't light, try wiggling it. Sometimes the base of the tube is slightly worn

The plain truth about tube testing

BY LARRY STECKLER

A drugstore tube tester can get your television set going again for the price of one tube

tubing bender: see convertible top, boat

■ THE MAN WAS MAD. There was no doubt about that. You would be, too, if you had just bought x-dollars worth of new tubes at the drugstore, installed them in your TV set—and still no picture.

I waited until his sputtering subsided and then offered to help him find the trouble. He welcomed the idea. So we checked all his new tubes on my Heathkit mutual-conductance tube tester. One, a 10DE7 (vertical oscillator-output), was defective. A good replacement cured the set.

That experience set me to wondering how many other people have had the same problem. Just how good are the replacement tubes you buy, how accurate are the drugstore testing machines, and what could and should the average Joe do about testing tubes on his home electronic equipment?

Before I found the answers, I had tested 105 radio, TV and hi-fi tubes on home, store and lab-

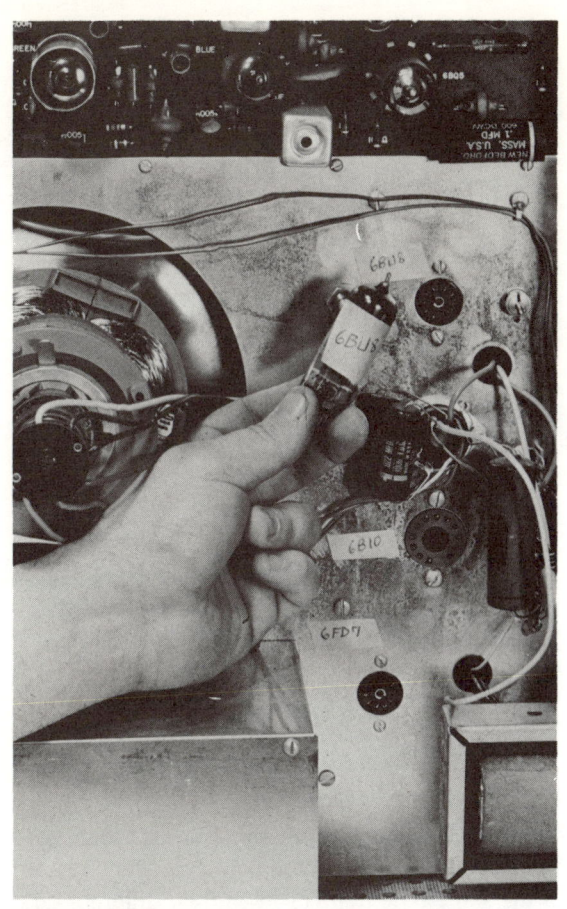

Label each tube and its socket with the tube type number to be certain that each one is returned to the same socket from which it was removed for the test. Use a tag or grease pencil on tape

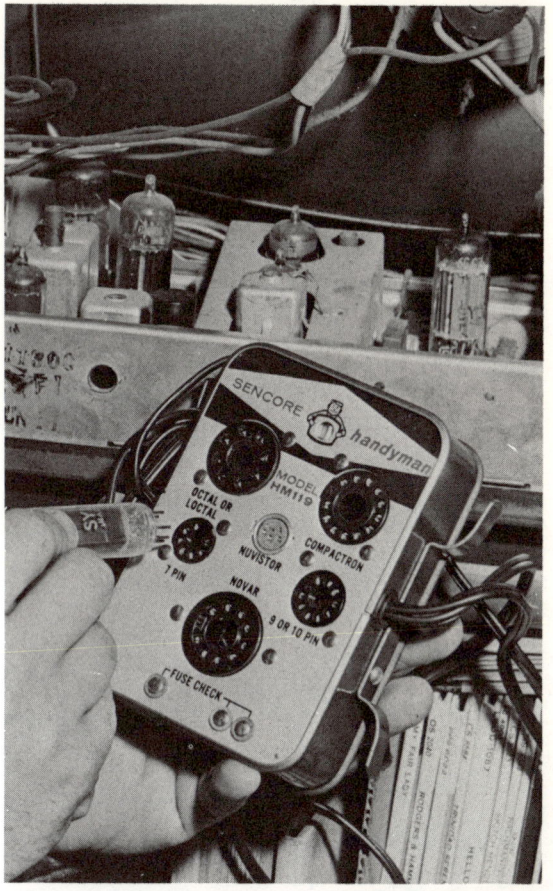

A continuity tester makes quick work of identifying a burned-out tube. In many TV and radio sets, when a single tube fails, the good ones won't light either. A continuity tester is not expensive to purchase

oratory-type testers, as well as in working electronic circuits. The results were fascinating.

I used as my good-bad standard the operation of the tubes in actual circuits. If a circuit worked with the test tube, the tube was called "good." If the circuit did not work, the tube was called "bad."

Several types of testers were used. First, I tried a *continuity* tester which tells you only whether a tube's filament is good or bad; that is, if the tube is burned out and will not light. Next, I used an *emission* tester, the type found in drugstores and used by many TV repairmen. It rates a tube according to the electron flow between the two main elements of a tube. It also reveals shorted and gassy tubes. Finally, I used a lab-type *mutual conductance* tester. This unit checks tubes under simulated operating conditions with all sections of the tube under test connected and loaded much as they would be in an electronic circuit.

The continuity tester—that's the sample, bargain-basement-type tester—found 5 bad tubes. All the tubes it called bad were bad; they did not work in an actual circuit. It did not locate any shorted or weak tubes, but it did provide a quick and easy test for the dead ones.

The drugstore emission tester and the repairman's emission tester gave identical results. They picked out the same 5 dead tubes plus 2 shorted and 3 gassy ones. They also listed 6 other tubes as "weak" and 4 others as "bad." One of the "bad" tubes and 3 of the "weak" ones were still in working order.

The mutual conductance tester did the best job of all. It found the 5 dead tubes, confirmed the 2 shorted and 3 gassy ones. And it also picked out one additional gassy tube the emission testers missed. It listed 11 "bad" tubes.

Now let's look at tube-testing procedures. The most important single point is to make sure the

2799

tubes, television

set is off and the line cord disconnected when tubes are removed. Next, remember that if a tube has a metal cap, you must ground this cap before removing the tube to bleed off any residual electricity. Do this by touching a screwdriver from the cap to some metal part of the chassis.

Another important point is to be sure you put the tubes back into the same sockets they came from. Get them mixed and you can cause a lot of

A "maybe" reading is the cue for a further check. Cover the tube with an empty frozen juice can and retest it. This gimmick raises the operating temperature, which may show up the tube's faults

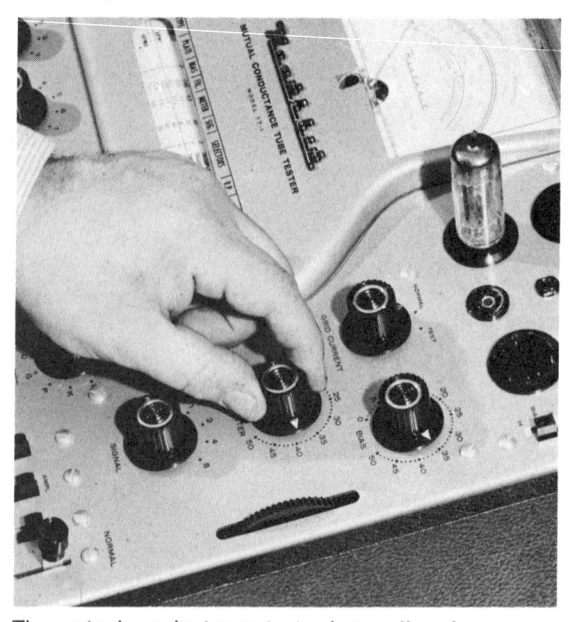

The mutual-conductance tester is excellent for accuracy but the proper setting of its many controls is a task for a technician experienced with its operation. Instruction for it is available

damage under the chassis—costly damage. Switch 2 tubes of the same type (you may have 2 of the same type number in entirely different circuits of the set) and a tube which worked in one socket might not work in the other.

There are several ways to tag tubes for identification—grease pencil, paper tags or numbers.

Which tester should you rely on? Well, if you have a lot of vacuum-tube equipment around the house, it may pay for you to get a tube tester of your own. The continuity tester becomes worthwhile if you have only one TV set. Prices range up to $15.00 or so. If you have two TV sets, a vacuum tube hi-fi or stereo set and a couple of radios, you probably have 40 or 50 tubes in action in your home and I'd suggest picking up an inexpensive emission tester. You can buy a good one for about $45.00 and with it you can do "drugstore testing" at home.

To use a continuity tester, just unplug the inoperative set and remove the back cover. Remove one tube at a time and plug it into the tester. If a tube tests "good," put it back in the same socket. Put a "bad" one aside, mark the empty socket with the tube type number and go on testing until you've tried every tube in the set. When you're finished checking, buy the proper replacements, have them tested at the time and put the set together. The chances are that it will now be back in business. One hedge is called for:

After the tube is warmed-up in the tester, tapping the tube very lightly with a pencil or a short length of dowel rod may reveal an internal short circuit. Otherwise, the tube might test as good

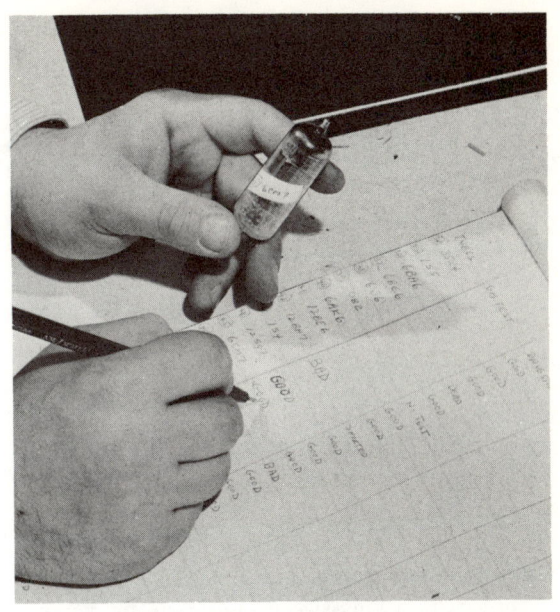

Detailed record-keeping is desirable when you have a large number of tubes to test. Enter each test reading of every tube. By doing this, you can later study each of the entries and compare the tubes

If any new tube also burns out in a short time, there is serious trouble in the set. You'll have to call for skilled assistance.

If you don't find any bad tubes with the continuity tester or if you don't have one, take your tubes to a drugstore tester or a TV service shop; both have testers of about the same quality. A few technicians use the more accurate mutual conductance unit, but there are $300-and-up instruments that must be operated by the repairman as the controls are much more complex than those on the emission unit.

The drugstore tester is easy to use and will tell you quite accurately which tubes are definitely burned out. It will also pinpoint shorted or gassy tubes. Its "good-weak-bad" scale will give a quality reading on the rest. Any tubes that test low down on the "bad" scale must be replaced. But hold off on those in the upper portion of the "bad" scale and on all of those in the "weak" section. Quite often they will still work, so don't replace them until after you have replaced all the really bad tubes (burned-out, shorted, gassy and low-scale) and find the set still doesn't work. My tests found seven borderline tubes.

Be sure to test any tubes you buy before leaving the store. This double checks the tester and the new tubes. If a tube fails to light and the new one also doesn't light, try wiggling it around in the tester socket. If you then find signs of life, the socket is worn. Try another tester in another store. Also be sure to use a tester that has a control marked "line adjust" or "meter set" atop the panel. Testers with either of these controls are almost impossible to rig to indicate more bad tubes than actually are in your set.

My expensive mutual-conductance lab tester gave about the same results as the drugstore testers but was much more accurate in picking out the bad marginal tubes, because it includes a "life" test. It did tip me off to some additional tubes that weren't going to last much longer. And the ideal procedure—if your budget permits it—is to replace a suspect tube with one you know to be good, which is just what your repairman does.

Paste that "known-to-be-good" comment in your hat. We made a check of tubes right off the shelf in one dealer's salesroom and found 5 bad ones in a lot of 200 that we checked.

After all testing is done and all bad tubes have been replaced, you will occasionally find that the set still doesn't work. About 15 sets out of 100 that don't work have circuit rather than tube troubles, and may need a repairman's expert touch. But at least when he tells you that the set has to go to the shop, you'll know that it's not just a bum tube—the trip is, in fact, really necessary.

See also: electronics; television repair; television servicing; television sets.

2801

tumbler

Trampoline doubles as wading pool

■ WHAT KID hasn't found great delight in bouncing on a bed only to be reprimanded for breaking the springs? Now, lively youngsters can bounce to their heart's content on an outdoor tumbler that will stand all the bounce they can give it. This one differs from others in that it is designed to convert to a king-size wading pool by removing the tumbling bed and lashing a waterproof plastic liner to the supporting framework.

The bed part of the tumbler measures 5 x 10 ft. and may be made of cotton or nylon duck, or strips of nylon webbing woven and stitched together. Nylon duck gives a little better bounce than cotton duck and is much lighter in weight. However, nylon webbing, woven or sewn, has more spring than nylon duck and gives the greatest bounce.

As detailed in the drawings, the supporting frame is made of doubled 2 x 6s, alternately lapped at the corners and nailed together with 12d common nails. The 2 x 6s are supported by 6 fence-post legs to which they are bolted se-

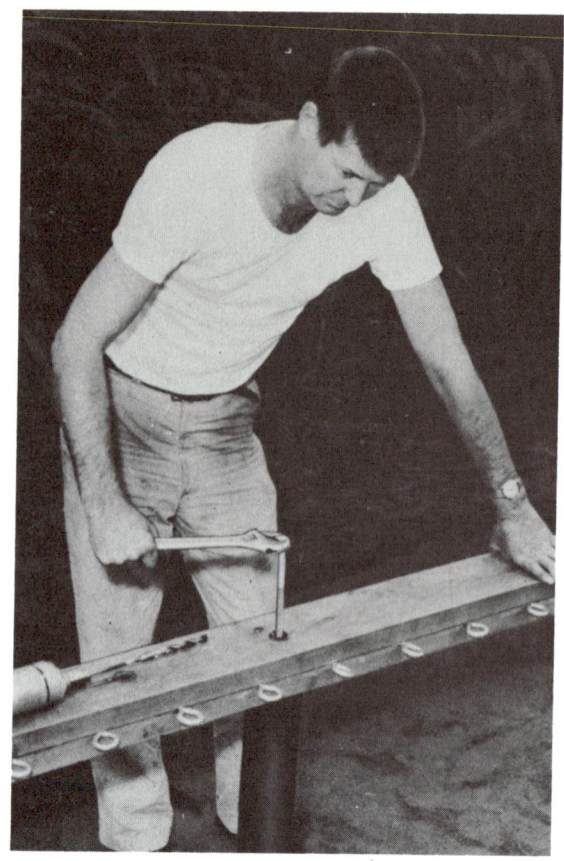

The wooden frame is lagscrewed to the 6 creosoted-fence-post legs which support it 30 in. above the ground. Pilot holes should be made in the posts for the 8-in. lagscrews

A plastic liner lashed to the tumbling frame converts your outdoor tumbler to a king-size wading pool. A 12-mm polyethylene film liner measuring about 12 x 17 ft. will make a good pool

Set the legs at the same height so the supporting frame of the tumbling bed is level. Check this with a level at the time the posts are set and again when the tumbler is completed

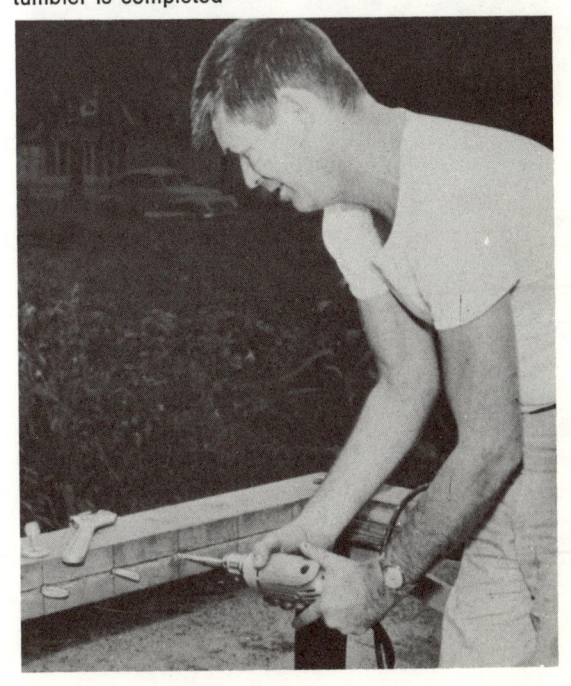

curely with 8-in. lagscrews. Three standard 7-ft. creosoted fence posts, sawed in two, will make the 6 legs. These are cross-braced at the ends with 1 x 2s. Make sure the legs are set the same height so the frame will be level. Check with a carpenter's level as you go along.

A total of 60 eyebolts, ¼ x 8 in., are required to attach the springs which support the bed. Holes for these are spaced 6 in. apart and bored edgewise through the 2 x 6s with the bit cutting across the joint. Ten eyebolts are installed at the ends of the frame, 20 along each side. Washers and nuts are placed on the outside.

A total of 61 coil springs are needed, the extra one being used as a hook when stretching the nylon bed. The edges of the latter should be rolled under to form hems, after which webbing is sewed to the underside for reinforcement. Then 60 grommets of the spur-tooth type are spaced around the reinforced edges of the bed. The job of stretching the springs to pull the bed taut works best with two persons working to-

tumbler

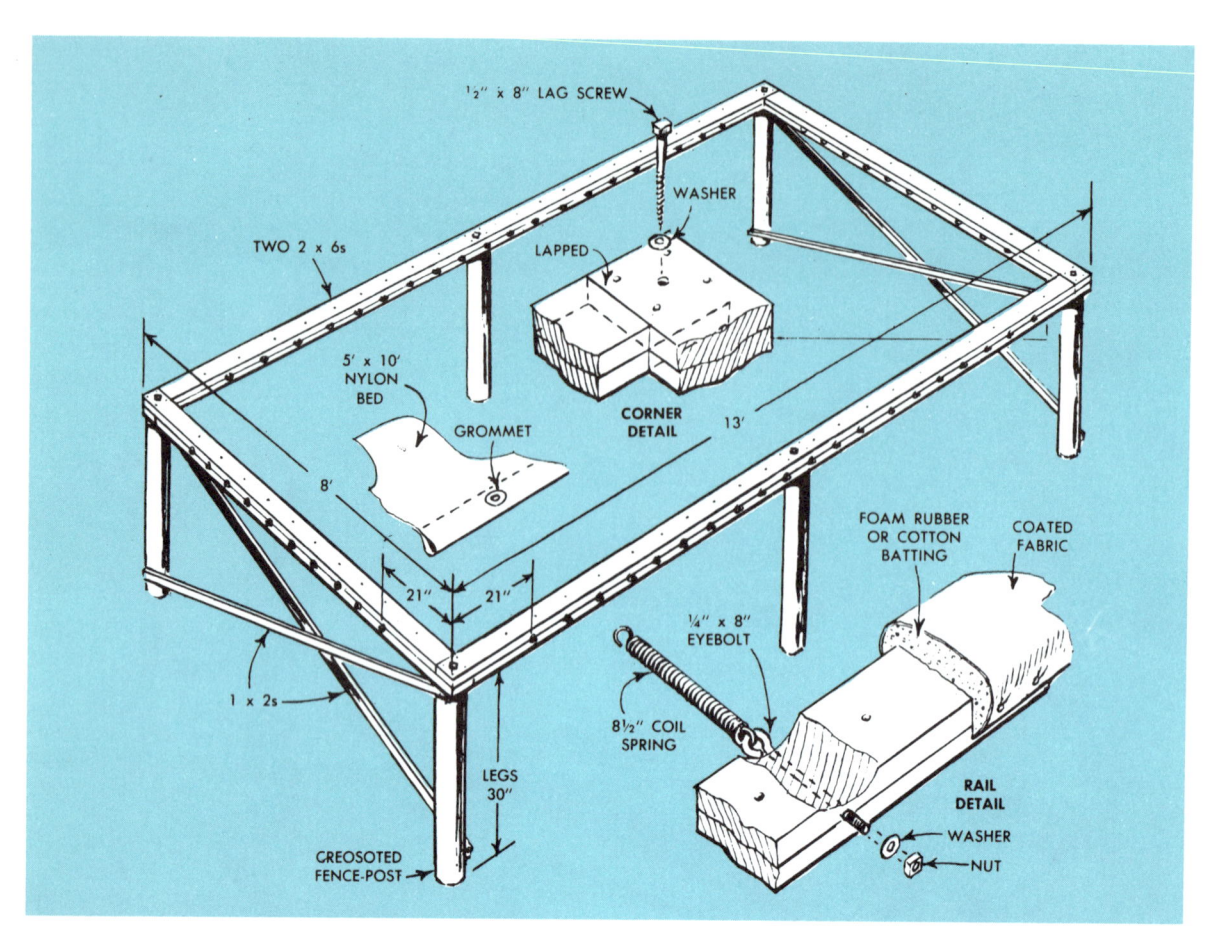

The holes for the eyebolts are made at the joint between the 2 x 6s as shown below. These are spaced 6 in., and washers are used on the outer ends of the bolts to prevent them from pulling through

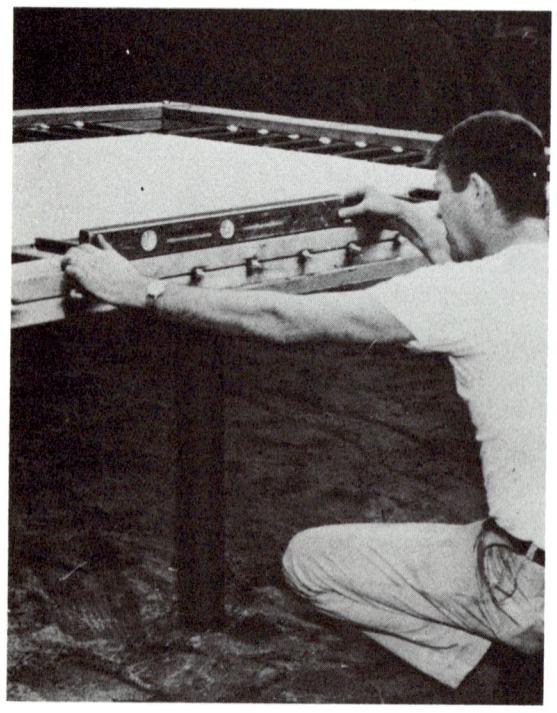

gether. Begin by hooking springs into the eyebolts and grommets at the corners at one end, then do the same at the opposite end. The extra spring is used as a stretching tool, hooking it to the spring being stretched and pulling on it until the spring can be hooked to the eyebolt. After the springs at the ends are hooked in place, the end springs along the sides are hooked in the same manner. With this done, the rest of the springs are installed, opposite springs being hooked in place alternately around the frame. Finally, the wooden frame is padded with a 1-in. layer of foam rubber and covered with a plastic-coated fabric tacked to the underside of the 2 x 6s.

Strong 12-mm polyethylene film makes a good wading pool liner. The edges are reinforced with webbing and then grommets are installed so it can be lashed to the eyebolts with light rope. Here an extra eyebolt is required at each corner of the frame to support the folded corners of the liner. A liner measuring approximately 12 x 17 ft. is available which will make a king-size wading pool.

See also: playground equipment; playhouses; sandbox; toys; tree houses.

tumbling machines

Tumbling machine gives high-polish finish

BY WALTER E. BURTON

■ ANYTHING FROM TABLESPOONS to jet-engine blades can be polished in a tumbling machine, or barrel finisher. The principle on which the tumbling machine operates is quite simple and effective. Parts to be polished are placed in a container, or drum, with a given quantity of abrasive and sometimes other filler materials such as sand or wood shavings, and the container rotated at a uniform speed ranging from 10 to 30 rpm.

Not only metal but wood, plastics of various types, also jewelry, can be given high polishes with the right abrasive and filler materials.

The small-shop unit illustrated in Fig. 1 and detailed in Figs. 5, 6 and 7 can be made from a couple of wringer rolls (those from a hand wringer or wringer-type washing machine will do very well), a spare ¼-hp motor, a few pieces of plywood, hardwood for bearings, 3 V-pulleys and a short length of ½-in. steel shafting. A 1-gal. paint can serves as the container, or barrel. These parts make up into about the smallest practical tumbler you can use for small parts. The unit can be made much larger by substituting larger and heavier rollers and a different drive assembly.

Figs. 2, 3 and 4 picture steps in the assembly of the unit as detailed in Figs. 5, 6, 7 and 8. As you can see, the whole thing is quite simple to make and easy to assemble ready for use. Note that only one roller is power driven; the other is simply an idler. In use, the container is placed on the rollers as in Fig. 1 and due to the reduction from the motor to the jackshaft, and again from the jackshaft to the driven roller, the speed of rotation of the tumbling drum is reduced to only a very few revolutions per minute.

The wringer rolls should be in good condition,

2805

tumbling machines

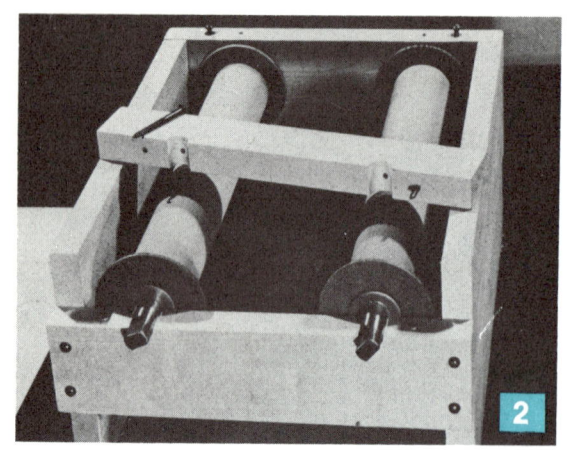

This boxlike frame carries rolls which turn tumbling drum at slow speeds. Rolls are washing machine wringers. Each roll is fitted with flanges at the ends

The jackshaft is mounted in hardwood bearings bolted to a vertical support that has been stiffened with a brace and cleat. Be sure bearings align

The jackshaft support, with its single brace and cleat, is attached to the machine base with screws and glue. The support must be vertical

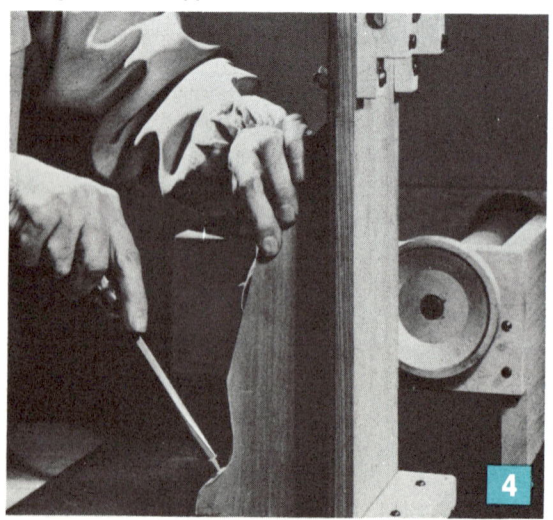

preferably new, as new ones are readily available as repair parts for washers. Old, worn rolls having hardened surfaces are not suitable, as the container will tend to slip and fail to rotate uniformly. This is especially true if it is loaded with metal parts. Hardboard flanges must be made and fitted to each end of each roll as detailed. After fitting they should be cemented in place. Bearings for the rolls are made by clamping the two supporting pieces together and then centering holes for the spindles on the line of the joint. The holes must be of a size to permit the rolls to turn freely, especially the idler roll, detail B, Fig. 7. A small smear of paste wax or beeswax in each hole will provide sufficient lubrication. When assembling the boxlike frame which forms a support for the rolls, be sure that the holes which provide bearings for the roll spindles are in line as otherwise the rolls may bind which can cause irregular rotation of the container. The side members of the frame which form the bearings for the roll spindles should be of maple as this is best for slow-speed bearings.

guide rollers

Note also in Fig. 7 the small rubber rollers, detail A, which are attached to the upper edges of the end bearings. These are referred to as rubber rollers, but they can be anything suitable for the purpose. A skate wheel will do very well. The purpose of the rollers is to provide rolling contact at the ends of the container when it drifts one way or the other on the rolls as it will do unless the unit is precisely level. If the ends of the roll spindles are milled to form flats, then the outer end of the driven roll should be fitted with a guard so that it cannot catch and wind a shirt sleeve or a glove when rotating. A metal drawer pull makes an effective guard, Figs. 5 and 7.

The box supporting the roll bearing assembly is mounted on a base of plywood which is cleated as in Fig. 5. The dimensions of the base given were found sufficient to provide space for the box and a motor mounting and jackshaft. The motor mounting, Fig. 8, is a simple arrangement making use of a wedge to tighten the V-belt. Any hinged motor mount can be used.

The jackshaft is mounted on a support consisting of a 5 x 15-in. piece of hardwood fitted with a brace of the same material. Both brace and support are screwed to the base, the approximate position of the brace and support in relation to the roll-bearing assembly being shown more clearly in Fig. 10. The support is screwed to a short cleat attached to the base as in Figs. 5 and

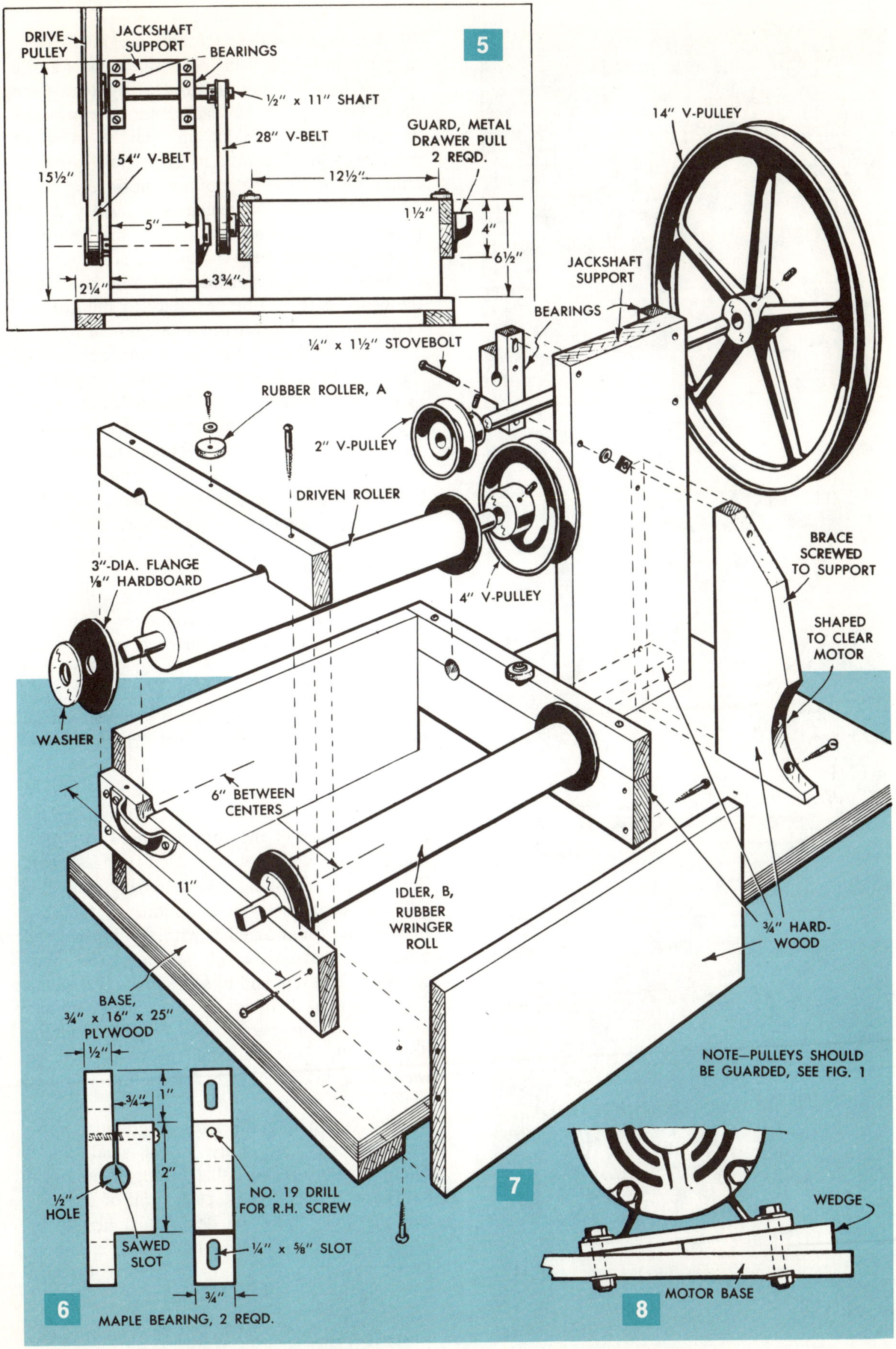
5
DRIVE PULLEY
JACKSHAFT SUPPORT
BEARINGS
1/2" x 11" SHAFT
28" V-BELT
54" V-BELT
GUARD, METAL DRAWER PULL 2 REQD.
15 1/2"
12 1/2"
1 1/2"
4"
6 1/2"
5"
2 1/4"
3 3/4"
14" V-PULLEY
JACKSHAFT SUPPORT
BEARINGS
1/4" x 1 1/2" STOVEBOLT
RUBBER ROLLER, A
2" V-PULLEY
DRIVEN ROLLER
3"-DIA. FLANGE 1/8" HARDBOARD
4" V-PULLEY
BRACE SCREWED TO SUPPORT
SHAPED TO CLEAR MOTOR
WASHER
6" BETWEEN CENTERS
11"
IDLER, B, RUBBER WRINGER ROLL
3/4" HARD-WOOD
BASE, 3/4" x 16" x 25" PLYWOOD
NOTE—PULLEYS SHOULD BE GUARDED, SEE FIG. 1
7
1/2"
3/4"
1"
2"
1/2" HOLE
SAWED SLOT
NO. 19 DRILL FOR R.H. SCREW
1/4" x 5/8" SLOT
3/4"
6
MAPLE BEARING, 2 REQD.
WEDGE
MOTOR BASE
8

tumbling machines

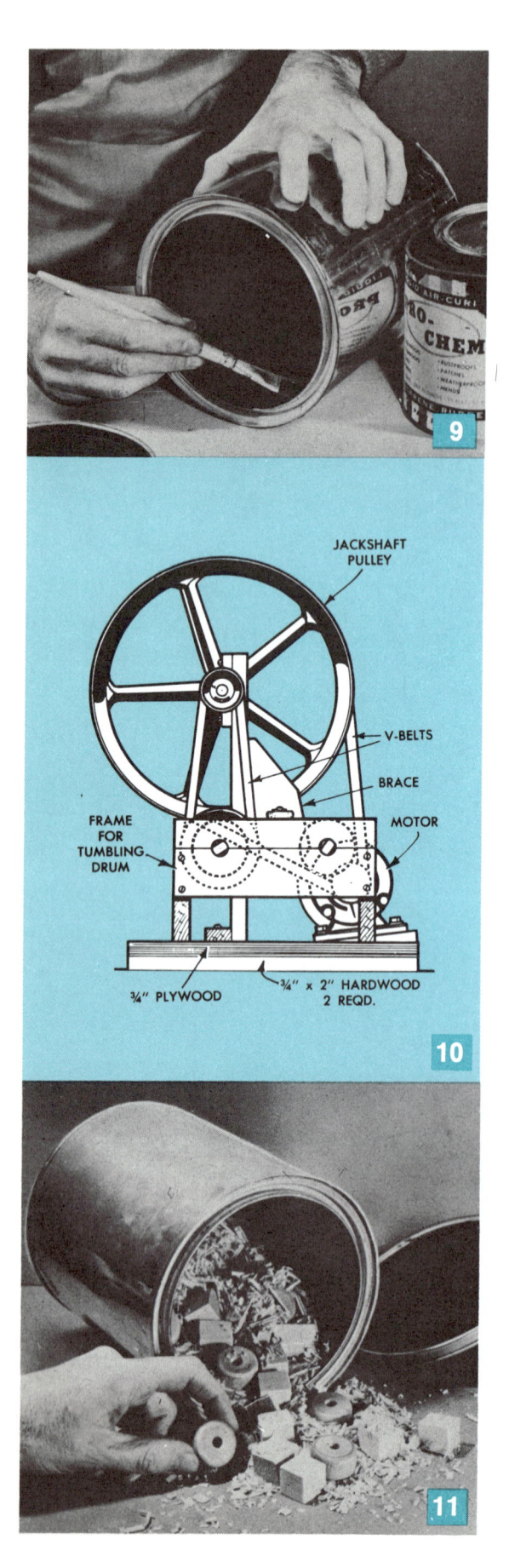

10. Bearings for the jackshaft are made from maple as in Fig. 6, using ¾-in. stock. Slots at the ends of each bearing provide for tightening the belts. The slot cut into each ½-in. hole provides an adjustment for taking up wear. A smear of paste wax or beeswax in each hole provides ample lubrication. Do not use lubricating oil in wooden bearings. No collar is necessary as the pulley hubs can be set against the bearings. When assembled there should be a slight amount of endplay. To prevent the shaft from binding in the bearings it may be necessary to shim one or both bearings to assure proper alignment.

If you use a spoked pulley on the jackshaft of the type shown in Fig. 7, it should be guarded as in Fig. 1. An exposed spoked pulley can cause a painful injury, even though it is turning at slow speed and is driven by a fractional-hp motor. A simple plywood guard cut to a contour slightly larger than the pulley's diameter and attached to the machine base will give protection.

tumbling drum

If you use a 1-gal. paint can as a drum, or barrel, the inside of the container should be coated with a rubber-base paint as in Fig. 9. Or you can line the inside of the can with sheet rubber (that from an inner tube will do). Cement the rubber to the metal with a suitable cement that will bond the rubber sheet firmly. Be sure the cement is dry before the drum is used. The coating of rubber-base paint or rubber sheet is necessary to protect the thin sheet metal from the abrading action of the abrasives used in polishing. The can must not be dented or misshapen.

In general polishing and deburring, rounding edges of small metal parts is done by tumbling them in the drum together with an abrasive and other filler materials which may consist of lubricants and cleaners and in some instances, water. The volume of the fillers usually must be greater than that of the parts to be polished and the drum is filled only half full, the water level (if water is used) even with that of the solids or slightly less.

Only the small-grade sizes of granular abrasives are practical for use in the small drum. These usually are available through your local hardware dealer. The exact amount of abrasive and the grade must be determined largely by experiment. The small-particle sizes cut more slowly and are generally more suitable for high polishing.

See also: grinding; toolpost grinder.

tumbling machines

Round and round go 4 quart jars of small parts. Abrasive agents (or steel balls) polish and burnish. The unit is set at table edge so the flywheel can extend below the base

Gang tumbler for small parts

■ THE LAZY WAY to remove burrs, sharp corners, rust and machine marks from small metal parts is to load them in a rotating container with steel balls or a granular abrasive. Since the burnishing is automatic, it spares you tedious hand work. And tumbling is often more uniform and thorough.

With this ganged tumbler you can work four different materials at once—or charge the four containers with various types of burnishing or polishing abrasives to take care simultaneously of several *stages* in the treatment of a single material. Lazy? Let's just say practical.

Each jar is filled from one-half to two-thirds of its capacity with a "charge." The burnishing or polishing additives vary in volume up to twice that of the work. The jars rotate approximately 34 rpm to give a tumbling speed of about 60 surface feet per minute (s.f.p.m.) for quart fruit jars.

To make the tumbler, start with the base, locating the positions of the three shafts as shown at the bottom of the next page. Then cut the 12-in. plywood flywheel which is to be driven by friction from a 1⅛-in. rubber wheel on the motor shaft. Or, you can substitute 14-in. and 1½-in. V-pulleys plus a V-belt. The latter arrangement will result in less vibration and noise than a plywood wheel having slight peripheral irregularities. Next, cut wooden pillow blocks (detail page 2811) and fit them with brass bushings, drilled to admit oil. Screw the blocks to the base at the positions indicated and fit with shafts. Or substitute two grinder heads.

One 7-in. and three 5-in. V-pulleys are used for mounting the cans. The tops are removed with a rotary can opener. Sandwich the bottom of each can between a pair of ¼-in. hardboard disks turned for a snug fit inside the can. One disk has a stepped edge to fit over the beveled portion adjoining the flat center area of most 5-in. pulleys. You can turn some or all of the disks at the same time by mounting them on a threaded arbor. As fruit jars sometimes vary slightly in diameter you must select jars that fit the cans properly. Both round and flattened jars

tumbling machines

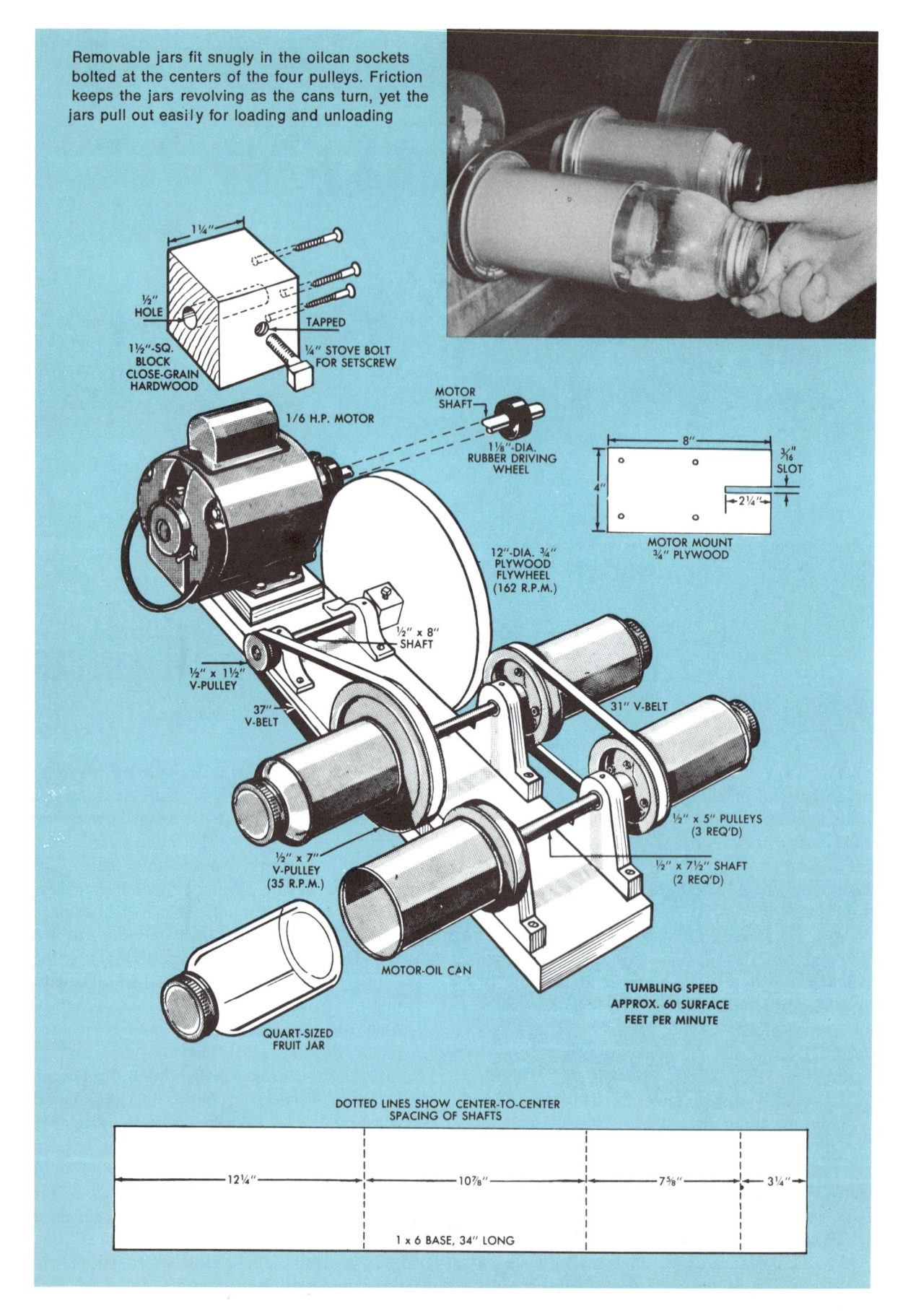

Removable jars fit snugly in the oilcan sockets bolted at the centers of the four pulleys. Friction keeps the jars revolving as the cans turn, yet the jars pull out easily for loading and unloading

1¼"
½" HOLE
TAPPED
1½"-SQ. BLOCK CLOSE-GRAIN HARDWOOD
¼" STOVE BOLT FOR SETSCREW

MOTOR SHAFT
1/6 H.P. MOTOR
1⅛"-DIA. RUBBER DRIVING WHEEL

8"
3/16" SLOT
4"
2¼"
MOTOR MOUNT ¾" PLYWOOD

12"-DIA. ¾" PLYWOOD FLYWHEEL (162 R.P.M.)
½" x 8" SHAFT
½" x 1½" V-PULLEY
37" V-BELT
31" V-BELT
½" x 7" V-PULLEY (35 R.P.M.)
½" x 5" PULLEYS (3 REQ'D)
½" x 7½" SHAFT (2 REQ'D)
MOTOR-OIL CAN
QUART-SIZED FRUIT JAR

TUMBLING SPEED APPROX. 60 SURFACE FEET PER MINUTE

DOTTED LINES SHOW CENTER-TO-CENTER SPACING OF SHAFTS

12¼" — 10⅞" — 7⅝" — 3¼"

1 x 6 BASE, 34" LONG

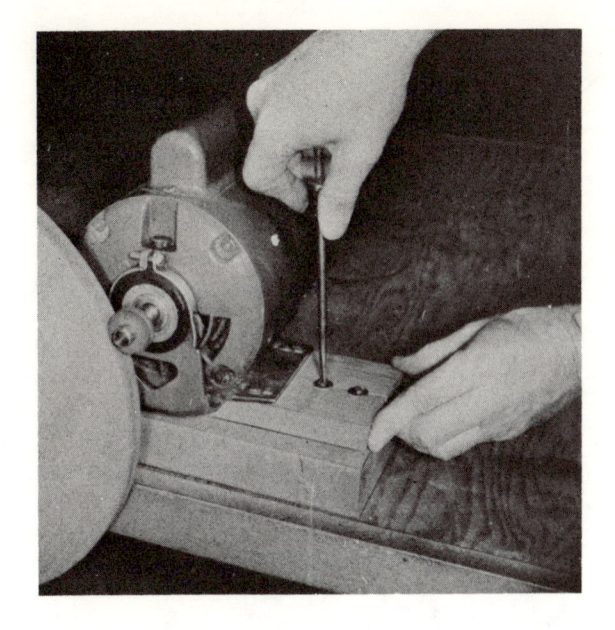

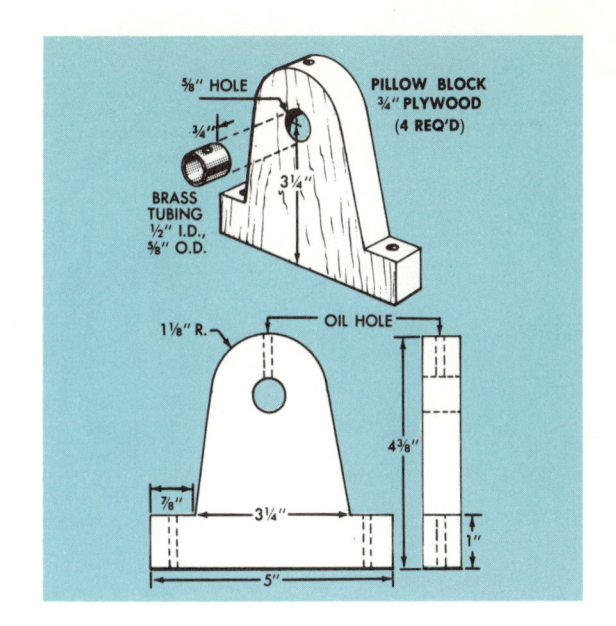

can be used. The corners on the latter aid in turning over the charge as the jar rotates.

A 1/6-hp motor was used on the model shown; it was fastened to a 4 x 8-in. piece of 3/4-in. plywood slotted to pass two wood screws which position it.

Tumbling speeds vary with the materials being finished. For polishing gemstones of the baroque or cabochon types (with suitable abrasives), a speed of 60 s.f.p.m. is sufficient. The first 3 or 4 consecutive polishing operations each require about 50 hours of tumbling at the above speed, and the final fine polishing step requires from 120 to 150 hours. For light burnishing of metal parts with hardened steel balls, which is the conventional technique, a tumbling speed of about 90 s.f.p.m. is used. For more vigorous action the speed may be increased to 250 s.f.p.m. To obtain speeds in excess of the 60 s.f.p.m. on the gang tumbler shown here, you simply put a larger pulley or rubber wheel on the motor shaft.

The abrasives used for polishing gemstones usually are silicon carbide, Nos. 100, FFF, 600 and 1200 grit, and tin oxide for final polishing. Successive tumblings use progressively finer abrasives. The work must be washed thoroughly after each operation to prevent coarse abrasive grains from mixing in with the finer ones. Tumbling is done either wet or dry. Besides the abrasive, the charge may contain chips of wood, pieces of felt, leather, cast iron, steel slugs or steel balls. In the first stage of gemstone tumbling the addition of iron screws (about 20 percent of the charge) has been found to decrease tumbling time from 15 to 20 percent.

In burnishing small metal parts with hardened steel balls, a rolling and hammering action replaces abrasive wear. The balls flatten the minute ridges on the work surfaces. Small balls contact more surface area than larger balls but also have less impact. Therefore you use the largest balls practical for the work. The volume of balls should be about twice that of the work. Soapy water is added until it stands slightly above the level of the charge. Frothing can be prevented by adding a few drops of liquid detergent.

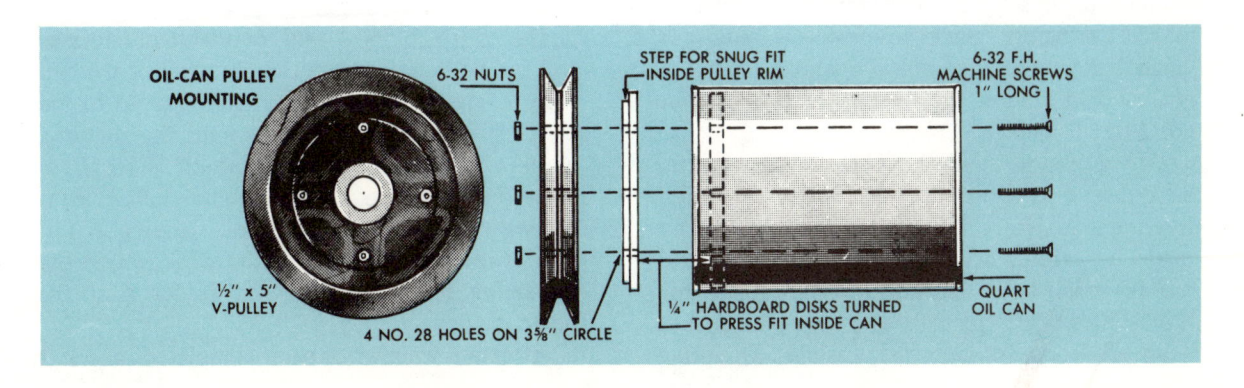

2811

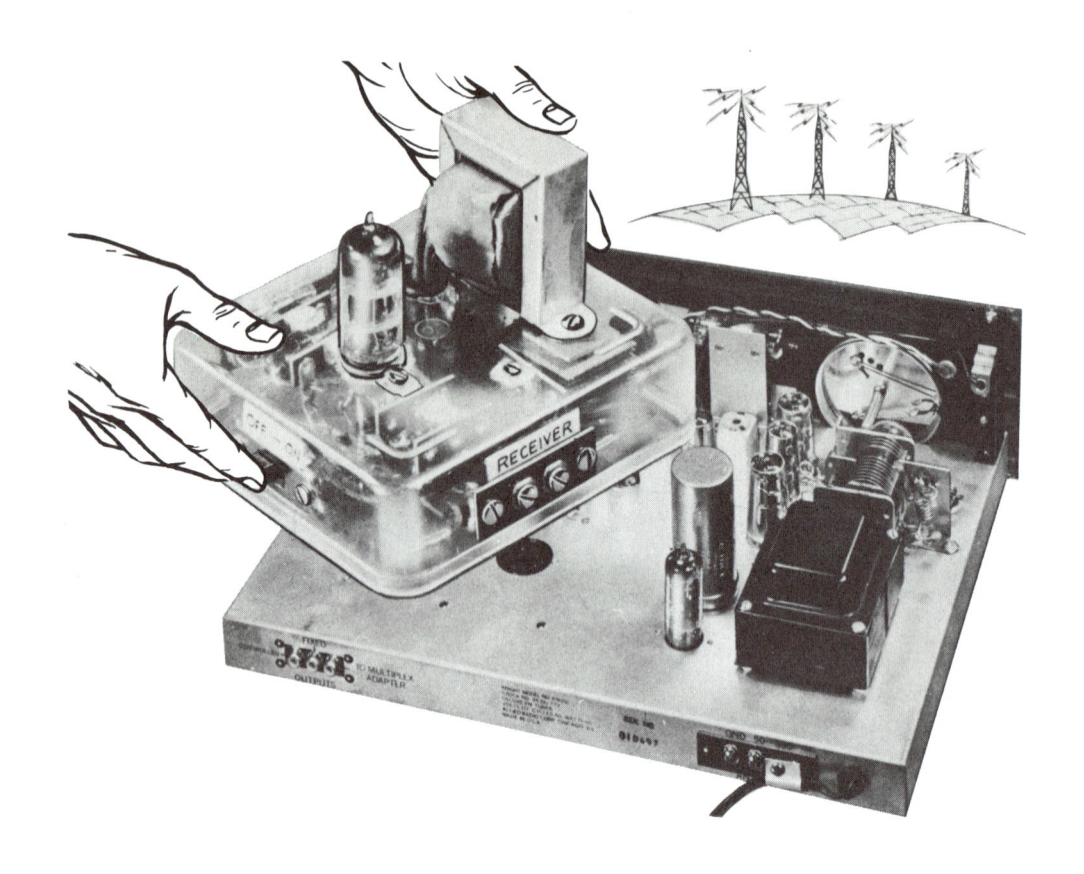

Give your FM tuner a longer reach

BY JOSEPH R. NOONAN

If you live in a "fringe area" or want to give your FM tuner the quality and clarity it is supposed to have, build this "signal sucker" and listen to the difference

■ BY ADDING THIS useful "signal sucker" to your tuner, you can make stations that sound weak seem as if they were just around the corner —and bring in some stations you were never able to receive before. Such a booster is almost a "must" if you are 50 miles or more from the nearest FM station, or if you are fussy about noise-free listening.

Use a plastic sandwich box as the chassis. Save the lid as a bottom cover when the wiring is complete. Holes for parts mounting can be made by careful drilling, or by using a heated nail for small holes and a heated knife-blade for larger ones. Parts placement is not critical, but keep all leads as short as possible. Mounting strips can be used to support small components such as resistors and capacitors. When mounting the coils L1 and L2, place them on opposite sides of the tube socket.

The coils use 5600-ohm, two-watt resistors as coil forms. Start by soldering one end of the coil wire to one of the resistor pigtails, close to the body. Evenly space the turns until the required number is reached. Where a tap-off is required, twist the wire into a small pigtail before continuing the coil. When the coil winding is finished, wrap the free end of the wire around the remaining resistor pigtail and solder near the body.

After the wiring has been completed, check it

carefully against the diagram. Connect terminal strip TS-1 to the antenna, and TS-2 to the FM receiver. Make these connections with standard 300-ohm twin-line. Turn on both the FM receiver and the booster. In order for a booster to operate properly, it must first be neutralized. While this is usually done with elaborate test equipment, here's how you can accomplish a fine neutralization simply with basic tools and a sharp ear. Adjust trimmer capacitors C5 and C6 to the point midway between where oscillation begins, as indicated by an excess of noise and distortion. Tune these for maximum noise.

Then adjust coils L1 and L2. Tune a station near the center of the dial and, using a toothpick, compress and spread the coil windings along the resistor body. Watch the FM tuning indicator, or listen very critically while adjusting, and space the windings for maximum signal boost.

Check station reception at both ends of the dial as well, to be sure a good compromise has been effected. When satisfied that maximum signal is coming through, coat the coil with Polystyrene "Q"-Dope to prevent accidental shifting of the windings.

Your booster will require no additional attention, except to turn it on and off. If you live in a fringe reception area, you will want the unit on at all times when the FM is on, in which case it might be wise to leave the switch in the *on* position and plug the booster line cord into the switched accessory outlet on the rear of the FM tuner, if one is available. This will turn the booster on and off with the tuner.

Should you find some stations in your area which are too strong when the booster is used, you can turn the booster off, and it will provide some measure of attenuation, reducing the signal to a usable level.

See also: cabinets, speaker; high fidelity; high-fidelity center; high fidelity, portable; preamplifier; stereo; record changers.

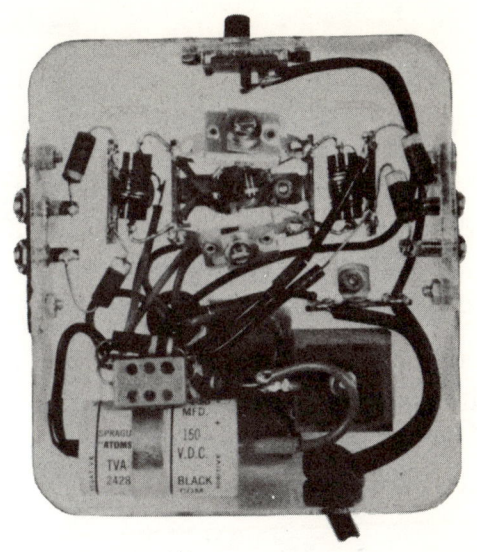

Bottom of chassis shows one possible arrangement of parts. Below is a schematic diagram of the booster and data on how to wind the coils

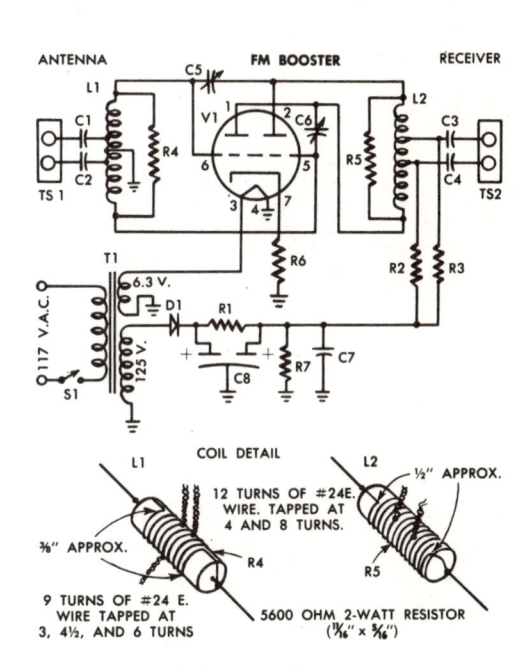

FM BOOSTER PARTS LIST

C1, C2, C3, C4—51 mmf., 1000-v. ceramic capacitor
C5, C6—3-30 mmf. midget trimmer capacitor
C7—100 mmf., 500-v. mica capacitor
C8—20-20 mfd., 150-v. electrolytic capacitor (Sprague TVA 2428 or equivalent)
D1—50-75 ma., 130-v. selenium rectifier
L1—9 turns of No. 24 enameled wire wound on resistor R4, and spaced 3/8 in., tapped at 3 turns, 4½ turns, and 6 turns (see text)
L2—12 turns of No. 24 enameled wire wound on resistor R5, and spaced ½ in., tapped at 4 turns and 8 turns. (See text)
R1, R2, R3—1000-ohm, ½-watt resistor
R4, R5—5600-ohm, 2-watt resistor (11/16 in. x 5/16 in.)
R6—47-ohm, ½-watt resistor
R7—100,000-ohm, ½-watt resistor
S1—SPST switch
T1—Power transformer: primary 117 v. a.c.: secondaries 125 v. a.c. @ 15 ma., and 6.3 v. a.c. @ 0.6 A. (Knight 54A1410)
TS1, TS2—2-lug screw-type terminal strip
V1—6J6A tube
1—7-pin miniature tube socket
1—plastic sandwich-box 4½ in. x 4 in. x 1⅜ in.
2—2-terminal mounting strips
Misc.—Grommets, power cord, etc.

tuners, FM

If your hi-fi rig lacks an electron-beam tube or an indicating meter, add one! The light patterns on the 6E5, at right, and EM84, opposite, show minimum shadow when you're right on station. Meters spell it out exactly for you

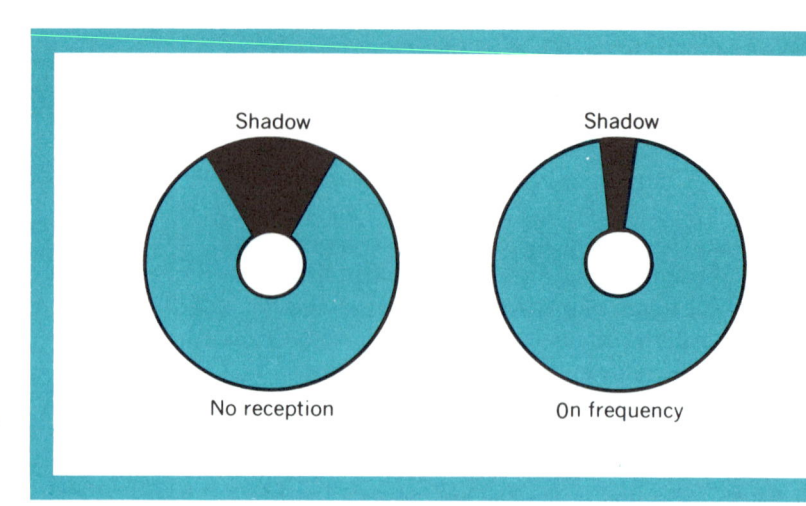

Stay on the beam with tuning indicators

BY WALTER SALM

■ THE IMPORTANT FUNCTION of a tuning indicator is to show you when your radio receiver is exactly tuned to the frequency you wish to receive. Tuning by ear may seem fine, but your ear is not as accurate as an electronic detector.

Proper center-of-the-channel tuning becomes even more important for FM stereo broadcasts. Slightly off-station tuning severely degrades the multiplex signal. If your component tuner or receiver or console stereo system doesn't have a tuning indicator, you can fit one into the existing circuits.

There are two types of tuning indicators: meters and electron-ray tubes. Each has certain advantages and disadvantages. The tubes are generally more sensitive than meters—they'll give more critical tuning and may be easier to use. But hooking them to your tuner is more complicated, and they draw an appreciable amount of power. Most tuner makers allow a safety margin in the design of their power supplies, so the tuning eye can be added without appreciably detracting from tuner performance.

green "magic eye"

Physically, the 6E5, the tube type, is larger and draws up to 4 milliamperes, opposed to about 1.5 ma. for the EM84. But you might already have a 6E5 kicking around the house. It was used very frequently on the more elaborate prewar radio consoles, and its circular green "magic-eye" still peeps out of many modern tape recorders as a modulation-level indicator.

The schematic diagram showing the connecting points for a 6E5 is of a typical FM tuner stage—in this case that of the EICO HFT-90. To power the indicator tubes, connect the filaments to the filament winding of the power transformer. Twist the filament leads together to cancel stray a.c. pickup. Find an appropriate B+ point of 200 to 250 v. You can find this with your vacuum-tube voltmeter or, if you don't have a meter, try one of the two B+ points indicated in the schematic.

The signal fed to the tube grid is the AVC voltage, obtained here from the last intermediate frequency (IF) transformer (point E). Look at the schematic for your own tuner and you'll find a similar point to make the connection.

The value of resistor R1 will vary depending on the signal strength at the IF transformer terminal. For low signal levels, a 150-ohm resistor will give just enough isolation to keep the indicator tube from affecting the tuner circuit. For higher signal levels, use higher resistance values up to about 1 meg. If you notice shadow fluctua-

Shadow — No reception

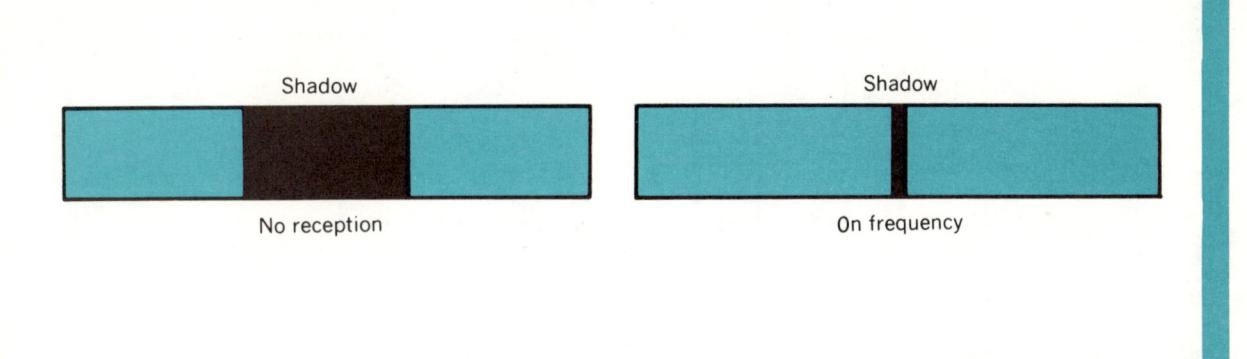

Shadow — On frequency

tions on the tube that vary with the sound, add the .01-microfarad bypass capacitor shown in dotted lines in the schematic. The 1-meg. resistor between the plate and target may already be wired into the tube socket if you took it from an old radio. Check its value with an ohmmeter.

The EM84 is somewhat more sensitive than the 6E5, has a target pattern that is easier to use, and is a 9-pin miniature type. The tube is really two tubes in one envelope. One is half a triode amplifier which provides the signal for the indicator section. A 470,000-ohm resistor connects the target and plate of the two sections. The plate of the triode half feeds the ray-connected electrode (grid) of the other section. A series resistor ties the triode grid to the AVC point in the tuner. Again, the value of this resistor may have to be selected as before, between 150 ohms and 500K.

The meter as a tuning indicator is easiest to install—and easiest to ruin by improper experimentation. The schematic shows connecting points for two types of meters—signal strength indicator and null point indicator. The advantages of meters over electron-ray tubes are that they draw very little current, require almost no additional hardware and are very easy to install. On the debit side, they are not quite as sensitive as most electron-ray tubes, since the meter movement has more mass than a stream of electrons.

Basis for a signal-strength meter is a 50-

Tuning indicators in front of EICO HFT-90 FM tuner are, from left to right: 6E5 electron-ray tube, 50-microampere meter movement and EM84 electron-ray tube. The EM84 is the same type of tube used in some newer color television receivers to indicate when the set is precisely tuned to a color-broadcast signal

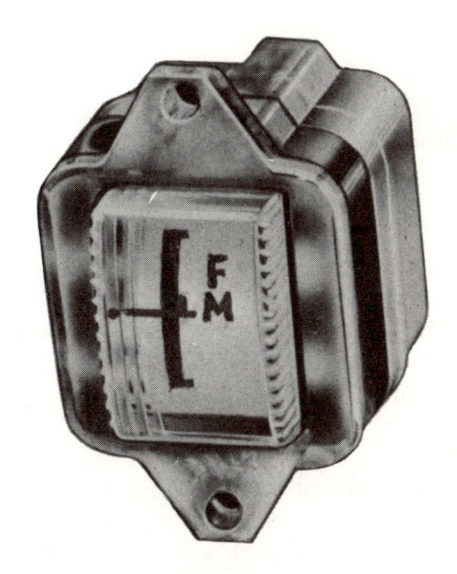

Lafayette FM tuning meter requires a scant 7/8 x 3/4-in. mounting area. The meter has a 50-microampere sensitivity above and below center null point. Solder lugs are on the back of the case

2815

tuners, FM

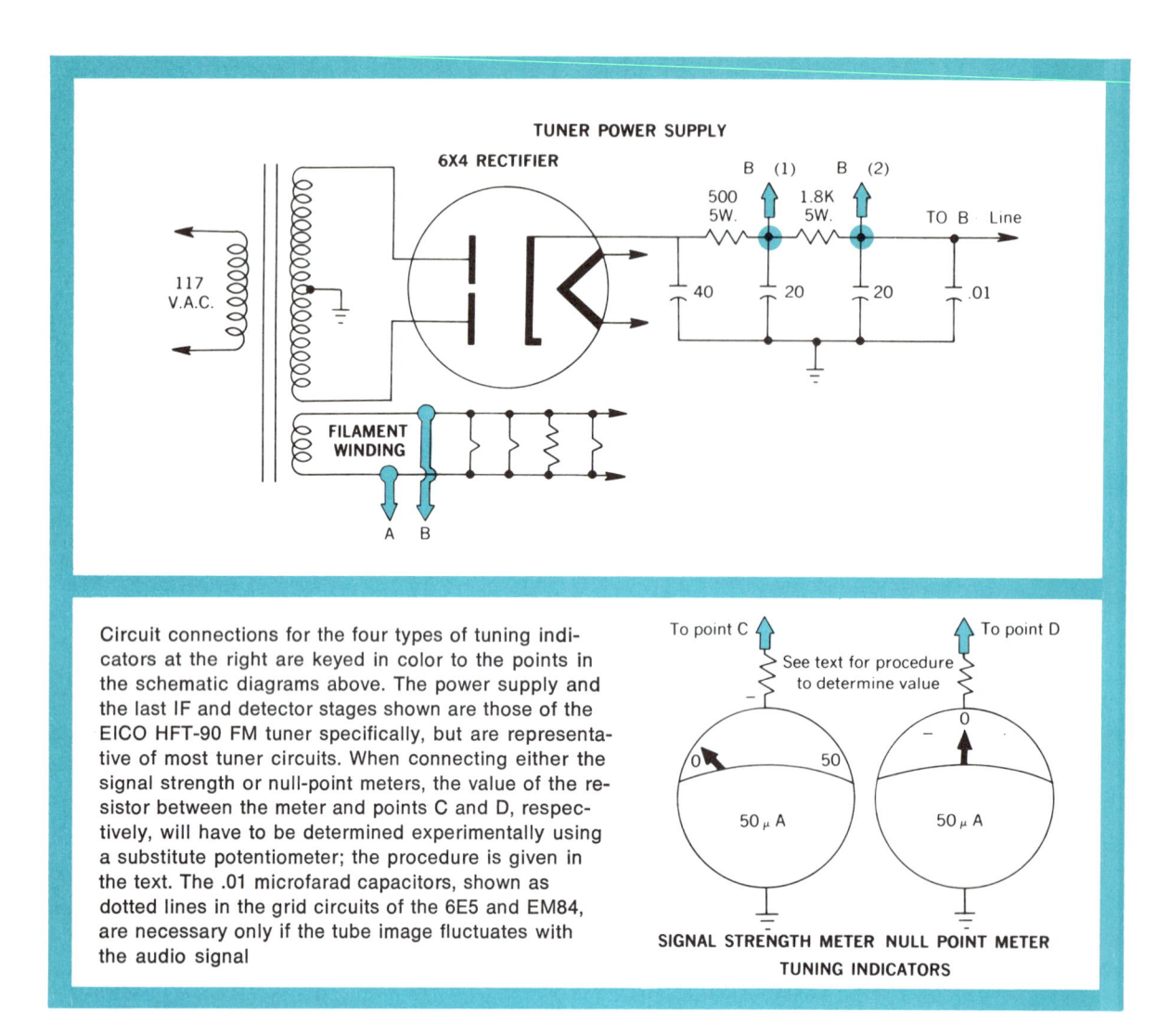

TUNER POWER SUPPLY
6X4 RECTIFIER

Circuit connections for the four types of tuning indicators at the right are keyed in color to the points in the schematic diagrams above. The power supply and the last IF and detector stages shown are those of the EICO HFT-90 FM tuner specifically, but are representative of most tuner circuits. When connecting either the signal strength or null-point meters, the value of the resistor between the meter and points C and D, respectively, will have to be determined experimentally using a substitute potentiometer; the procedure is given in the text. The .01 microfarad capacitors, shown as dotted lines in the grid circuits of the 6E5 and EM84, are necessary only if the tube image fluctuates with the audio signal

SIGNAL STRENGTH METER   NULL POINT METER
TUNING INDICATORS

tuning indicators, continued

microampere meter movement. You can buy the big easy-to-read or the small edge-reading type from electronic parts distributors.

With the signal-strength meter, connect the *positive* side to chassis ground and the *negative* side to the center terminal of a 500,000-ohm potentiometer set at maximum resistance. (The potentiometer will be used to determine the value of the fixed resistor to be wired into the circuit between the meter and point C.) Now connect one of the other terminals of the pot to point C in the schematic.

Tune in a strong station and then back off the pot slowly until the needle reads about 75 percent of full scale. Without changing the potentiometer setting, remove it from the circuit and measure its value with an ohmmeter. It will probably be somewhere between 100,000 and 300,000 ohms. Now wire a fixed resistor of approximately the experimentally determined value into the circuit.

For the null-point indicator, you'll need a 50-microampere meter with zero at the center of the scale. This time connect the *negative* side of the meter to the chassis ground, the *positive* side to the pot center terminal and other side of the pot to point D in the schematic. The potentiometer adjustment will require some experimentation for a null point (zero).

As you approach the center frequency of the station you're tuning, the needle will climb up the plus side of the meter and then drop back for an instant. This is the null point, the spot that you want. Adjust the pot so that the needle doesn't move much more than half the scale width on either side of zero. When you get the right setting, measure resistance and wire in a fixed resistor.

LAST IF AND DETECTOR STAGES

(Schematic: 6AU6 Last IF Transformer and 6AL5 Ratio Detector stage, with component values including 470K, 100K, 47 μμf, .01, 15K, 15K, .005 μμf, 1K, 330 μμf, 330 μμf, 6.8K, 6.8K, 10, 1.5K, 68, 330 μμf, 68K, .001, .05. Labels: From Previous IF Stage, To First IF, AVC Voltage Point E, To Audio Stage, Point D, Point C, To Grid of DM70/DM71, Multiplex Jack, B.)

TUNING INDICATORS

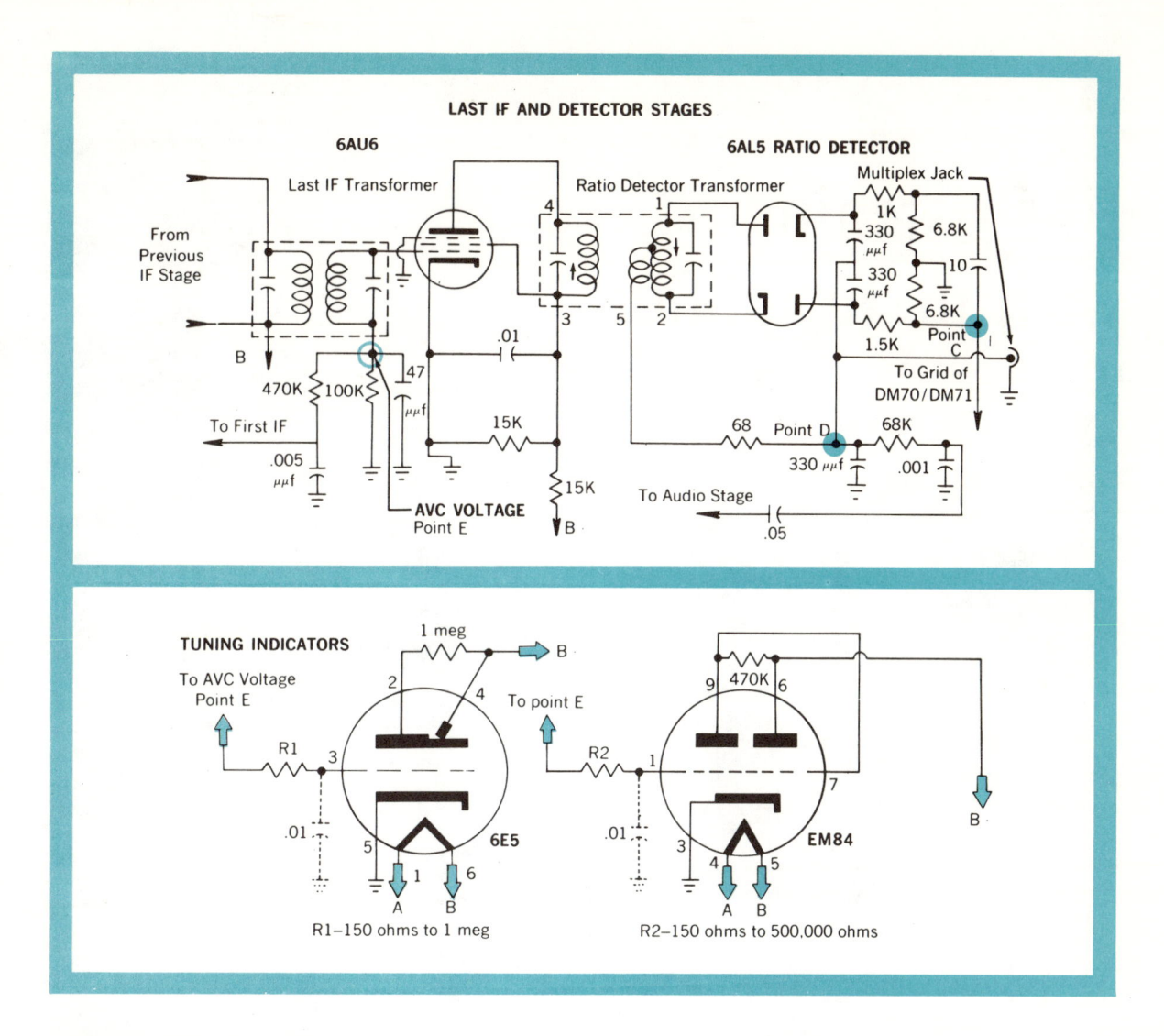

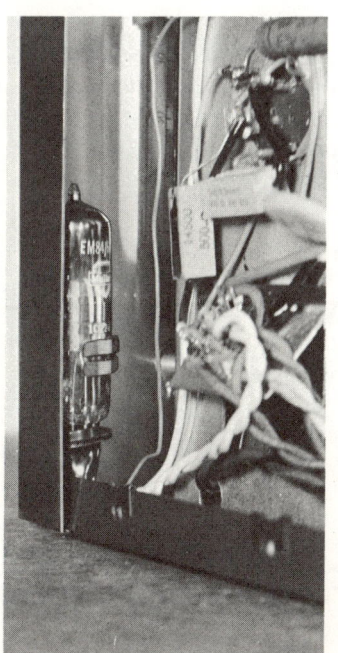

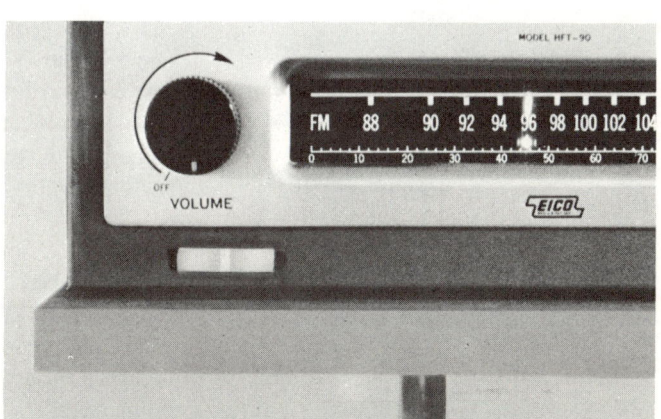

(Schematic showing 6E5 tube: pins 2, 4, 3, 5, 1, 6; with 1 meg resistor, R1, .01; labels "To AVC Voltage Point E", "B", "A".)

R1—150 ohms to 1 meg

(Schematic showing EM84 tube: pins 9, 6, 1, 7, 3, 4, 5; with 470K resistor, R2, .01; labels "To point E", "B".)

R2—150 ohms to 500,000 ohms

Installation of EM84 indicator tube in EICO HFT-90 Tuner is shown at left and above. Lower left corner of tuner immediately behind the front panel allows adequate room for the tube. Rectangular cut in the front panel was made to correspond to dimensions of the beam on the surface of the tube. In making your own custom installation, locate the tube—or meter—in a position convenient for wiring and viewing, and route leads to the tube socket or meter lugs close to the chassis. If the front panel cannot be worked easily, consider a mounting behind thin dial-face backing plate somewhere that won't allow it to interfere with the mechanical or electronic operation of the tuning mechanism

tuners, FM

FM listening with no amplifier

BY ART TRAUFFER

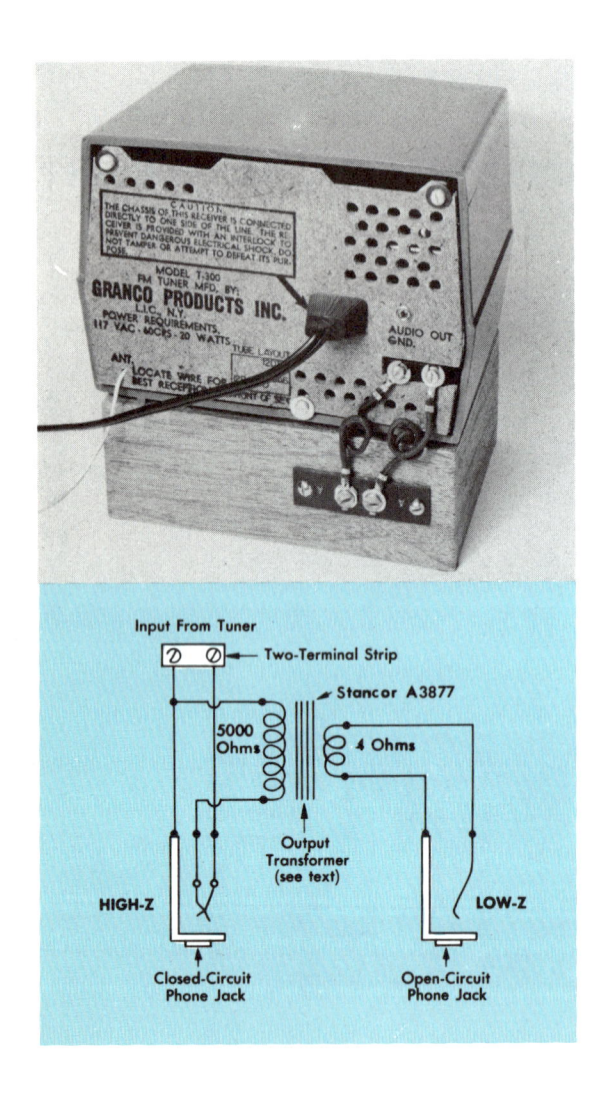

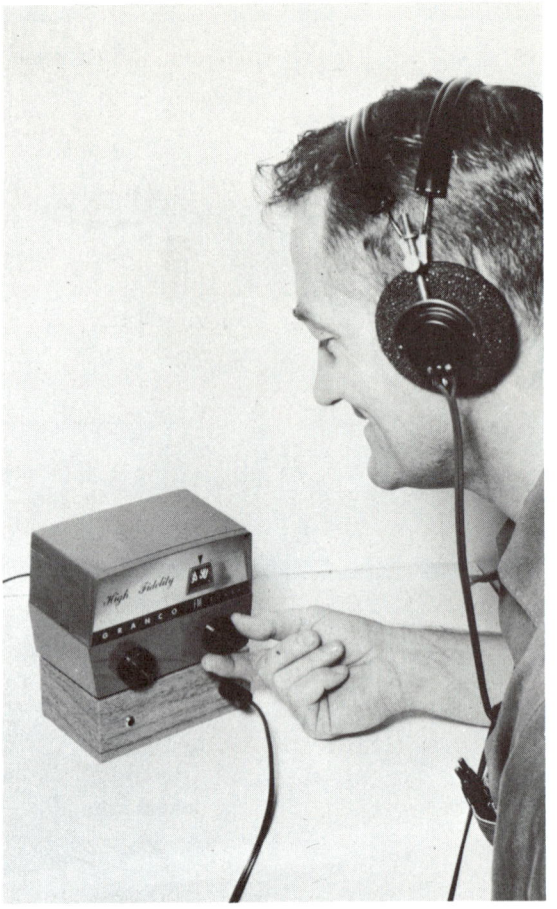

Left, rear of FM tuner is shown on top of the earphone box, with two short leads connecting the two units. Above, the listener uses FM volume control to adjust sound. There is no tone control on unit

■ WHETHER YOU HAVE ONE of the new hi-fi headsets or an old pair of army surplus "cans," here's a versatile device that neatly solves a matching problem. It allows you to hook any style earphone directly to the output of an FM tuner for private listening.

As detailed in the schematic, four components are required. These are mounted and wired in a small wood box with lengths of hookup wire. You needn't be concerned about the polarity of the transformer leads. For example, either wire from the primary winding may be run to the terminal strip.

If you don't know whether your earphones are high or low impedance, simply try both jacks, one after the other, and use the one that provides the loudest sound.

Be sure your phones are monaural and that their jacks are simple, two-lead units. If you must use stereo phones, hook leads from each earpiece in parallel when connecting to the jack.

turbojob: see jet runabout
turning, metal: see lathe techniques
turntable, modeling: see potter's wheel
twin closets: see closets
two-car garages: see garages
tying knots: see rope

clever ideas

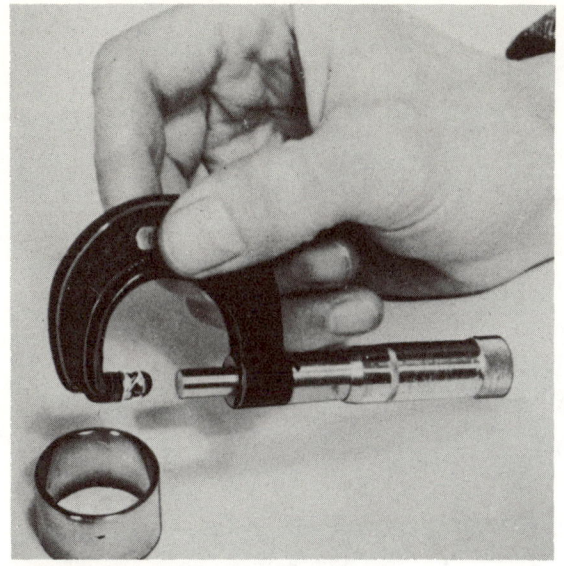

Work in job shops often requires that the machinist know the exact wall thickness of tubing. Although stock specifications usually give this as inside and outside (I.D. and O.D.) diameter, if a light cut has been made inside or outside it still may be necessary to know the precise thickness of the wall. You can take this measurement with an ordinary mike by taping a steel ball to the anvil with cellophane tape. This serves the purpose and, when removed, the accuracy of the mike will not be affected.

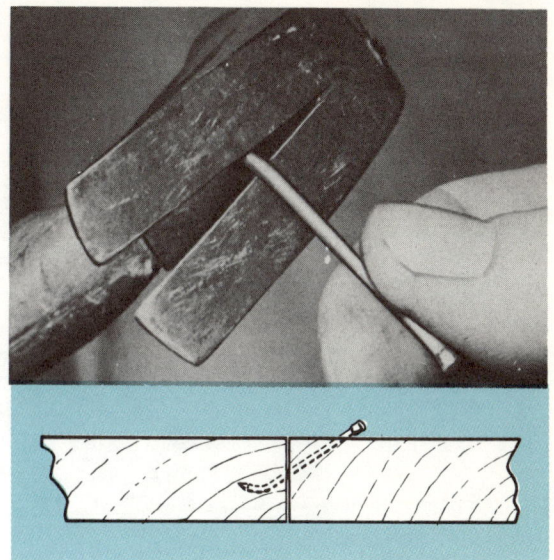

You need to join two boards edge to edge—no glue, no corrugated fasteners at hand. What to do? There are other ways, of course, but they take time, and time you haven't got. So you make use of an old, old trick—"draw-nailing" they called it. You butt the boards edge to edge and stand or kneel on each one to hold it in position. You bend the tip end of the nail by catching it in the hammer claws as pictured, and then start and drive the nail at an angle as shown in the detail above.

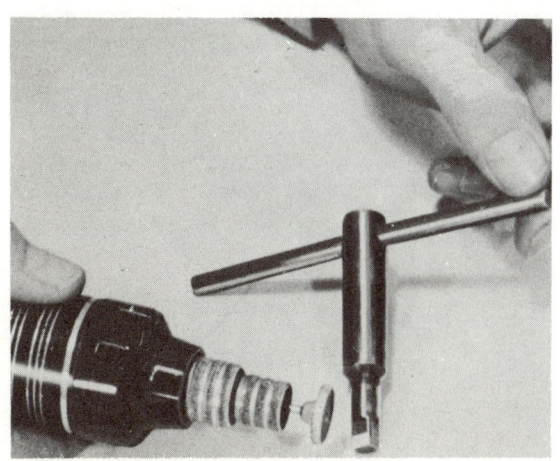

Perhaps you have thought about it, and again maybe not. At any rate you've never got around to grinding a slight taper on the four flats of the squared end of your chuck wrench. The squared end of the average chuck wrench is purposely sized to a fairly close fit in the socket head of the chuck screw. That means the wrench must be closely aligned with the screw before it will drop in place. Grinding a slight taper on the four flats will cause it to slip easily in place and will not impair its efficiency.

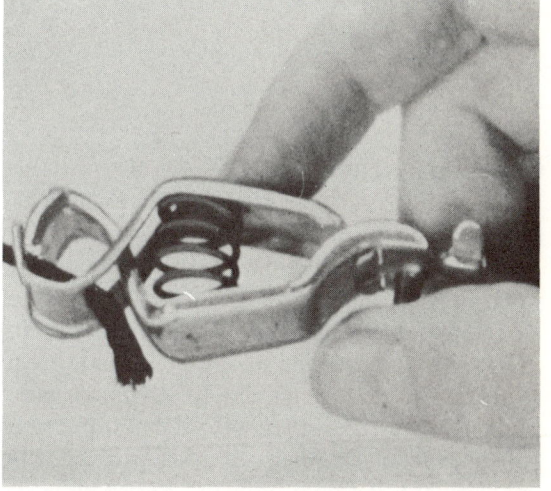

Rather than cut and pare insulation from wires with a pocketknife when making electrical connections, use a battery clip as an emergency stripper. File the notched grippers, or jaws, of the clip to a sharp edge. Then just slip the opened clip over the wire, release the jaws and give the clip a slight twist. It will cut through the insulation cleanly. Then pull lightly on the clip and off comes the insulation, just as it would if you used wire strippers. Regular use of the clip is not impaired.

underwater camera cases

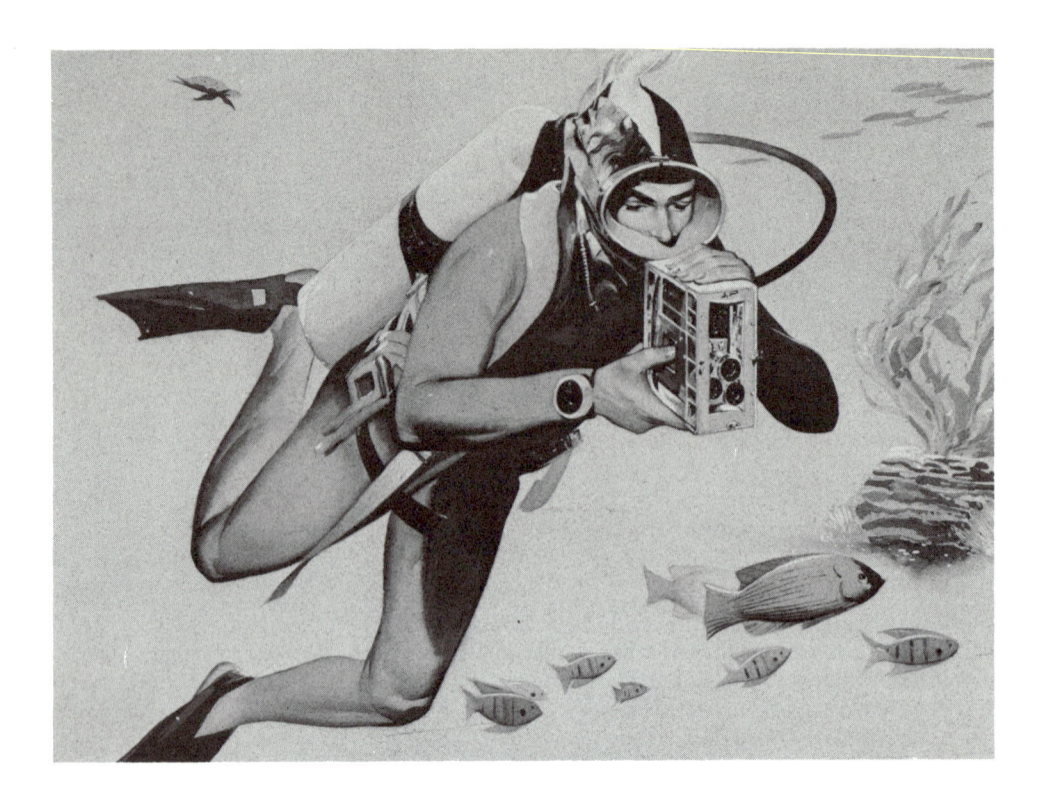

Waterproof camera box for underwater movies

After placing the movie camera inside the housing, snug down the wingnuts to compress the foam-rubber gasket. The gasket will provide a watertight seal

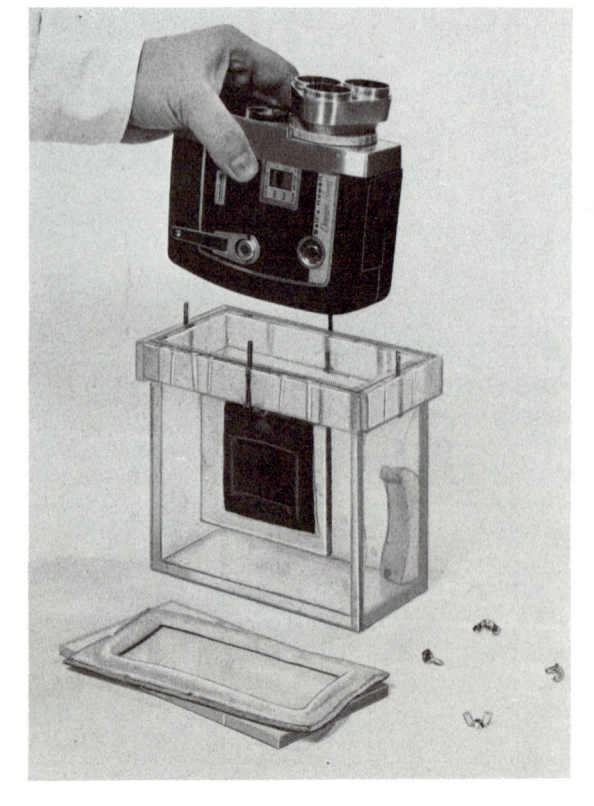

BY HANK CLARK

■ FOR THE SCUBA DIVER who is also a home movie enthusiast, here's a project that will combine both hobbies. It's a watertight housing for a movie camera that allows you to make underwater movies with no special equipment.

Actually this underwater camera case is nothing more than a simple plastic box. Made from ¼-in. acrylic plastic, it's amply strong to withstand the pressure 20 ft. below the surface. If you plan to make some really deep dives with your camera, it would be better to use either ⅜ or ½-in. plastic.

The waterproof box detailed here is dimensioned for an 8-mm Bell & Howell turret rig. Cameras of different size and design will, of course, require adaptation of the plans. An opening cut in the side of the box provides handy access to the camera's release button. A small square of thin rubber cut from a bicycle inner tube or patch kit is bedded in epoxy or Pliobond cement to seal the opening. It is important to

2820

DOUBLERS — FINDER IS SIGHTED THROUGH PLASTIC

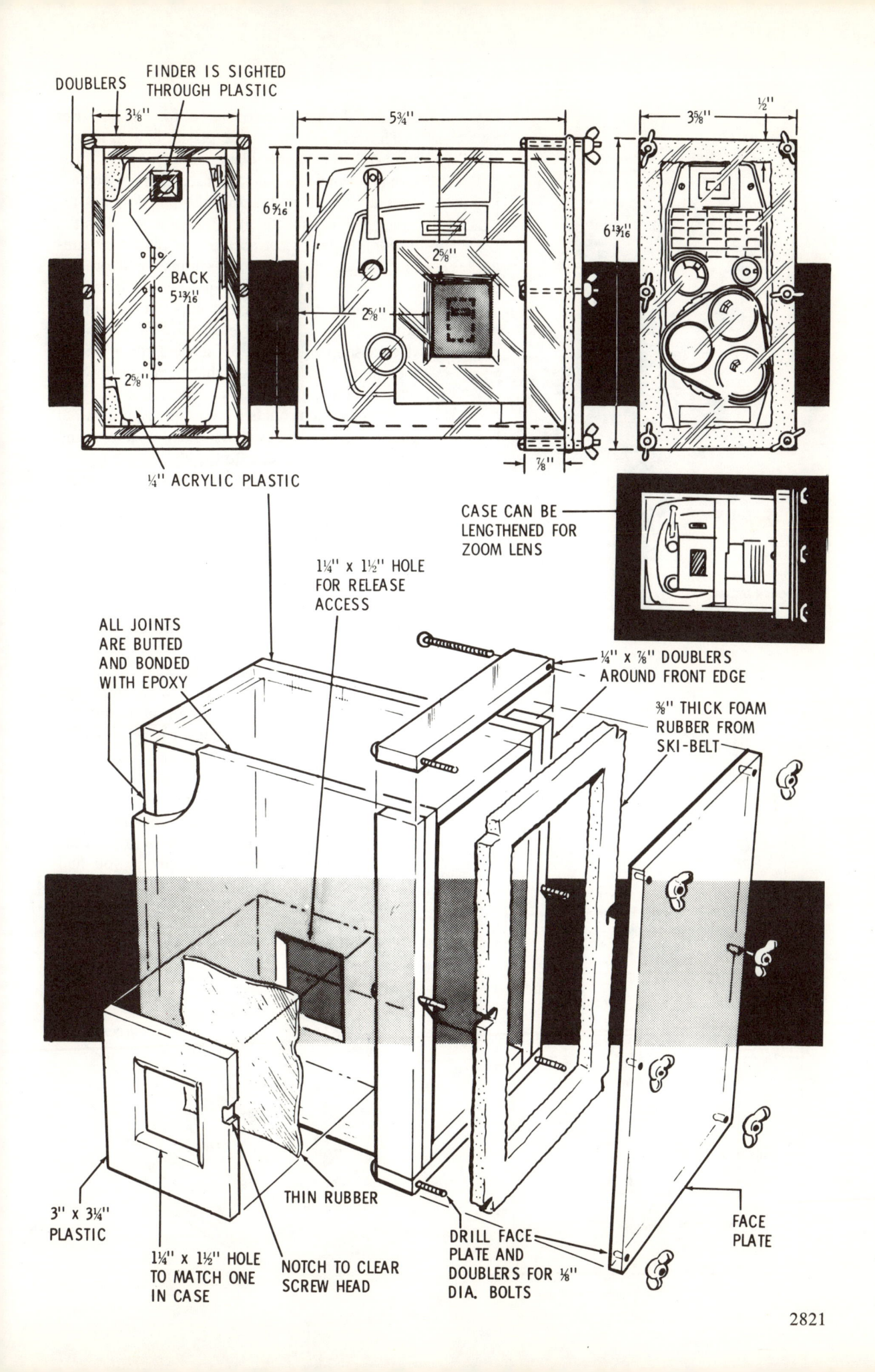

3⅛" 5¾" 3⅝" ½"

6 5/16"

BACK
5 13/16"

2⅝" 2⅝" 6 13/16"

2⅝"

⅞"

¼" ACRYLIC PLASTIC

CASE CAN BE LENGTHENED FOR ZOOM LENS

1¼" x 1½" HOLE FOR RELEASE ACCESS

ALL JOINTS ARE BUTTED AND BONDED WITH EPOXY

¼" x ⅞" DOUBLERS AROUND FRONT EDGE

⅜" THICK FOAM RUBBER FROM SKI-BELT

3" x 3¼" PLASTIC

1¼" x 1½" HOLE TO MATCH ONE IN CASE

NOTCH TO CLEAR SCREW HEAD

THIN RUBBER

DRILL FACE PLATE AND DOUBLERS FOR ⅛" DIA. BOLTS

FACE PLATE

2821

underwater camera cases

The release button is operated by pressing on a flexible piece of rubber cemented to the housing with either Pliobond adhesive or epoxy

The cutting diagram below should be followed exactly. The optional handle is cut in two pieces which are then cemented together to form a double thickness

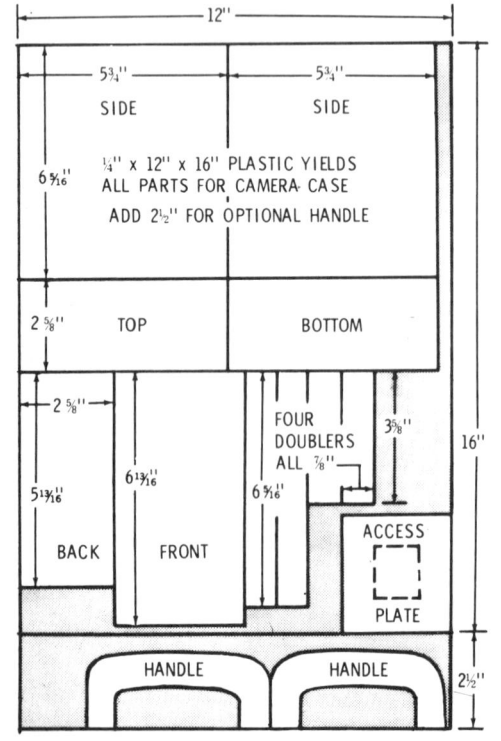

choose a flexible piece of rubber for this purpose.

The best way to cut the plastic is with a fine-toothed circular saw blade. In a pinch, a fine-toothed hand saw may be used. Epoxy cement does a fine job of bonding the plastic parts together but it is absolutely essential to roughen the meeting edges or surfaces of the plastic by rubbing with a coarse grade of sandpaper before applying the epoxy. Though epoxy is thick enough to fill minor nicks and other imperfections in the edges, it's best to joint each edge after sawing. If your shop equipment doesn't include a jointer, the simple sanding block shown in the drawing will true the edges quite accurately.

Epoxy cement holds with a bulldog grip, so to guard against epoxy oozing from joints and bonding the plastic case to the workbench top, be sure to lay down a sheet of wax paper before starting work.

Drilling the faceplate and doublers for ⅛-in. bolts should be done with care. To assure accurate alignment of the holes, it is best to clamp the faceplate to the doublers and drill through both in one operation. After the holes have been drilled, pass the bolts through and anchor their heads in place with epoxy.

The ⅜-in. foam-rubber gasket that fits underneath the faceplate provides a watertight seal when the wingnuts are tightened sufficiently to compress the gasket to a thickness of about ³⁄₁₆ in. As a precaution, test the empty box under water.

If desired, two accessories may be added: a double-thick handle and a wire frame viewfinder. The handle will help you keep a firm grip on the case. The finder is necessary only if you find that your face mask makes it awkward to sight through the camera's built-in viewfinder.

See also: cameras, used; photography; skin diving.

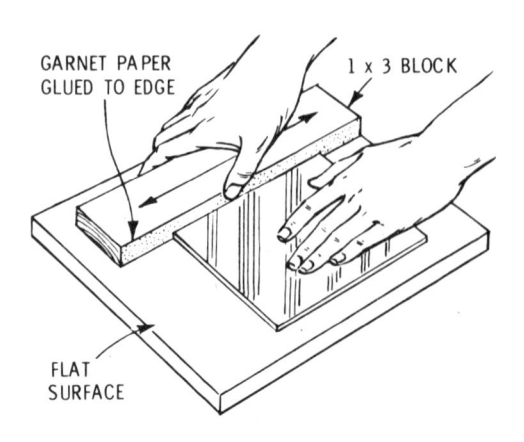

clever ideas

A vacuum-bottle holder which hangs from the inside of the car door can be made by riveting a strip of light metal to a tin can slightly larger in diameter than the bottle. Bend the end of the strip into a hook.

Upholstery covers are often difficult to slip back over foam cushions once you have removed them for cleaning. You'll find that dusting the cushions with talcum powder will make them slide in easier.

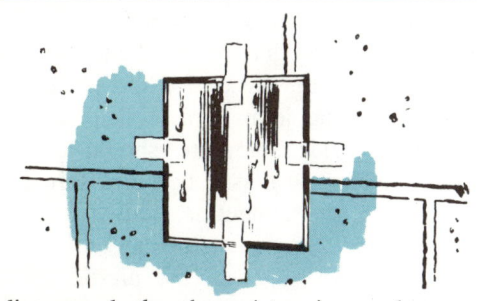

To discover whether the moisture in your basement is condensation or seepage, tape a small mirror over a moist zone. If condensation is the problem, the mirror will soon be covered evenly with condensate.

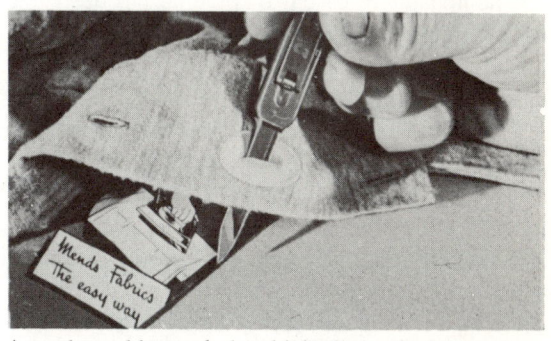

An enlarged buttonhole which allows the button to slip out is an annoyance. To repair it, mount a piece of press-on mending tape on the reverse side and make a slit in the tape with a knife or razor blade.

Want an extra shelf in your basement without all the bother of installing masonry anchors? For the extra one, make up a pair of U-shaped hangers from 1 x 2 stock, and nail these to the joists to support the shelf.

An easy way to remove a jelly glass from boiling water is to slip a dipper under it and insert a wooden spoon in the top. Use the dipper to lift the glass out, holding it with the spoon.

2823

underwater camera case

Camera case for scuba shutterbugs

BY EARL WOBECK

■ TAKING PICTURES under water no longer is a novelty, nor is it any more difficult to learn than surface photography. At least, not since scuba (self-contained underwater breathing apparatus), high-speed roll film and a suitable compact camera have been made available at affordable prices. By "suitable" camera, it is meant one that has most of the automatic features, ground-glass viewing, built-in light meter and a size that will produce a 2¼ x 2¼-in. negative or larger. Most twin-lens reflex cameras score high on all of these points, making them ideal for ordinary underwater photography.

The housing or case presented here is designed to accommodate such cameras. It is easy to make, costs only a few dollars for materials and operates beautifully.

Ground-glass focusing eliminates underwater focusing problems of view-finder cameras. Everything you see underwater appears about ¼ larger than its actual size, requiring a focus setting of ¼ less than the actual camera-to-subject distance, when a nonreflex-type camera is used. Reflex cameras are a good compromise between 4 x 5-in. press-type cameras and 35mm, eliminating most of the bulk of the former, while retaining the roll-film loading and compact features of the latter. If there is occasional need to take more than 12 shots on one loading, 35-mm film adapters are available for many models.

While the controls shown are designed for one popular make of reflex camera, slight modification of the end fittings is all that's necessary to accommodate other makes. Here's the step-by-step procedure:

1. First, clamp one end of the ⅜ x 5¾ x 32-in. plastic to the back of the forming block and make the 4 bends required. Use a torch to soften the plastic, and then press evenly against the point of bend with a wooden block.

2. After making the previous bend, the end is overlapped onto the back edge and cemented to it by dipping the joint in a V-shaped tray of methylene chloride. The latter should just cover the joint. When the plastic becomes soft, clamp the joint until the cement sets. Methylene chloride is used for cementing all joints.

3. Sand down edges of the plastic on both sides of the case, first smoothing wrinkled corners. Make sure you keep the edges square.

4. Cut out side pieces, check them for tight fit against the case edges and cement right side to

After clamping one end of the plastic to the back of the forming block, soften the plastic to make the 4 bends. Press against the bends with a block

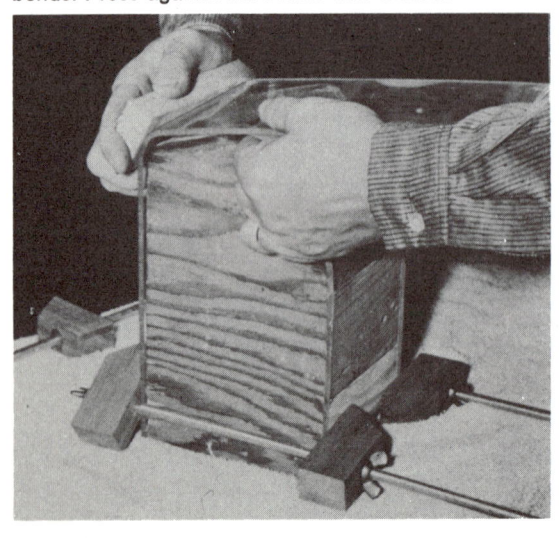

Holes for the shutter speed and aperture-control shaft are located by positioning a spike over the centers of the controls, marking the right-side hole first

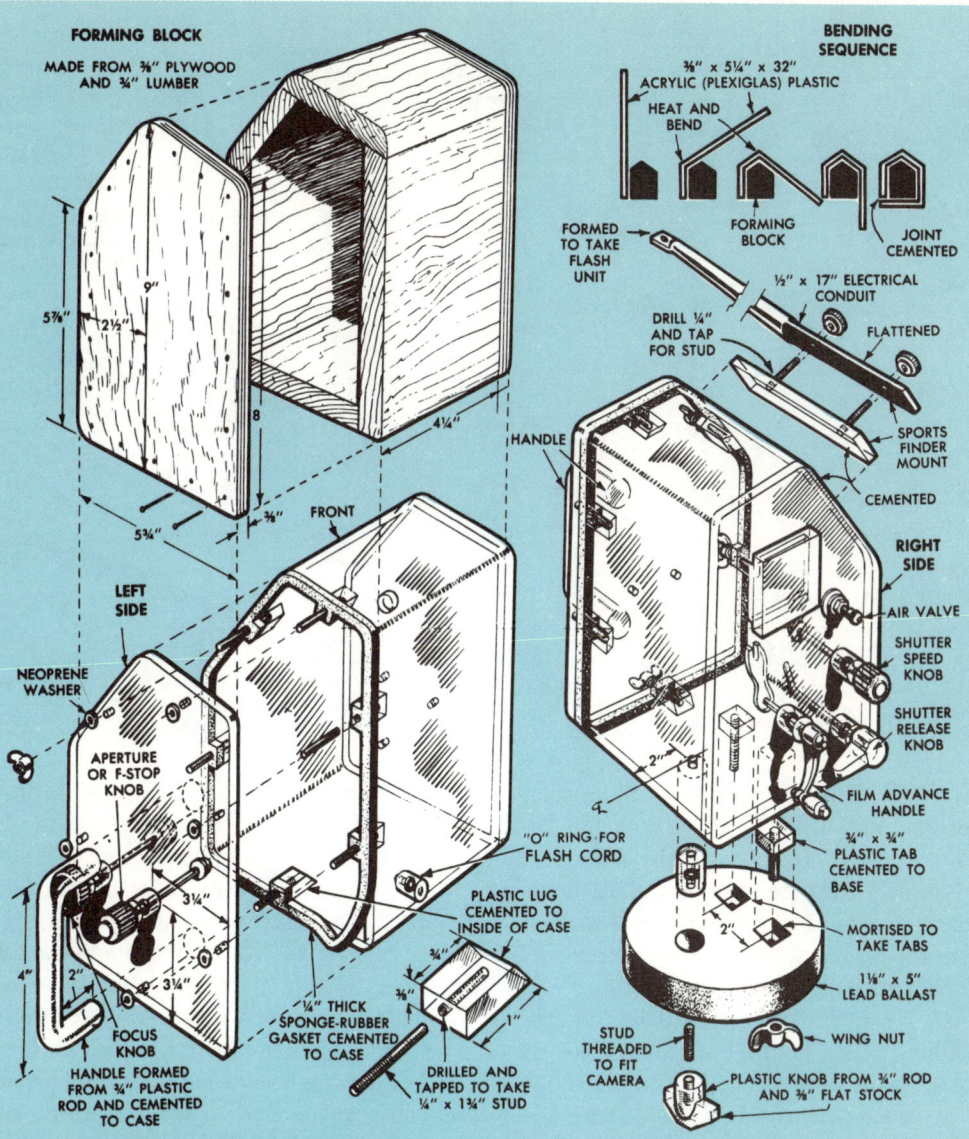

FORMING BLOCK
MADE FROM ⅜" PLYWOOD AND ¾" LUMBER

5⅞" · 2½" · 9" · 4¼" · 5¾" · ⅜" · 8"

BENDING SEQUENCE
⅜" × 5¼" × 32" ACRYLIC (PLEXIGLAS) PLASTIC
HEAT AND BEND
FORMING BLOCK
JOINT CEMENTED

FORMED TO TAKE FLASH UNIT
½" × 17" ELECTRICAL CONDUIT
DRILL ¼" AND TAP FOR STUD
FLATTENED
SPORTS FINDER MOUNT
CEMENTED

FRONT
HANDLE
RIGHT SIDE
AIR VALVE
SHUTTER SPEED KNOB
SHUTTER RELEASE KNOB
FILM ADVANCE HANDLE
¾" × ¾" PLASTIC TAB CEMENTED TO BASE
MORTISED TO TAKE TABS
1⅛" × 5" LEAD BALLAST
WING NUT
STUD THREADED TO FIT CAMERA
PLASTIC KNOB FROM ¾" ROD AND ⅜" FLAT STOCK

LEFT SIDE
NEOPRENE WASHER
APERTURE OR F-STOP KNOB
"O" RING FOR FLASH CORD
PLASTIC LUG CEMENTED TO INSIDE OF CASE
¼" THICK SPONGE-RUBBER GASKET CEMENTED TO CASE
DRILLED AND TAPPED TO TAKE ¼" × 1¾" STUD
FOCUS KNOB
HANDLE FORMED FROM ¾" PLASTIC ROD AND CEMENTED TO CASE
3¼" · 4" · 2" · 3¼" · ¾" · ⅜" · 1" · 2"

The camera is mounted in the case after drilling a hole in the bottom to take the fastening screw, as shown in the photograph

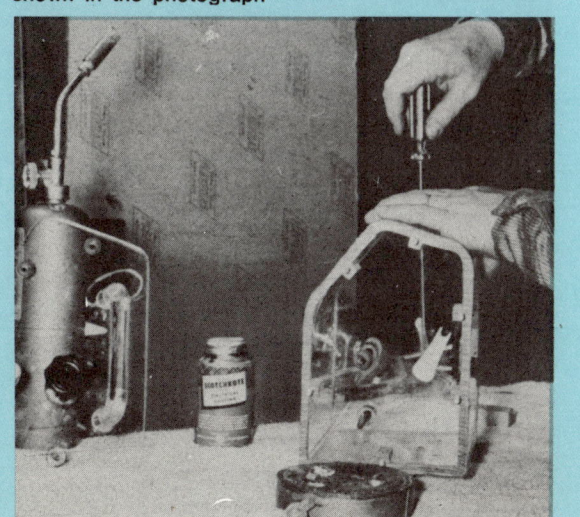

A hole is drilled in the case side for the film advance as shown. Holes also are drilled for the shutter release and focus shafts

2825

underwater camera case

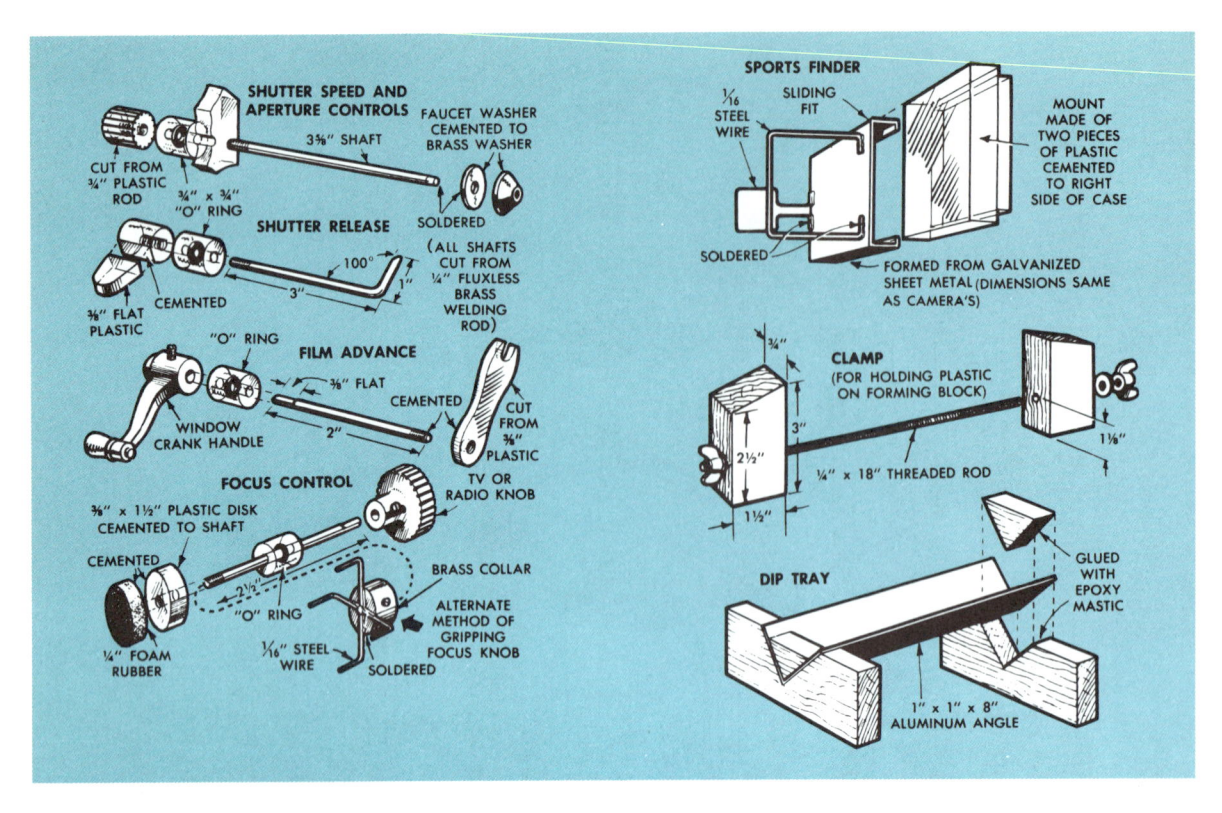

the case. (Cement is poured in a shallow stainless or enamel pan to ¼-in. depth, then the case is placed in it, right side down. At the same time, cement is brushed on the mating surface of the side piece.) Plastic lugs are made next and cemented to the inside of the case to take the left side, which then is drilled to take the studs.

5. Next, the camera is mounted in the case, after drilling a hole in the bottom to take the fastening screw as shown. The lens board should be fully extended when doing this to assure adequate focusing clearance. Shutter speed and aperture-control shaft holes are located by positioning a spike (large nail) over the centers of these controls on the camera and marking for the hole on the right side first. A ¼-in. hole then is drilled through at the mark, after which the left side is fastened in place temporarily and the same procedure used for marking it to take the aperture-control shaft. The holes to be drilled in the case sides for the shutter release, film advance and focus shafts are best located by first making a template of each side of the camera, with the axial centers of the camera's controls (handle, in case of film advance) marked on it. The template then is taped in place on the appropriate case side and the holes drilled as marked.

6. Each control and through-case connection is fitted with an O-ring cemented to the outside of the case to seal out water. To assure proper alignment of the O-ring hole with the case hole, insert one of the ¼-in. shafts in the latter, then apply methylene chloride to the mating surface and slide the O-ring in place on the shaft. All control assemblies are detailed.

7. The air valve is a standard tubeless tire valve, which is installed on the case with the parts that come with it. Air pressure from a few strokes of a tire pump before each submersion will leave a trail of bubbles in the event of a leak and give you time to surface before water enters.

8. The lead ballast at the bottom of the case is necessary to counteract the buoyant effect of the entrapped air in it. About 8 lb. of lead are required (enough to allow the camera and case to settle slowly in the water) so that it won't float away when you set it down. A 1-lb. coffee can makes a good form for casting the weight.

9. When forming the handle from plastic rod, be sure to apply heat entirely around the point of bend. The ¼-in. sponge-rubber gasket that seals the removable side of the case is cut in one piece from a bathroom mat and cemented in place with electrical coating dope, such as Scotchkote. The thick part of a truck inner tube also may be used for gasket material. The sports finder is an optional accessory.

Acrylic plastic scratches easily, so when making the case and later when transporting or storing it, protect the surface with a soft cloth.

unicycle

No one would look twice at a youngster because he was riding a bicycle. But who would fail to notice the boy who comes pedaling down the street on this homemade unicycle?

As can be seen from the drawing below, a unicycle is a fairly simple assembly requiring few parts. The wheel, fork and pedals are taken from the front-wheel assembly of an old tricycle. The tricycle fork is then bolted between a larger fork made of two lengths of ½ x 2-in. plywood which supports the seat. Buy or make a comparatively narrow seat or saddle of the type shown. It's easier to clamp between your legs while learning to ride the unicycle.

And make no mistake: learning to ride one of these solo wheels is not a simple one-day course. It takes practice and more practice.

See also: bicycles; bicycle boat; exercise equipment; paddleboat.

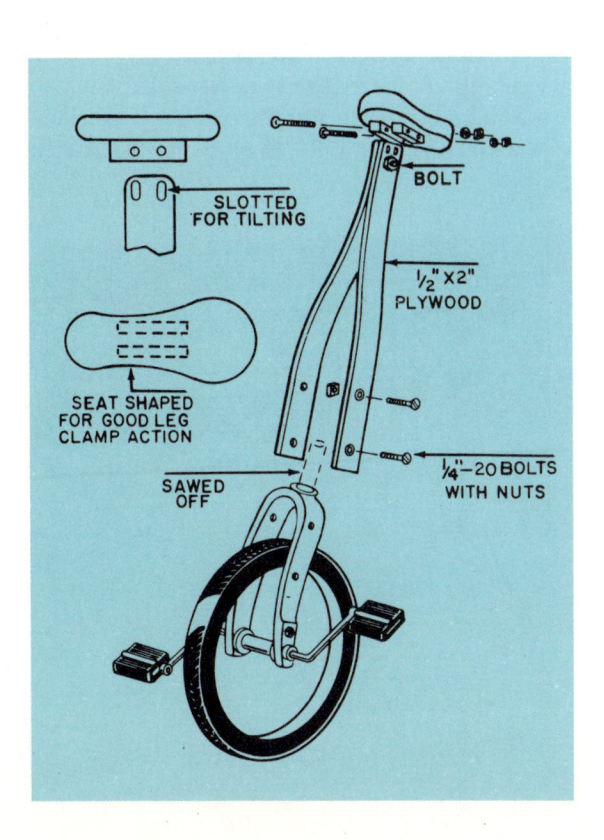

For fun, try a unicycle

BY HANK CLARK

You'll have the most unusual vehicle on the block once you build this unicycle. All you need is some plywood and an old tricycle

universal bending jig: see benders
universal holder: see holder, bench-top

upholstery

Uplift for tired old chairs

BY E. R. HAAN

■ COIL-SPRING SEATS that sag, lose their comfort and good looks often can be put back in good shape permanently by using steel webbing.

First diagnose the chair's condition. Set it upside down and remove the dust cover under the seat. Then, with the aid of a flashlight, examine the spring assembly. If the springs have not broken away from the twine tied across their top coils, and are not bent, all you have to do is truss up the spring assembly with steel webbing which you nail or screw to the underedges of the seat rails. The old webbing is not removed.

To determine the amount of steel webbing needed, you measure the total length of the old webbing and add a few feet for waste. The average easy chair requires less than 25 ft. Two steel webbings are shown below; one is corrugated, the other is flat and perforated. Both are available at upholstery shops or can be purchased from mail-order houses.

Also get a steel-webbing stretcher. One for flat-perforated webbing is shown in detail C. If you can't get one, you can use a pair of large pliers, preferably the self-locking type. Also needed are some 1½-in. ring-type nails to fasten

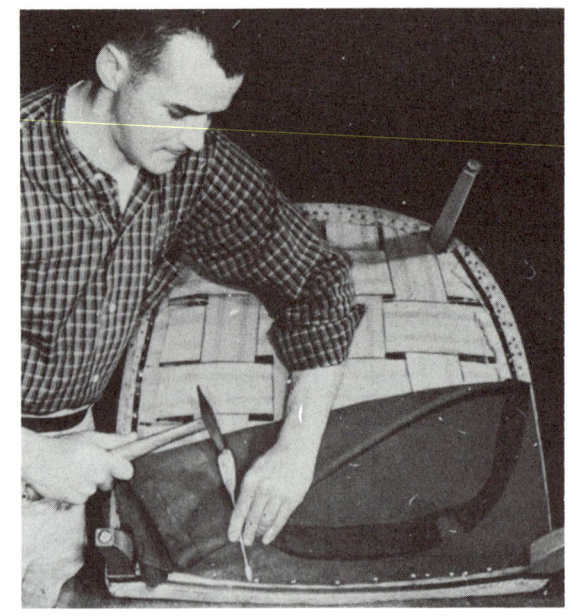

Turn the chair upside down on a table or bench and remove the dust cover. Replace this with a new dust cover made of black cambric sold for the purpose

the webbing. Purchase black cambric to replace the dust cover.

Next, cut two 1 by 2-in. wood strips a couple inches longer than the maximum span between seat rails. These are used to compress rows of springs to eliminate strain on the webbing when installing it. Drill holes through the strips edgewise to take the wood screws, which you drive into the rails. Drill pilot holes in the rails for the screws.

Start by compressing the center row of springs from front to back, and nailing the end of the webbing to the front rail not less than ½ in. from the rail edge. Then use the webbing stretcher or pliers at the rear rail. When using the stretcher

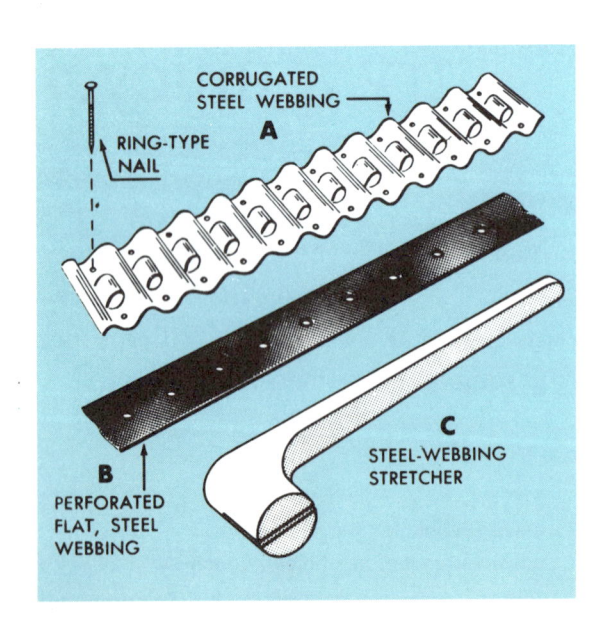

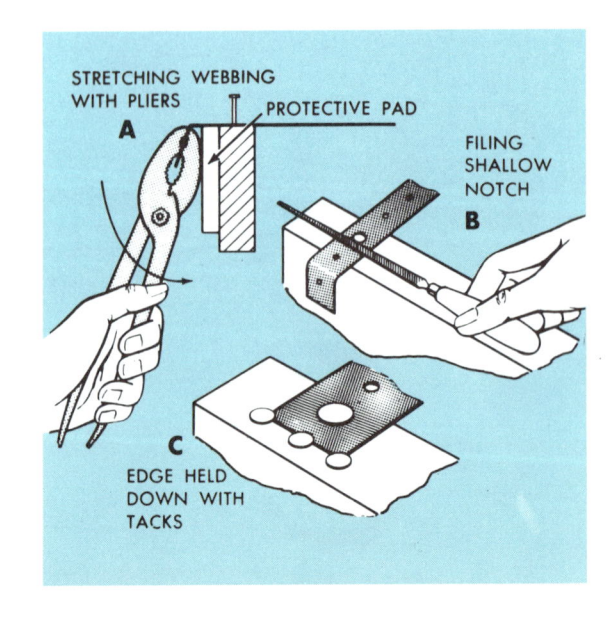

Check the spring assembly with a flashlight. Springs should be tied with twine across their top coils. If they are, you can start applying steel webbing

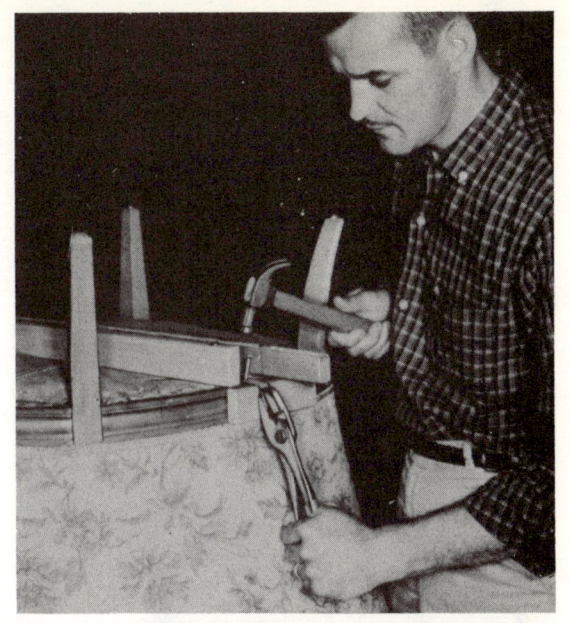

Pliers or a webbing stretcher can be used to pull the webbing taut at the rear rail after it has been nailed securely to the opposite rail

cut the webbing after it has been nailed, but when using pliers, cut the webbing off about an inch beyond the edge of the rail before pulling the webbing taut and nailing it. In either case use a piece of hardboard or plywood from ⅛ to ¼ in. thick as a protective pad under the tool to prevent marring wood finish in detail A. Should the nail hole of perforated webbing come too close to the edge of the rail, drill an extra hole.

After you have nailed the webbing to the rear rail, cut it off inside the rail edge so that it won't show when the dust cover is installed over it, and so that a sharp projecting edge cannot cause injury. To saw, cut the webbing near the nail head, file a shallow groove with a three-cornered file as in detail B, after which you bend the waste portion up and down with a pair of pliers until it breaks off. If the broken end is high, fasten it down with two or three tacks as in detail C.

Follow the same procedure with the other two front-to-back and side-to-side rows of springs. The cross strips of webbing usually are "interwoven" with the front-to-back strips. Finish the job by replacing the dust cover.

See also: bedroom furniture; children's furniture; legs, furniture; step table; tables.

Use wood strips screwed to the chair rails to compress the rows of springs. Apply the steel webbing between the wood strips. Pre-drill screw holes for strips

This is an easy-chair seat, restored by applying steel webbing across the bottom to raise the springs. Applying a dust cover completes the job

upholstery

Because the chair with a sagging seat (above right) had a sound frame, it was perfect for foam rejuvenation. The beautiful result is shown above. Foam rubber is now firmer because of the staggered pattern of many small holes in both sides, as shown below

Reupholstering with foam rubber

---

urethane finishes: see finishes, urethane
used boats: see boats, used
used cameras: see cameras, used

2830

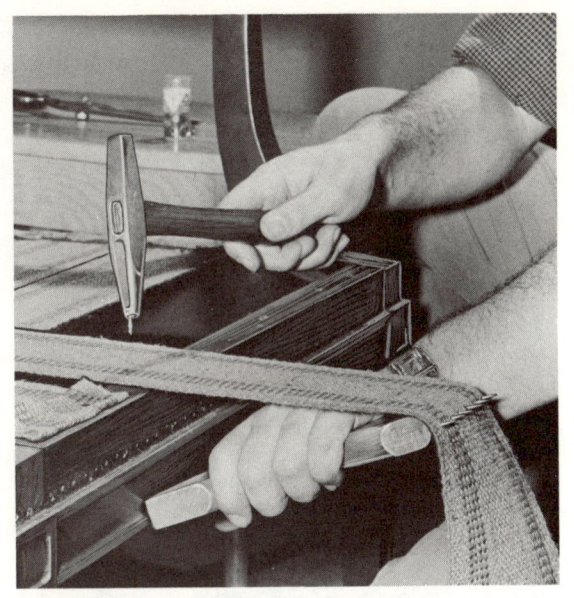

A webbing stretcher makes it possible for you to put leverage on the webbing in order to pull it taut across the frame before nailing it securely. This inexpensive special-purpose tool is almost a must for any reupholstering job

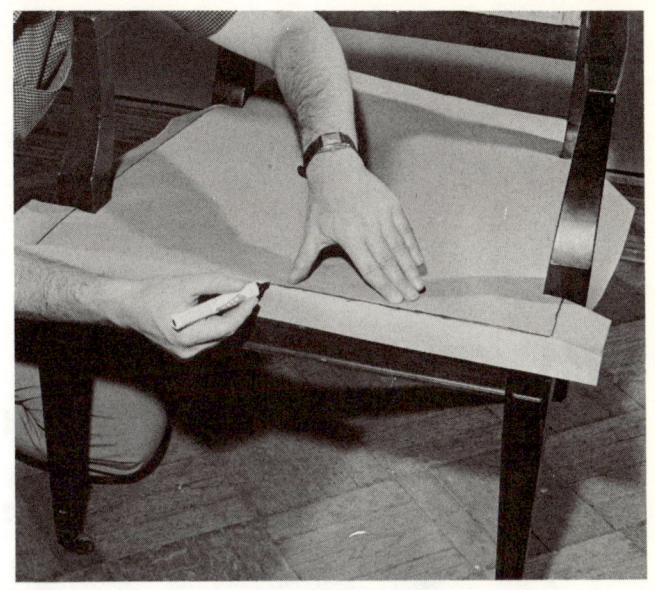

Make a pattern of the chair seat from a piece of wrapping paper so that you will have something to use as a guide when cutting the foam rubber to size. This is especially useful if the cushion has a curved or unusual outline

■ THOSE TRICKY reupholstering jobs you've shied away from now surrender meekly to modern do-it-yourself materials and techniques. By using a new form of latex foam rubber, you can avoid the complicated and time-consuming chore of tying and replacing loose and broken springs. What's more, foam eliminates the fuss of cotton padding.

Instead of the large core holes found in the

Trace the outline of the cushion on a piece of 2-in. pincore latex foam rubber, using a felt-nib marking pen. Be sure to allow an extra ½ in. of foam rubber beyond the pattern outline. This extra rubber serves as an upholstery allowance

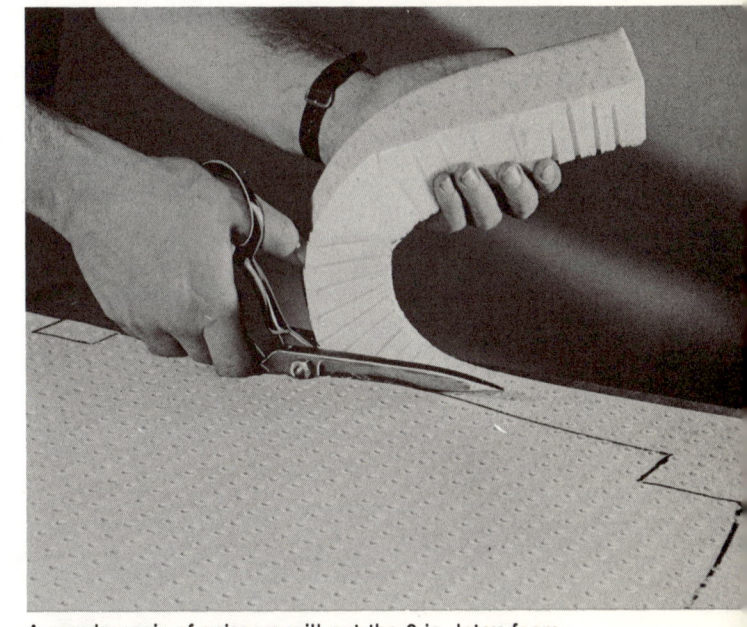

A regular pair of scissors will cut the 2-in. latex foam with ease. However, if you're working with foam more than 3 in. thick, it's best to cut it with a bandsaw. Many upholstery shops will cut cushions to size

upholstery

upholster with foam, continued

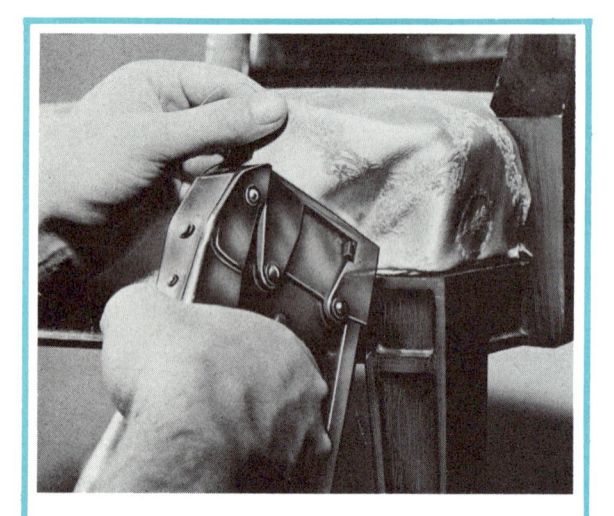

Making corners with the upholstery fabric may look difficult, but it's actually quite simple if you try this easy method. Pull the material around the corner, lift up the excess fabric; then staple the fabric that is flat against the frame and drop the remaining cloth straight down. Remove the excess material, leaving only enough to fold neatly underneath as shown below. Then staple or tack the fabric to the chair frame

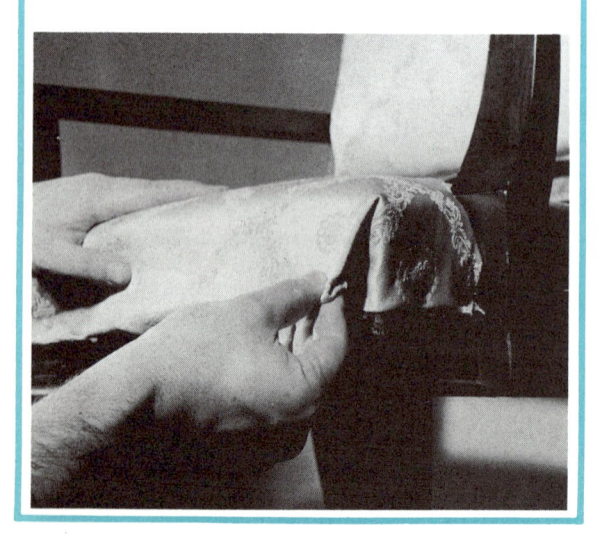

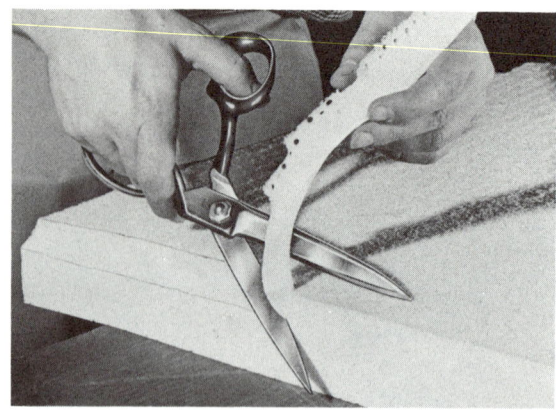

When the edge of the cushion is to be rounded, undercut it slightly with the scissors, as shown. This will make it easier for you to pull the edge down and tuck it underneath when you are installing the cushion

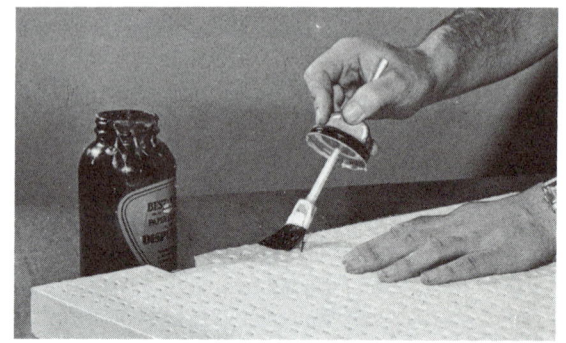

Cement strips of muslin along the top edges of the cushion. They will be tacked to the frame later. These strips serve a dual purpose—they not only hold the foam rubber cushion in place, but also help to give it its shape

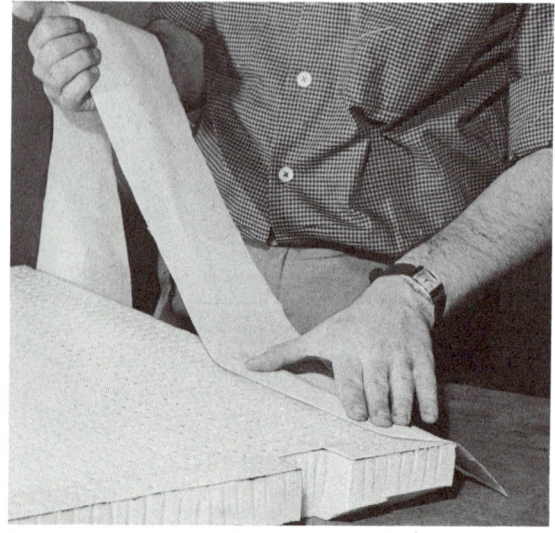

Apply two coats of rubber cement to the edges of both the cushion and the muslin, allowing the first coat to become practically dry before applying the second. When this gets tacky, press the cushion and the muslin together

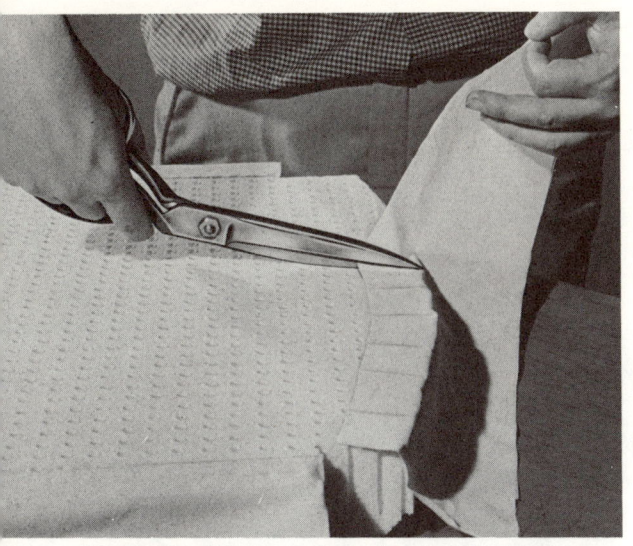

If the cushion has a curved edge, cut V-shaped notches in the muslin as you apply it so the cloth will lie flat on the cushion. The width of these notches will depend on the sharpness of the curve; the sharper the curve, the wider the notch

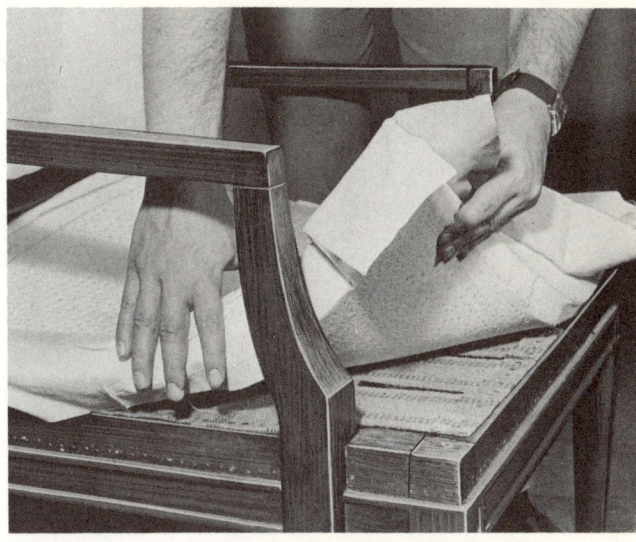

After positioning the latex foam cushion over the jute webbing, you are ready to tack the muslin strips to the chair frame. Be sure the rubber cement you applied to the muslin and the cushion is thoroughly dry before you begin tacking

underside of foam rubber when it was first introduced, this new kind, which the industry calls pincore, has hundreds of tiny holes, top and bottom. These pass only halfway through the slab in a staggered pattern so they do not meet. This now makes the rubber pad fully reversible and provides a firmer foundation.

The photos on these pages take you through the steps of reupholstering a chair the easy way.

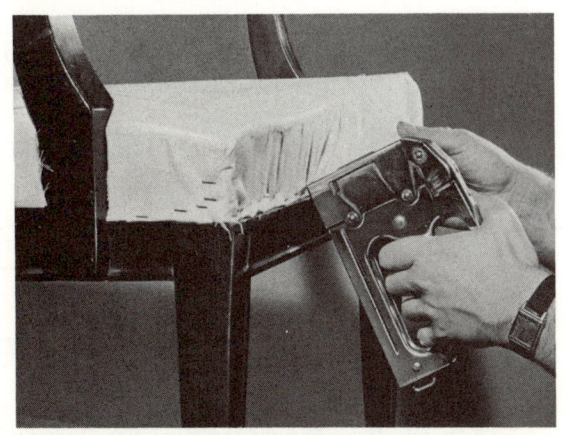

Pull down on the muslin and then tack or staple it to the chair frame. The cushion shown here is being given only a slight rounded edge. By pulling down harder on the muslin and tucking the foam rubber under, the curve can be increased

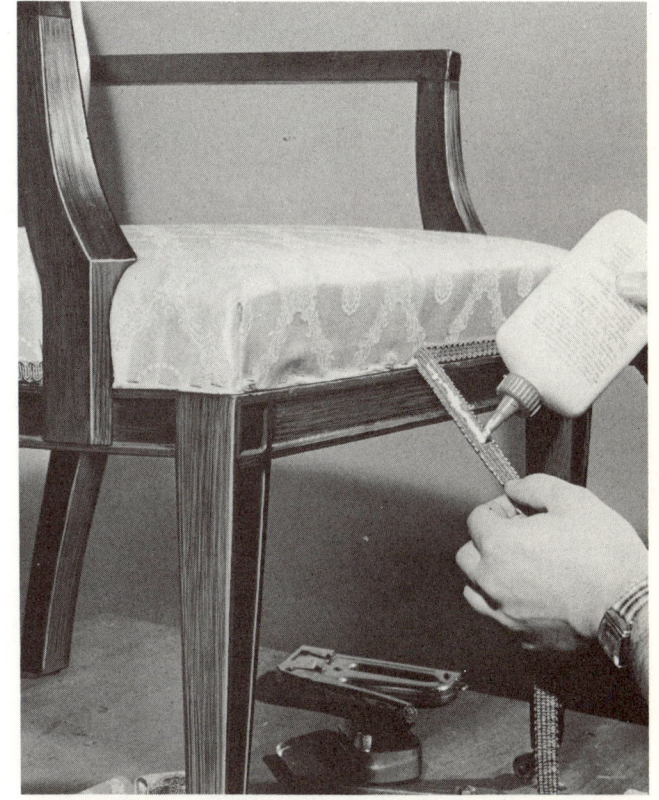

The final step is to add a decorative gimp to cover the fabric staples. You'll find it easier to apply the gimp if you glue it on but of course it won't remove as easily. Run a bead of glue on the back, then press in place

2833

used-car reconditioning

A modest investment
in reconditioning materials,
plus a weekend of
inexpensive elbow grease,
will pay off handsomely
at trade-in time

How to get more for your old car

BY JAMES B. COLBORNE

used outboard motors: see outboard motors, used
used pianos: see pianos
utility garages: see shelters
utility trailers: see trailers

■ How WOULD YOU LIKE to get up to $200 more than you think you can when the time comes to trade or sell your car? It's possible, if you are willing to invest a weekend of work and about $20 to $25 for supplies. All you have to do is perform a basic appearance reconditioning job on the old bus. And that's not too hard if you will take the time to do a professional-like job. The necessary supplies are so packaged today that even a rank novice can do a job that will add many dollars to the value of his automobile.

Car dealers have known for some time that the appearance of a used car can make or break a sale. They also know a reconditioned car will bring more money than one that hasn't been reconditioned.

The front and rear under-panels below the bumpers are the hardest hit by dirt streaks, road tar, paint nicks, flying pebbles, and shine-dulling film (top photo). After cleaning, polishing and a touch-up in this area, the car looks 100 percent better (lower photo). Rust has also been removed from the bumper, which now shines

To match your paint for a good touch-up job, look for this identification plate on your car. It will give the code numbers for the original colors

Not too long ago a dealer I know purchased an older model at auction. Appearance-wise, the car was a mess. He had a basic reconditioning job performed at a cost of about $20 and took the car back to the auction where it was resold to another dealer for a net gain of $155. Because of similar experiences, many dealers today are reconditioning their used cars before placing them on the resale lot.

To recondition your car, start with the engine compartment. The first step is to clean the engine and its compartment thoroughly.

Remove the air cleaner and cover the carburetor opening with a waterproof material such as

2835

used-car reconditioning

The grime-encrusted engine above looks old before its time, and can hurt the car's resale value just by its grimy appearance. It suggests that the car has not been taken care of by the first owner

Above is the same engine as shown at left, now with a degreasing bath, new paint and polish. This transformation will pay off in added resale dollars. Below, a fresh coat of paint on the tools takes only a few minutes

more for your old car, continued

polyethylene film to prevent any foreign matter from entering the carburetor. If the car is more than two or three years old, it is a good idea to cover the distributor. This can be done easily with a polyethylene sandwich bag.

Clean dirty underhood insulation by cutting into the material about 3/16-inch deep and peeling off the dirty layer. The remaining insulation will look like new. If the insulation is beyond saving, replace it. New material can be purchased from a dealer or at an automotive supply house.

Brush a degreasing compound over the entire engine and engine compartment, following the manufacturer's instructions. Be sure not to overlook the underside of the engine block and A-frame. Apply the degreaser to the underside of the hood if the insulation has been removed. Degrease the radiator, firewall and battery, and don't forget the air cleaner. Clean and replace the windshield washer bottle and radiator cap. Re-

CHECK THESE 10 KEY SPRUCE-UP SPOTS
1. Paint engine and compartment and polish bright metal.
2. Renew convertible window with plastic cleaner; if badly scratched, replace.
3. Restore convertible top with special top dressing.
4. Scrub out trunk; clean and repaint tire-changing tools.
5. Touch up nicks; remove rust spots; restore paint luster with rubbing compound.
6. Remove scuff marks; tint material if necessary.
7. Clean and paint floor pads; replace if badly worn.
8. Clean upholstery; recolor faded areas if necessary.
9. Coat walls of tires with special tire dressing.
10. Polish chrome trim; remove rust from pitted areas.

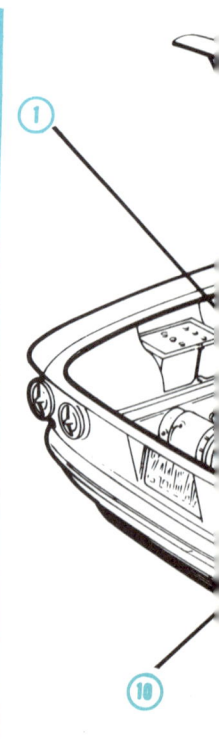

2836

The inside door panels take a rough beating at their lower edges (above). Scuff marks can be removed and the material retinted for a like-new look, as shown below. Sometimes a good washing is enough

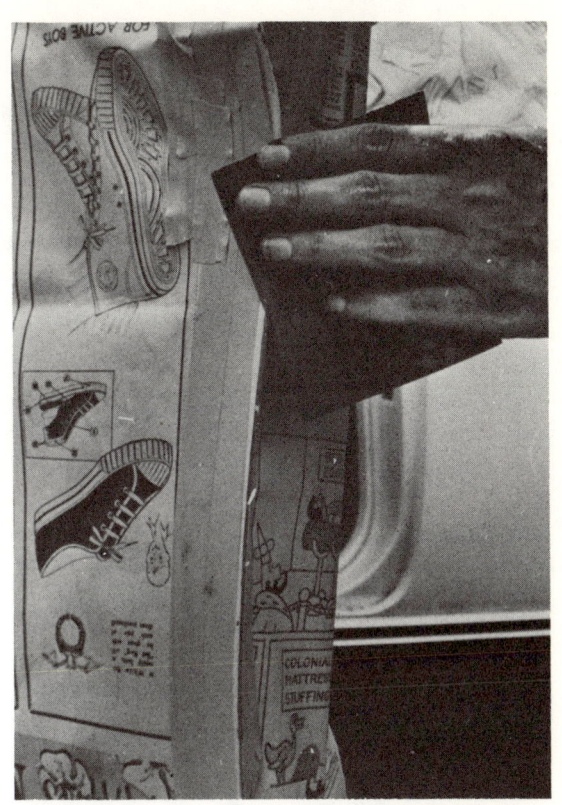

A slick paint job calls for careful masking of the surrounding areas with newspaper and masking tape. Sand any rough chipped spots around the door edges, so that the new and old paint will blend evenly

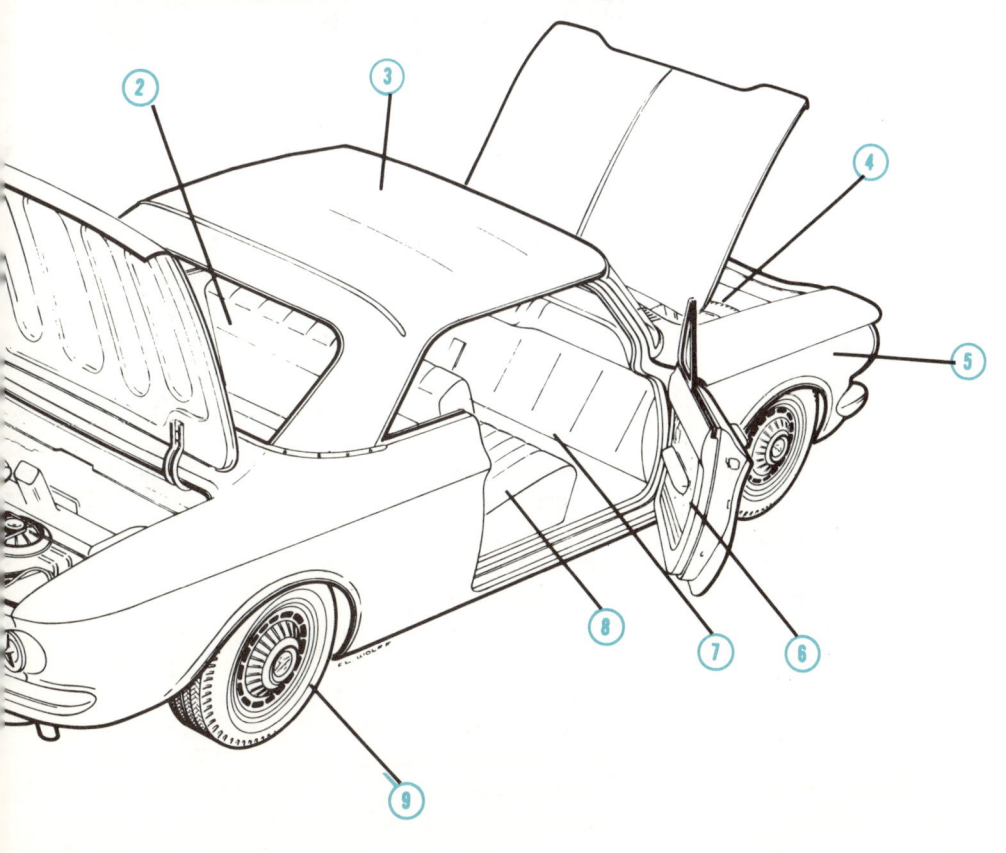

used-car reconditioning

more for your old car, continued

move all masking paper and clean white metal surfaces with steel wool.

The next step is to restore the interior. Start with the headliner. This area contains at least 80 percent of a used car's odor, so it behooves an owner to make sure the headliner is cleaned thoroughly.

restoring headliners

Fabric headliners can be restored by cleaning with an upholstery cleaner or by spraying with a color tint. If you are going to scrub the headliner, start at the rear left corner and clean one section at a time. Work the suds into the fabric with a circular or back-and-forth motion. When a section is cleaned, finish by sponging the nap in one direction. This is necessary to prevent some sections from looking darker than others. Repeat the process, overlapping the sections about 3 in. to prevent streaking. Scrub the sun visors in the same manner. Don't let yourself be interrupted once you start as uneven drying may cause streaks.

If the headliner is stained or faded, it can be tinted. Aerosol packaged tints are available for the home craftsman. When buying the tint, make sure it is compounded for the type of material in your headliner. Natural fabrics have a nap; nylon or synthetic fabrics usually do not.

remove sun visors and hooks

Remove sun visors, garment hooks and window moldings and mask off the beading, dome lights and windows. Start at the back left corner and spray from left to right in a continuous motion. Never let the spray stop momentarily in one spot, but keep it moving. A light coating of the tint is all that is necessary. Cross-spray the headliner with a second coating, moving from the front to the back of the automobile. Remove the masking tape and paper when the headliner is dry. Overspray can be removed with a spot remover.

Clean vinyl headliners with an appropriate vinyl cleaner and wipe dry. If the headliner has to be tinted, mask the area as before. Wipe the headliner with a lacquer thinner to increase the adhesion of the tint material. Spray with a vinyl tint in the same manner as for a fabric headliner. If the first coating is not even, cross-spray a second time.

The type of upholstery material will dictate the restoration method to be used. First, remove dirty spots with a spot remover. Next, use a stiff brush and scrub the upholstery with an appropriate cleaner. If fabric, brush the nap in one direction and wipe the cleaner from the upholstery with a clean absorbent cloth.

how to clean nylon

Dirty nylon upholstery and door panels can be cleaned with an upholstery cleaner. If the nylon is faded or stained, wash the material and let it dry. Mask off the area to be tinted and spray with a nylon tint. Allow plenty of time for drying before applying a second coating. When the material is completely dry after spraying, sponge the area with an upholstery cleaner to remove any chemical odors that may remain from spraying and to impart to the material a soft, natural feel. *Do not use nylon tints on wool or cotton.*

Vinyl or leather upholstery can be cleaned by brushing with a recommended cleaner. If tinting is necessary, wipe the surfaces with a lint-free rag soaked in lacquer thinner. This will remove all oil dyes from the surface. When the material feels tacky, it is ready for coloring. Spray on a first coat and wait until it is dry before applying a second.

spraying two colors

Keep spraying until the new color matches the old. If two different colors are required, let the first color dry overnight before masking it. Otherwise the first color coat may be removed when the masking tape is pulled off. After the coloring is dry, sand the material lightly with No. 400 paper to restore a silky feel to the upholstery. *Caution:* Foreign car leathers are usually oil-tanned and will not readily accept a surface dye.

Torn, stained or warped kick panels and package shelves can be replaced by cutting new pieces from heavy cardboard or fiberboard. Use the old piece as a template. Seal the new material with clear shellac and dye it to match the original.

Wool or cotton floor coverings should be scrubbed clean with an upholstery cleaner and stiff brush. Brush the nap to lay in one direction. Tint stained or faded material. If badly worn, replace the mats.

Discolored rubber floor mats should be scrubbed with an upholstery cleaner. After cleaning spray them to restore their color.

Replace damaged door sill plates. Stained or discolored plates can be brightened with steel wool. Clean door jambs with upholstery cleaner. Cement loose weatherstripping back in place.

A can of silicone spray lubricant comes in handy during this refurbishing. Spray all hinged parts on doors and tailgates so they will work easier and have no squeaks. Also spray the hood hinges and latches, the accelerator-pedal hinges or fittings. If any of the instrument-panel fittings don't work smoothly, sometimes a quick spray will loosen them.

Check the accelerator and brake pedals for wear. On some models, these may be replaced with only a little effort; on others it is a pretty big job. If the wear is considerable, replace if possible.

replace burned-out lamps

If any of the instrument lamps are burned out, replace them, too. The cost is small, and the effect is important. Buyers know that the car has been taken care of.

If yours is a station wagon, pay particular attention to the inside of the rear compartment. Station wagon buyers judge the kind of life the wagon has had by the way this compartment looks. In some wagons, the compartment is painted; in others, it is lined with vinyl or other material. Refinish the entire compartment, checking the tailgate and side walls particularly, since they get most of the scratches.

Now that you are trading the car, you obviously don't want to spend a lot of money on it, but only as much as necessary to raise the trade-in value. Thus, a complete engine tune-up might be too costly. But if you can get a smoother running engine by retiming it, by replacing the points, or by cleaning and regapping the sparkplugs, the time invested would be worthwhile. Make sure the air cleaner isn't partially clogged; this is often the cause of a rough-running engine.

exterior is final step

The final step in the reconditioning process is to restore the car's exterior and touch up all nicks and scratches.

To get an exact match of the paint color and type, look for the paint identification plate on the car. Depending upon the make you own, this plate will be located on the firewall, fan shroud, engine compartment wall, door post, or in or under the glove compartment. The paint and trim numbers can be taken to a paint supplier and translated into the information you need to purchase paint of the matching color and type.

If large areas of bare metal are exposed, sand the metal to remove all rust and dirt. Feather-edge the surrounding paint, tapering the edges with sandpaper so the paint slopes down to the bare metal. This will permit a paint job that will look better than one painted over a sharp break in the old finish. Clean the area with a cleaner to remove any grease or car polish.

paint carefully

Prime the bare metal and feather-edged area. A red oxide primer in an aerosol package is suitable. Apply two coats of primer as directed in the manufacturer's instructions. Smooth the primer with No. 400 sandpaper. Wash with clear water and let dry. Apply the paint as directed.

If you are painting with a lacquer, you will have to apply four or five coats. If you're using enamel, apply two or three coats. Apply a light coat of paint, let it dry, and then apply another. Repeat until you build the paint up to the correct thickness. Don't try to apply all the paint in one coat.

Go over the entire car with a rubbing compound to polish the paint. Small marks in the finish can be rubbed out if the paint is a lacquer. Do not use an abrasive rubbing compound on an enamel finish; a mild auto polish is all that's necessary.

polish depends on method

If you decide to use an electric drill fitted with a wool polishing bonnet to apply the rubbing compound, be sure to use a machine-type compound. A compound designed for hand rubbing contains too harsh an abrasive for machine work, and you may spoil the car's finish by breaking through the paint. Follow the compounding with a coat of polish.

Finally, use a chrome cleaner and polish to restore the metal trim. Small rust spots around the chrome can be cleaned up by using a toothbrush and chrome cleaner or rubbing compound.

A word to the wise: *Read the instructions on the supply containers before you begin.* This will not only make the job easier, but will help keep you out of trouble and will give you the assurance you are getting a job worthy of your time and money spent.

After all of this effort—in most cases not much more than a Saturday's work—you'll have what the dealers call a "clean" used car. Clean cars get the top bluebook price at auctions. If you increase your trade-in by $100 or more, you'll have been pretty well paid for the time you spent.

See also: auto repair; chassis, auto; cleaning, auto.

vacation homes

Three year-round vacation homes

Do you want to be a two-home family but you're afraid the budget won't take the strain? Look again. These three year-round vacation retreats can be built for less than you might guess

■ THE OLD DAYS of shuttering and battening down the hatches on the vacation cabin have gone the way of the dodo. This is the era of the year-round vacation home. Modern materials, designs and construction methods have placed these homes within buying reach of most budgets. Now anyone can have his own weekend retreat for a modest outlay.

Today you can buy a shell that goes up on your lot in a day, and finish it at your leisure. There's another design that can be put up and taken down when you decide to move. You can have a geodesic dome or an A-frame or a squat rancher. You can have one built over a stream, or a ski cabin with an indoor pool.

The three exciting vacation-home designs presented here were designed for Simpson Timber Co. by the architectural firm of Robert Martin Engelbrecht, A.I.A., of New York City. All are year-rounders, yet each is distinctly different. You can adapt your new vacation home from one of them.

The *Olympic* is an aerie built on stilts, aesthetically and commandingly "at home" on a mountainside where an unimpeded view is offered from three sides of the house.

The *Engelframe Saranac* uses the geometry of the isosceles trapezoid to combine strength, beauty and simplicity. Like the *Olympic*, the *Saranac* can be erected on uneven terrain by varying the lengths of the supporting structural members as required.

The utility and symmetry of the square is highlighted by the design of the *Tidewater,* another vacation home adaptable to virtually any site. This one features a spacious deck surrounding a compact living area, creating the effect of an open pavilion. But if you think this covered deck

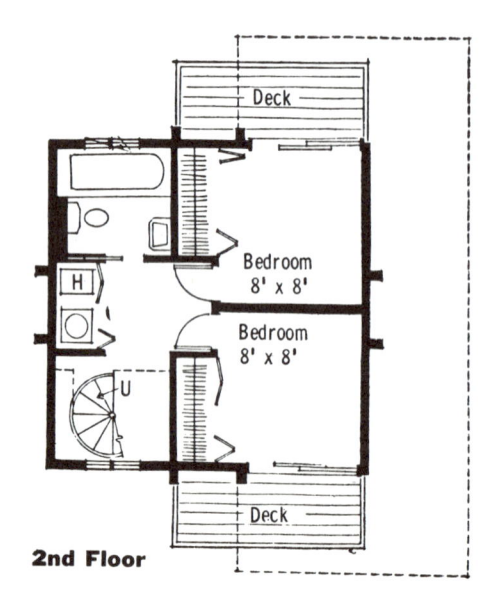

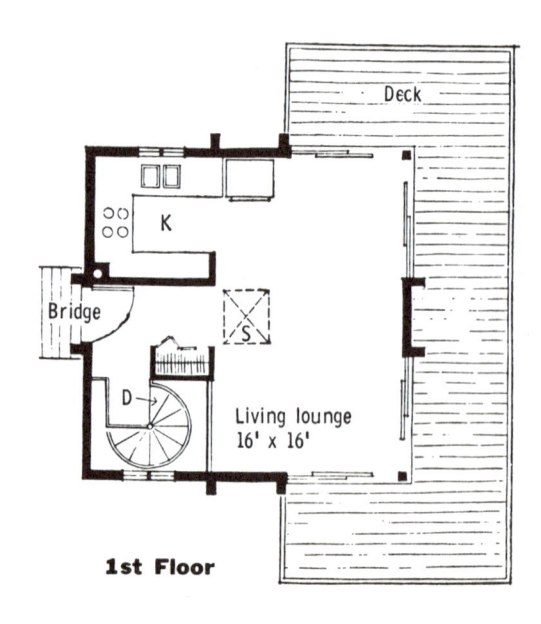

2nd Floor

1st Floor

Pick your mountain, then build. This eagle's nest of a house—the *Olympic*—is supported by eight strong pillars. A footbridge leads to the entrance. The living lounge and a spacious wrap-around deck constitute the upper level. The two bedrooms, bath and utility area on the lower level are reached via a spiral staircase

vacation homes

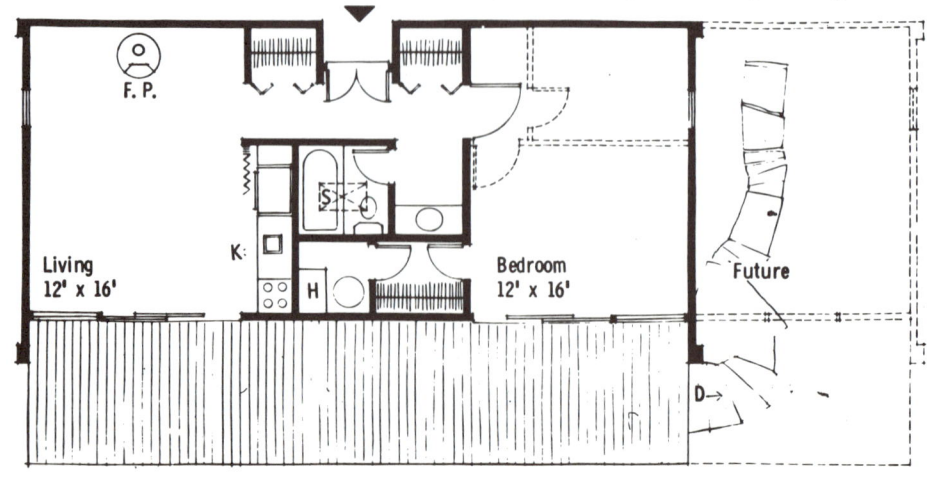

Seaside, lakeside, riverside, hillside—*Engelframe Saranac* can be locked into place just about anywhere. A single-story structure, it can be built as a one- or two-bedroom house. Its simplicity of design would facilitate building an addition on to the house as indicated in the plan. A main feature of this hideaway is the full-length redwood deck which encourages casual indoor-outdoor living. The glass walls and doors flanking the center section of the house permit taking full advantage of the day and night view

deprives the house of light—you're wrong. Sunlight and starlight flood into the house through a cluster of skywindows centered in the high, peaked roof.

Remember, while these are but a sampling of vacation-home designs created by *one* architectural firm, they point up the imaginative strides that are being taken in this field. Today's buyer selects his vacation home from hundreds of styles, sizes and prices. Plainly, the day of the "voting booth" cabin has passed into history.

See also: building; framing; garages; home additions; home buying; home improvement; home sites; measurements; remodeling; roofs; storage buildings.

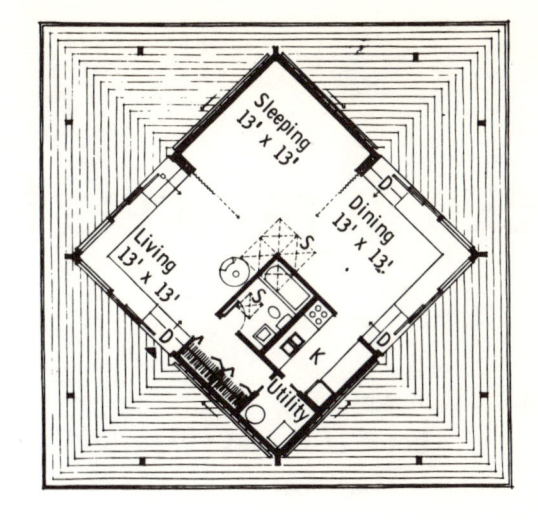

You'd be definitely *in* with the "in crowd" if you brought them to this square retreat. The *Tidewater* vacation home, like the *Saranac,* is designed to go anywhere. Different areas of the roof-covered deck surrounding the living quarters are in shade and sun throughout the day. Daylight floods into the house through a cluster of skywindows centered in the peaked roof. A unique feature of the house is that you step down into the living room from the sun deck. The corner window seat converts into bunks

vacation homes

Weekend projects for hideaway homes

There's no reason why your home at the lake can't be as convenient as your year-round home. Here are five ideas to make that lake home more comfortable

FLOOR-TO-CEILING shelves like these are easy to knock together, and do a great job of sharpening the appearance of a room while delivering more stowaway space. The shelves are mounted flush against the wall and attached at the ceiling and floor. Metal clips set into notched metal runners support the shelves. When you want to shift the position of a shelf, just move the clips. If your weekend home has a big picture window, these shelves could flank it. They're endlessly adaptable and give that second home a look of sophistication.

turn the page

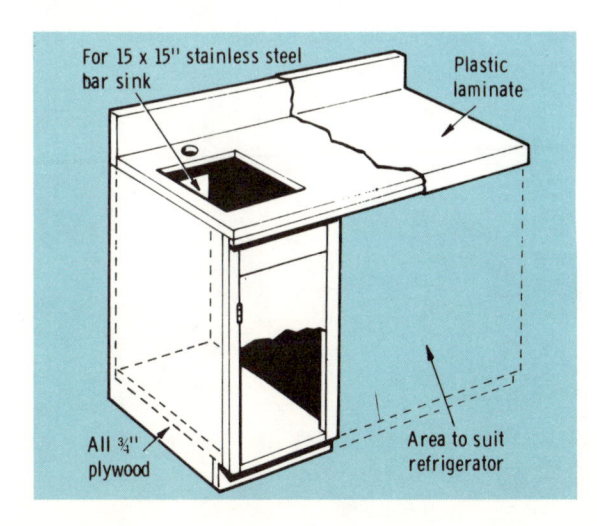

Typically, a weekend home is designed for plenty of living and allots the minimum for a kitchen work center. And why not? You go there to unwind, not to spend hours over a hot stove. Curious to know the absolute minimum-sized kitchen using separate appliances, we asked designers to give us the answer, based on the measurements of the smallest units made throughout the industry. What you see is a 19½-in.-wide range and oven combination and a 6½ (6.6)-cu.-ft. undercounter refrigerator. You simply add the wood-frame surround, cabinet door, counter top, and drop in a bar-sized sink—in this case a unit made by Just Mfg. Co. It fits a 9 x 12-in. opening.

2845

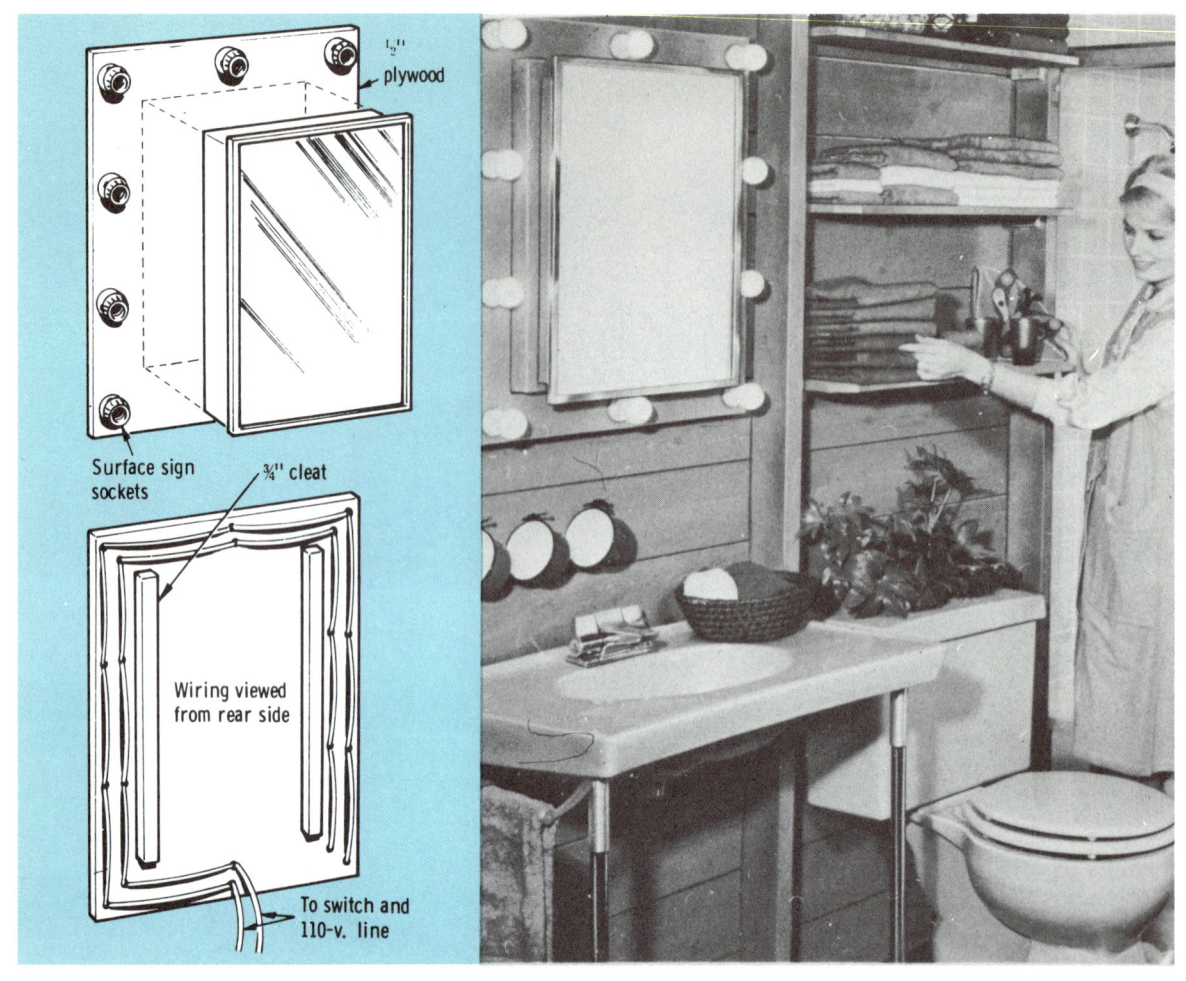

vacation homes

■ A BACKSTAGE MAKEUP mirror will do a lot to glamorize a cottage bathroom. To make it, simply attach a medicine cabinet to a plywood panel and surround it with ten 25-watt bulbs wired to a single switch.

second-home projects, continued

■ POTATO AND ONION storage always seems to be a problem. You might try this handy solution—even in your year-round home. The frame for the drawer has 2 x 6 sides to support the weight of the refrigerator.

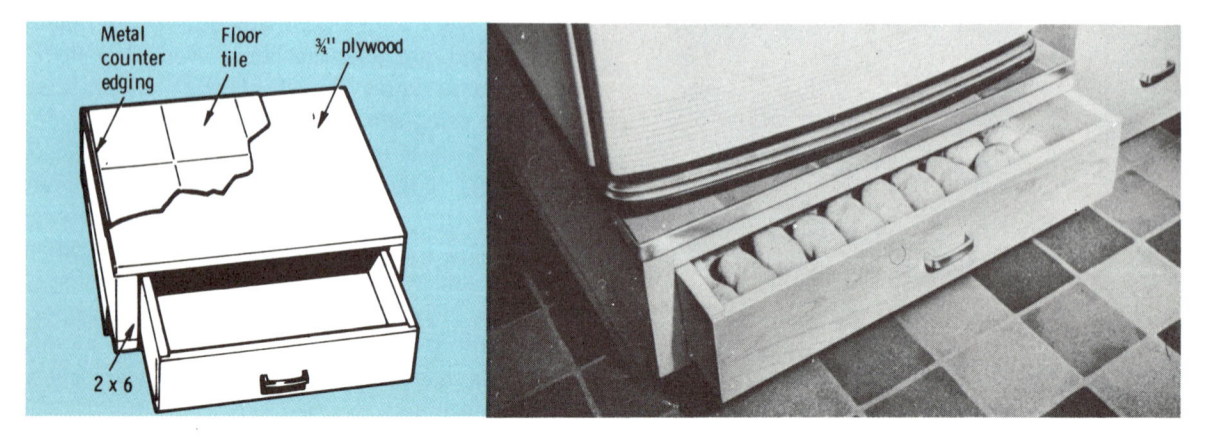

Screwed to wall

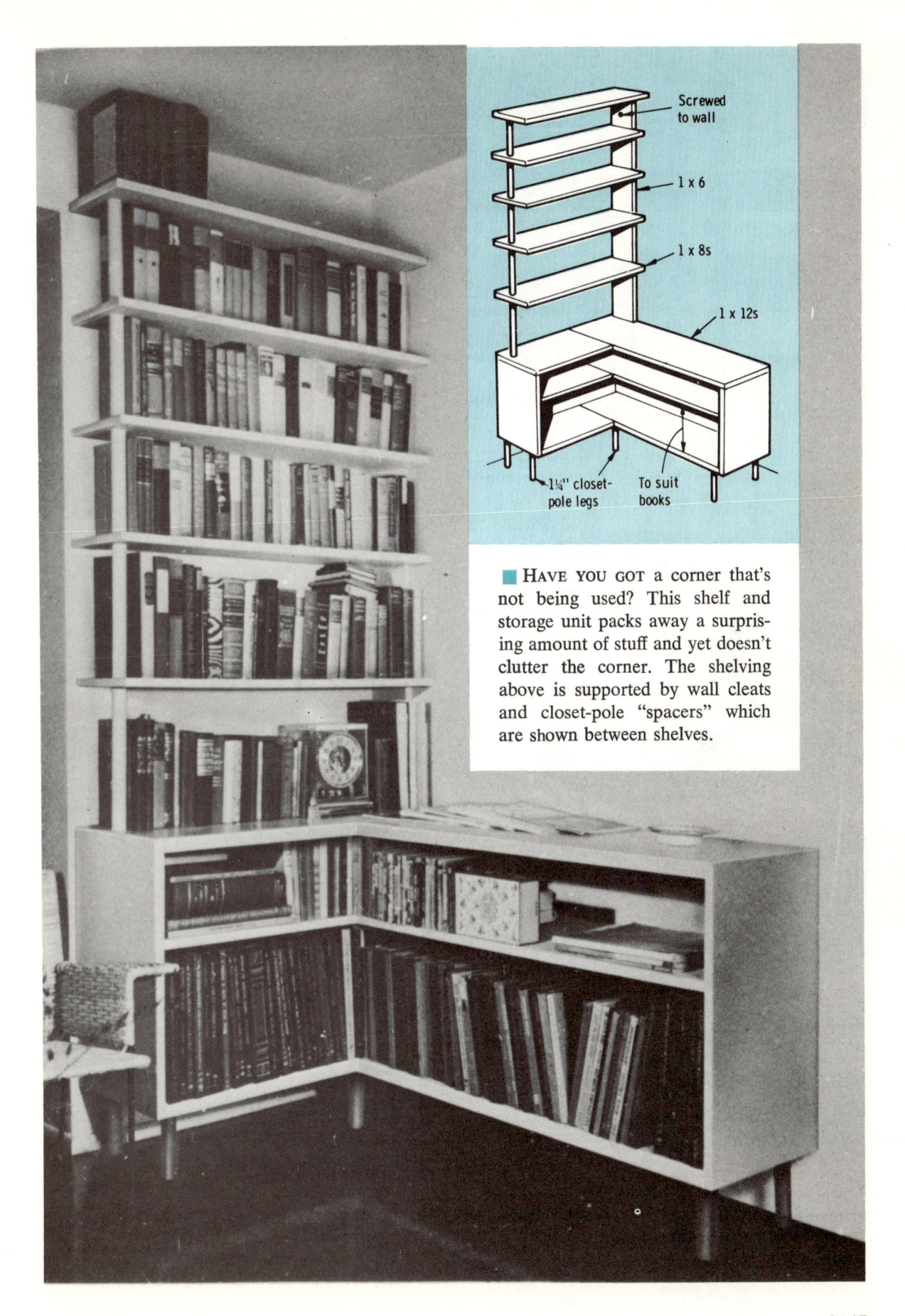

1 x 6

1 x 8s

1 x 12s

1¼" closet-pole legs

To suit books

■ HAVE YOU GOT a corner that's not being used? This shelf and storage unit packs away a surprising amount of stuff and yet doesn't clutter the corner. The shelving above is supported by wall cleats and closet-pole "spacers" which are shown between shelves.

vacation homes

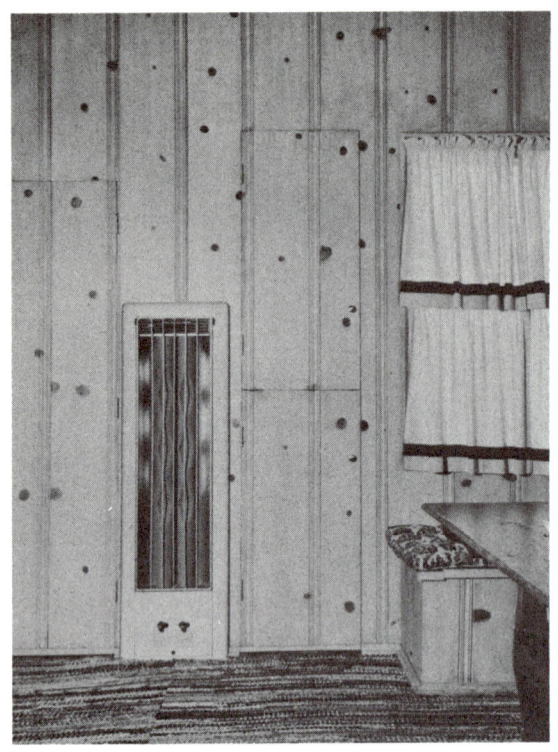

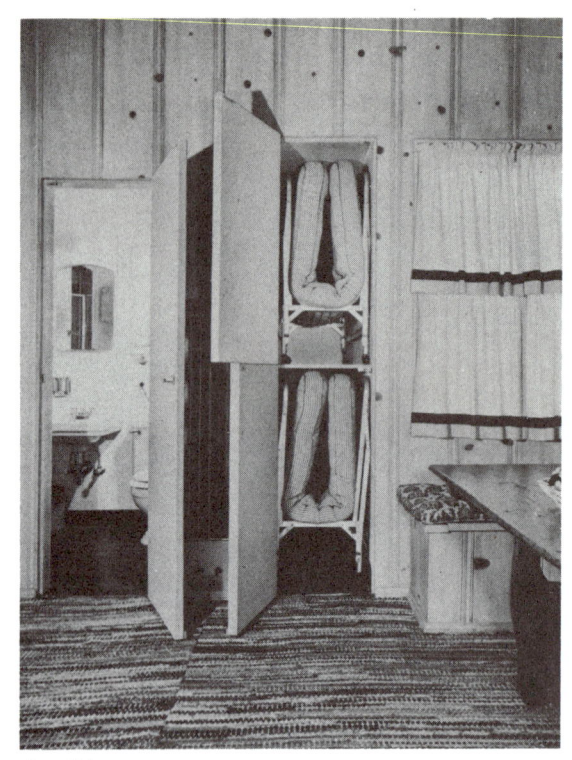

You're sure to have guests at least once during vacation. Here's a trim, space-saving way to store the beds you'll need. Figure about 45 in. for height of folded cots. The shelf is a piece cut from ⅜-in. plywood. There's also storage in the window bench

vacation homes, continued

Why not build in your own beach party? This cabana can serve hot and cold snacks and beverages. Built of cypress, it has a sheet-metal roof and glass behind the counter to break the wind. There are receptacles for plugging in appliances. The space at the right takes the refrigerator and there are storage bins for orderly stowing. Designer is John Pugh

Stack the firebrick vertically and give yourself a smart, economical hearth and spark fence. Bed-sofa and built-in shelves squeeze every inch of use from space available

Redwood enclosure gives privacy. The slats set at 30 deg.; they measure ½ x 4 in.

for more ideas, turn the page

Go topside and stretch out in the sun. Put up a rig like this and soak up the sun even on windy days. Any well-supported flat roof will do. Here, the owner lashed a dark-green canvas to a metal pipe frame, laid down a fir deck, and added steel steps leading to a canvas gate. Lacing is plastic

vacation homes

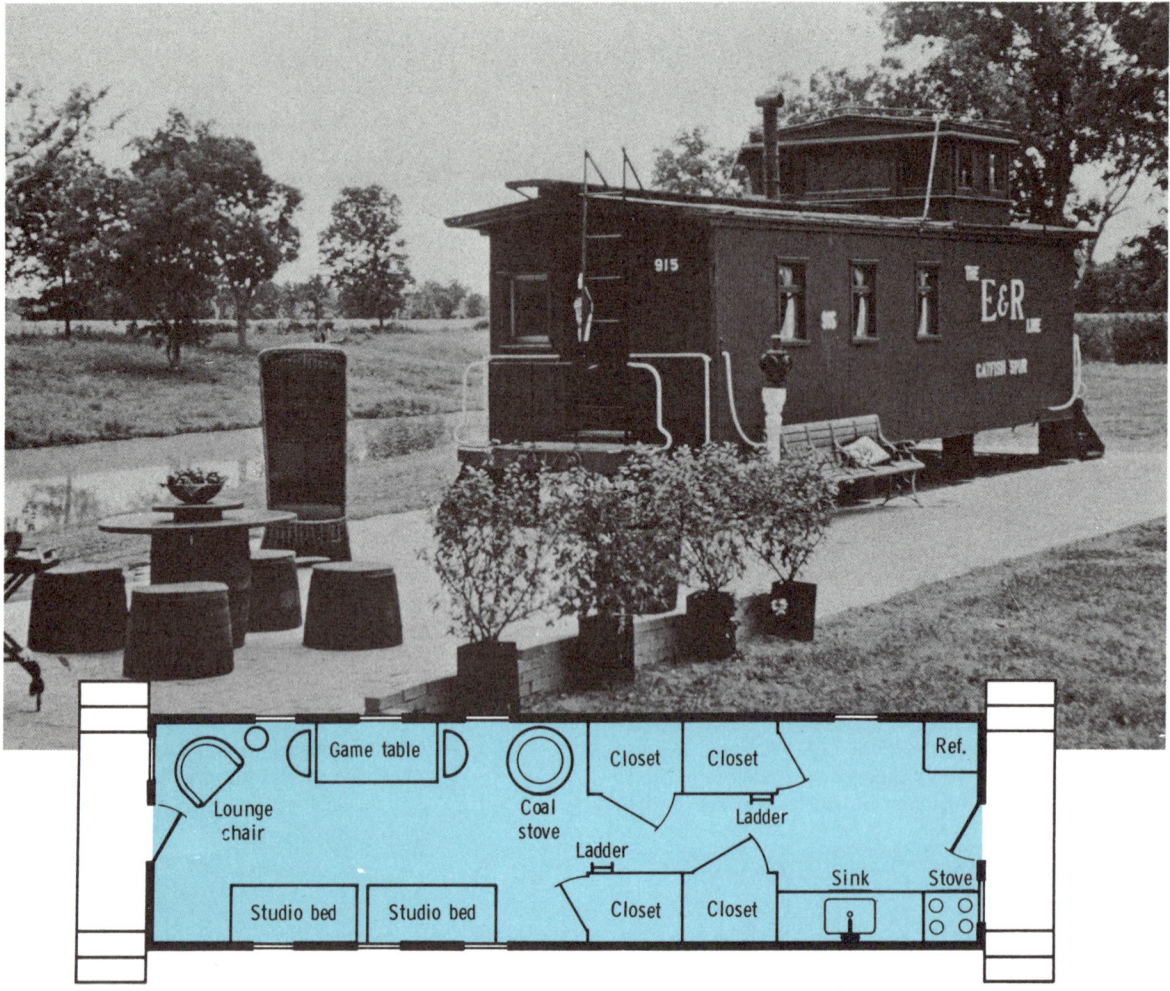

You're not seeing things; that's a real caboose you're looking at. If you're willing to persevere a bit you can probably latch onto one like it at nominal cost. There'll be a trucking charge, but a few pieces of new lumber, some fixtures and paint can turn it into a cottage

The leggy creature below is a Virginia coast beach house that will stay put in a hurricane. High water, not high wind, is the real wrecker in a coastal storm. The water rushes right under this home because it's on stilts. The framing is of the post-and-beam construction

2852

Storage wall or simple partitions are smarter-looking and easier to build if you use prefinished plywood wall paneling. Just frame out and nail up the panels. You can buy molding and doors to match the grain of the paneling you use

Does a swim before breakfast appeal to you? It's not hard to do here, since double, wood-framed jalousie doors open out from the bedrooms for a quick getaway to the beach or pool. George Matsumoto, AIA, designed this house for Masonite Corp.

Cut down time waiting to wash in the morning. This built-in bedroom lavatory backs up to bath plumbing. The double doors close to make it look like a closet. Four-drawer chest is built-in

At least 6 storage ideas are visible here. Pick those that fit your needs best. Stud-deep storage shelves back up to a living room cabinet. The wood is western pine; the desk has a plastic top

clever ideas

Spot removal will be a breeze if you use a carpet-backed caster cup as an applicator for the cleaning fluid. The raised pile of the carpet insert is ideal for brushing cleaning fluid into the fabric.

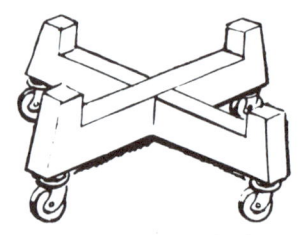

Heavy floor plants can be moved from room to room or outdoors effortlessly with this simple plant dolly. Make it from 2 x 4 stock, using a half-lap joint at the center, and notch pieces to fit the plant's tub. Use socket casters and make sure holes taking the sockets are drilled straight.

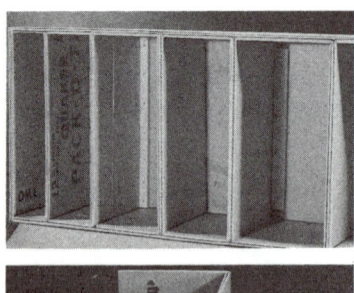

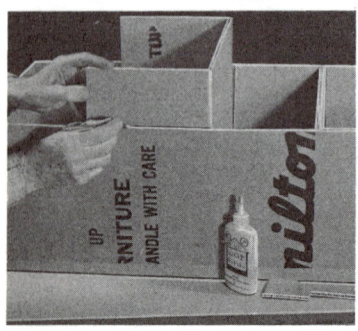

Cardboard strips bent U-shaped to fit snugly into a rectangular cardboard box form shelves in this cabinet. The wings of the U serve as supports for each succeeding shelf as shown in the photos. Glue the wings in place or hold them with tape. Cover the cabinet with wallpaper or other decoration.

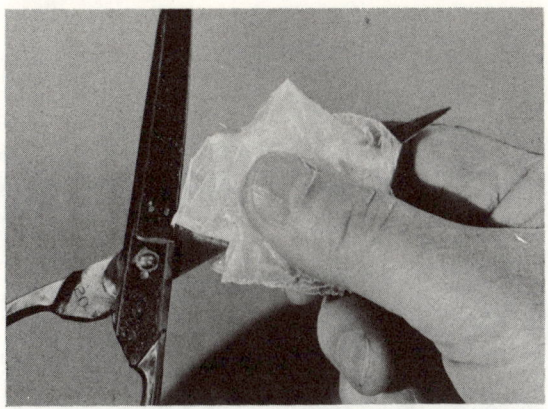

To rustproof scissors, rub the unplated inner surface of each blade with a wad of ordinary wax paper. If you plan to store them, protect the edges by folding a piece of waxed paper and cutting it.

Push pins can substitute for grooves to hold china plates standing edgewise on shelves. Press the pins into the wood so that only the heads project. For large plates or platters use two pins.

Emergency ice creepers can be made from strips of fly screen. Wrap a strip around each shoe and tie it with a cord looped around your ankle. They'll get you from your house to the garage, across the street or anywhere you want to go, safely.

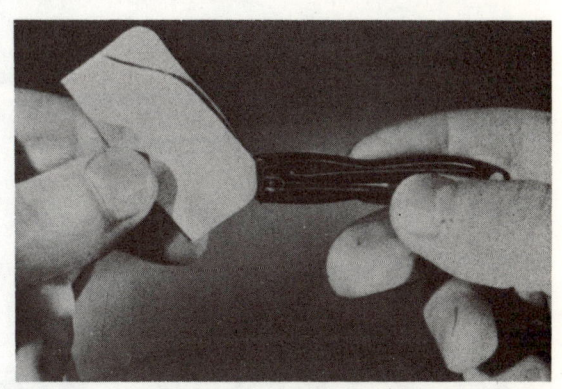

Press-on mending tape holds better and won't lift if the corners of each patch are rounded. A quick, neat way to do this is to fold the patch and then clip the corners with a fingernail clipper.

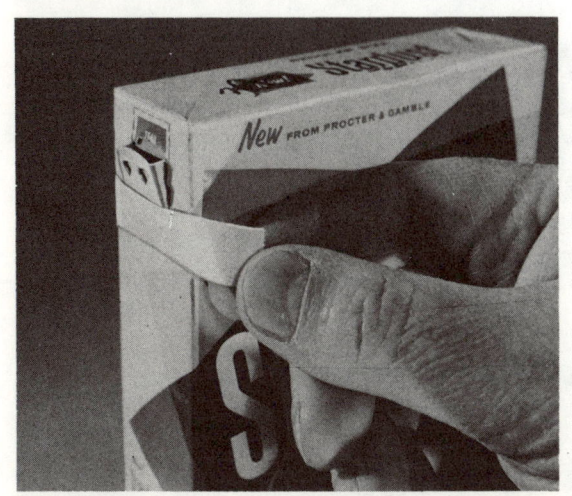

Pull-out spouts on boxes of kitchen products often open so wide that you accidentally pour out too much material. To slow the pouring rate, run tape around the spout to hold it partially closed.

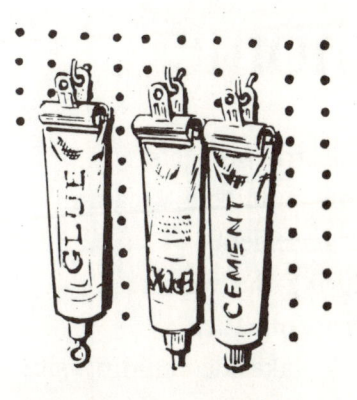

Having trouble keeping track of all those tubes of repair compounds in your workshop? It seems that you can never find the one you want, and when you do, it's empty. You can tell at a glance how much is in each tube if you clip each one in a spring-type paper clip and hang it on the wall.

2855

vacation homes

Start your vacation home at home

Prefab construction lets you build this vacation house in your basement during the winter, ready for trucking to a lakeside building site the following spring

2856

■ EVER THOUGHT you'd like to build your own vacation home? You probably have the very spot already picked out, a choice site overlooking a beautiful lake where the family could spend a carefree summer and you the weekends, plus your vacation.

A lake home takes the bother out of those family weekend outings. You always know exactly where you're going and how to get there, and there's no need to stuff the car full of suitcases since you'll have most necessary items already stored in your second home.

Of course, there's that one big drawback: Who has the time to build his own vacation home? Traveling back and forth would leave little time for working. It would take forever to build it. It's just too big a project to ever consider as a spare-time job. Or is it?

Building a vacation home at some distant spot weekends is out of the question, to be sure. But suppose you could get a head start by building at least half of it at home in your basement or garage?

In building such a home within your home it's obvious that almost everyone would be faced with a shortage of time. The answer is a simple modular affair, the floors and walls of which can be prefabbed at home in standard 4-ft. sections, stockpiled until spring and carted to the building site where they could be erected by the builder within a two-week vacation period.

With this idea in mind Home Planners, Inc. was commissioned to design such a vacation home. Two features were especially stressed: that it should be built of stock materials in modules that would go together like toy building blocks. In addition, it was to be designed to grow with the builder's future needs.

The vacation home you see here incorporates these basic requirements. Designed as a three-stage, add-on affair, the modest basic unit has a modular floor plan measuring 24 x 24 ft., or a total of 576 sq. ft. It features a living room, a kitchen, a bedroom and bath, large enough to sleep and house a vacationing family of four. While the basic unit alone may very well fill your needs, both familywise and budgetwise, the house is designed so it may be expanded at any future time with a minimum of work and expense. For example, if you find you need more sleeping area than the basic unit provides, a 12-ft. two-bedroom addition can be added. This involves little more than hitching on more 4-ft. prefabbed floor, wall and roof sections to the basic unit and cutting a doorway through the existing end wall. If in time you feel a need for a porch and the

Here's what your vacation home will look like when the add-on sections are attached to the basic unit, giving a total area of 1152 sq. ft.

vacation homes

Footing forms are 2 x 4s, set on grade and then dug out for an 8-in. poured footing

prefab a vacation house, continued

Stub tie-ins are laid at basic foundation corners when future addition is planned

Foundation goes faster when several concrete blocks are buttered at the same time

STAGE 1

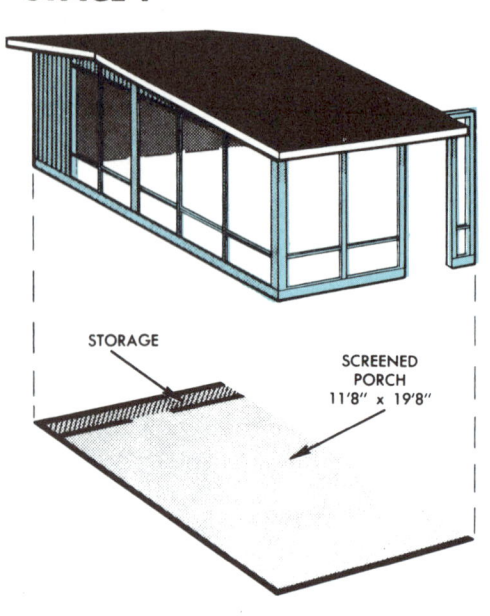

STORAGE

SCREENED PORCH 11'8" x 19'8"

storage it provides, here again it's a case of simply hooking on another 12-ft. addition to the opposite end of the basic unit, over the existing patio slab. In each case, the wall and roof line is not disturbed, only a few roof shingles would have to be removed to tie in with the new, plus the fascia boards on the gable ends. The third stage gives you a total floor area of 1152 sq. ft., sufficient for even year-round living.

Now, can you actually build this home yourself? In the strict sense, no. Working alone you'll have the problem of lifting the heavy and bulky prefabricated panels. This will be less of a problem at home where your wife can give you a hand in wrestling with the panels. However, when it comes to erecting them and framing the roof, you'll need a helping hand. There's the problem, too, of a well, a septic system and of getting the crawl space bulldozed. Actually, it makes sense to have the footing and block foundation laid for you so that when you are ready to take over, this part of construction is already done. In the case of the foundation it might be well to weigh the future possibility of building stage II. If so, you will be ahead to have the footing for the bedroom addition laid at the same time as the footing for the basic unit and to have a portion of the foundation wall extended. Such long-range planning not only will save you money but will

2858

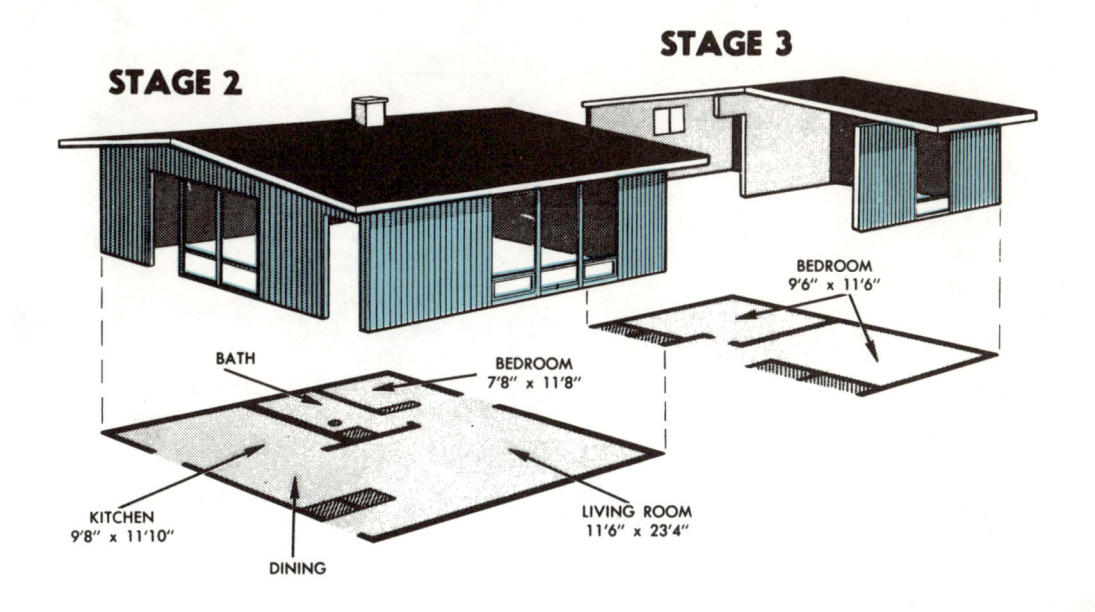

also provide foundation stubs for tying-in the new wall. Both footing and stub walls can be graded over and uncovered later.

What will the house cost? Materials for the basic unit will run about $3000.00. This figure is based on material costs in a high-cost area and could very well be less in your particular locality. To this you will have to add the cost of the lot, the cost of a well, septic system and whatever additional labor you will have to hire.

What tools will it take? The perfect power tool for mass-cutting duplicate members to the exact same length is a radial-arm saw. But it doesn't mean you have to own such a saw. In fact, if you've got what it takes, musclewise, to whip through 2-in. lumber with a handsaw, you can build this home with a minimum of common carpenter's hand tools. On the other hand, if you're not so good at hand sawing, it will pay you to invest in or rent a portable electric saw. It is important that the members be cut squarely, so the prefabbed sections will fit together accurately.

Now to go to work. Prefabbing the floor is your first step. Based on a module of 4 ft., the floor of the 24 x 24-ft. basic unit requires eighteen 4 x 8-ft. sections. In studying Figs. 1 and 2 you'll notice they are not all alike, although several of the group are made in duplicate. For example, 6 of (B) are made alike, 4 of (F), 2 of (A) etc. All require 4 x 8-ft. panels of ⅜-in. material which are nailed to a framework of 2 x 6s placed on edge. Here, even though a couple of the sections require only one of a kind to be fabricated, you'll find it will pay to take the time to make a nailing jig. Rigged up on a couple of horses and fitted with stop blocks to position duplicate parts uniformly, such a jig will make the work go faster in an assembly-line manner. Some of the assemblies are left open at the ends, others are closed at one or both ends. In some cases the 4 x 8-ft. sheets are kept flush with the 2 x 6 members; in other cases the sheets are centered on the 2 x 6s to provide nailing ledges for the adjoining sections. Use 8d coated nails spaced 6 in. apart to fasten the ⅜-in. material, 16d nails to nail the 2 x 6s. As each section is completed, letter it so you will know the order in which it joins the others. If you lack the space to store the completed sections indoors, stockpile them outside on a level surface and cover with a protective tarp.

Figs. 2 and 3 will give you an idea of how the floor sections will eventually rest on the foundation of the basic unit. Supported by two beams which are built up of 2 x 8s to rest on concrete-block piers and pilasters, the floor sections are toenailed to a 2 x 8 plate atop the foundation wall. The plate is anchored here and there with

vacation homes

prefab a vacation house, continued

Holes in the wall plates are located for anchor bolts in the foundation by placing 2 x 8 members against the bolts and using a try square to mark the position of the bolts

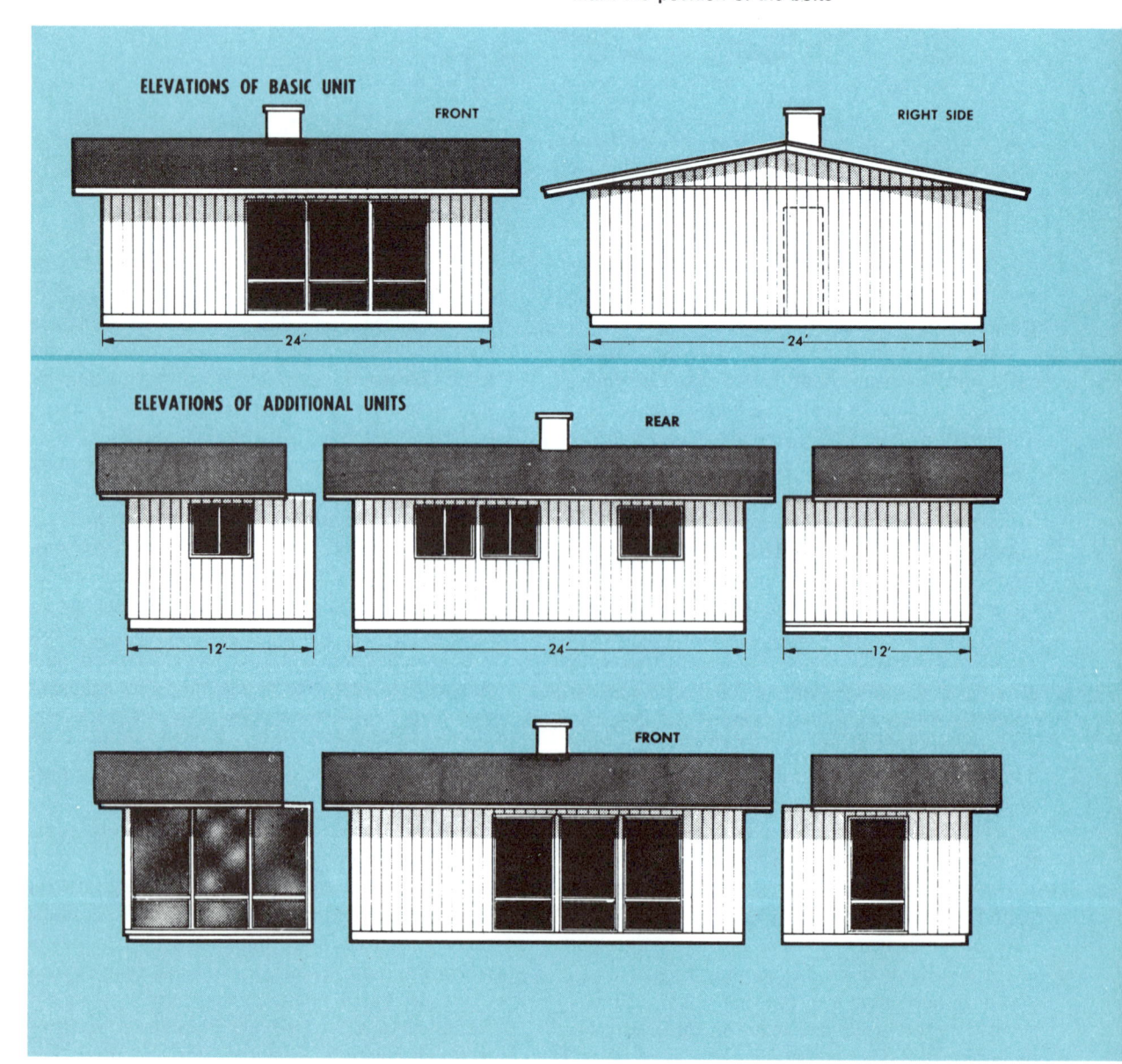

ELEVATIONS OF BASIC UNIT

FRONT — 24'

RIGHT SIDE — 24'

ELEVATIONS OF ADDITIONAL UNITS

REAR — 12', 24', 12'

FRONT

2860

bolts mortared in the cores of the top course of blocks. In addition to being toenailed to the plate, the floor sections are nailed to each other from under the crawl space, as well as being nailed along the lapped joints.

Assuming that you have the 18 floor sections for the basic unit completed and stockpiled, you are ready to prefab the exterior and the interior walls. Where 2 x 6s were used in the floor sections, 2 x 4s are used in the walls, and where ½-in. sheathing was used to cover the floor sections, ⅝-in. sheathing is used to cover the wall sections. Other than this, assembly of the wall sections is similar to that of the floor sections, these being covered as before on the outside only.

Of the 24 sections required for the exterior

Each pilaster in the foundation wall of the basic unit is built up with a 4-in. block backed with a common 8-in. block in each course of the wall. Basic unit is 24 x 24 ft.

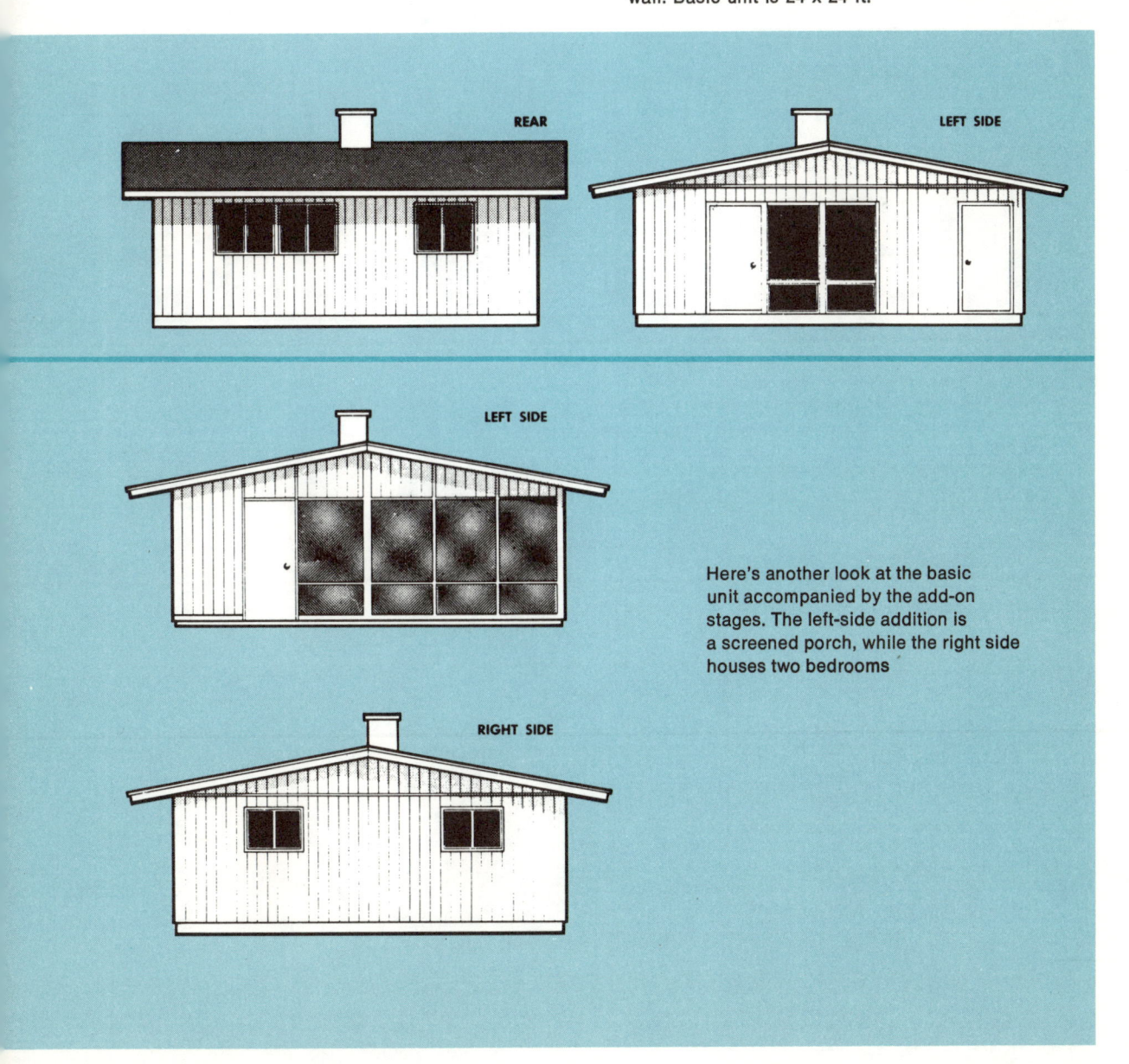

Here's another look at the basic unit accompanied by the add-on stages. The left-side addition is a screened porch, while the right side houses two bedrooms

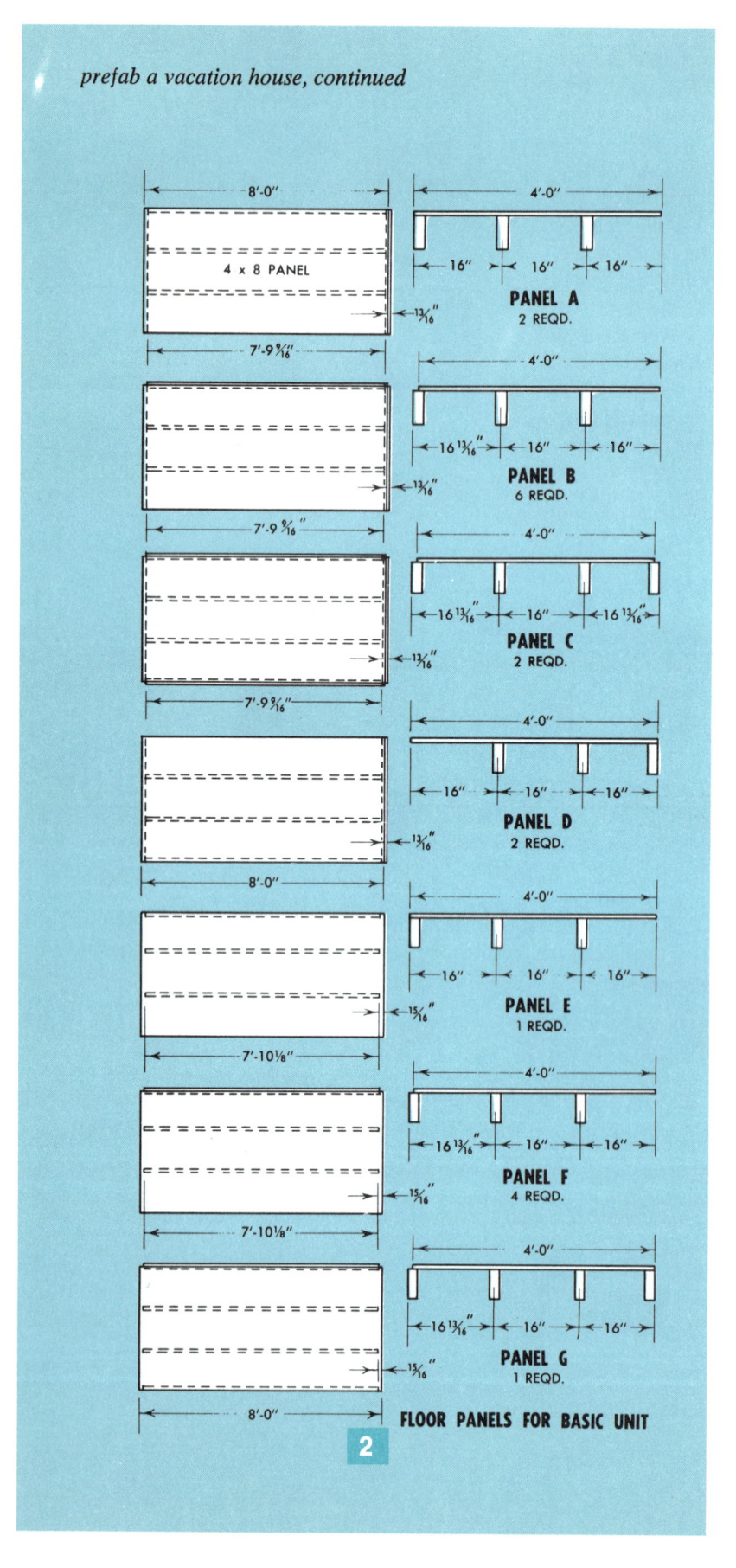

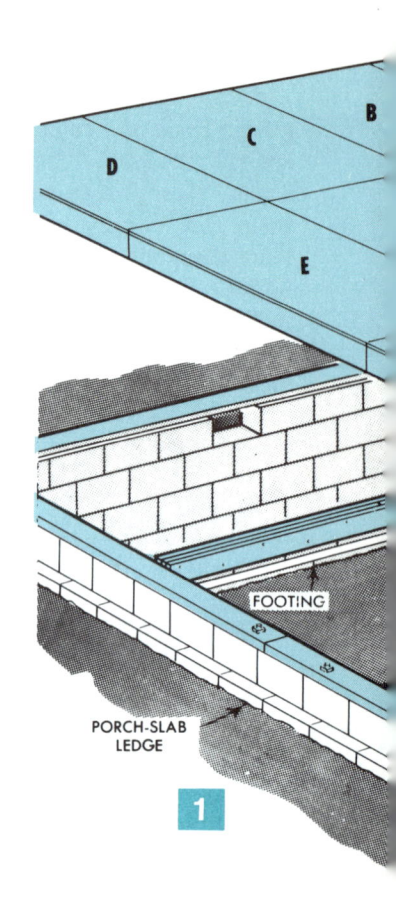

vacation homes

prefab a vacation house, continued

PANEL A — 2 REQD. (8'-0" × 4'-0", 4 × 8 PANEL, 13/16")

PANEL B — 6 REQD. (7'-9 9/16" × 4'-0", 16 13/16" / 16" / 16", 13/16")

PANEL C — 2 REQD. (7'-9 9/16" × 4'-0", 16 13/16" / 16" / 16 13/16", 13/16")

PANEL D — 2 REQD. (7'-9 9/16" × 4'-0", 16" / 16" / 16", 13/16")

PANEL E — 1 REQD. (8'-0" × 4'-0", 16" / 16" / 16", 15/16")

PANEL F — 4 REQD. (7'-10 1/8" × 4'-0", 16 13/16" / 16" / 16", 15/16")

PANEL G — 1 REQD. (7'-10 1/8" × 4'-0", 16 13/16" / 16" / 16", 15/16")

FLOOR PANELS FOR BASIC UNIT

2

1 FOOTING / PORCH-SLAB LEDGE

2862

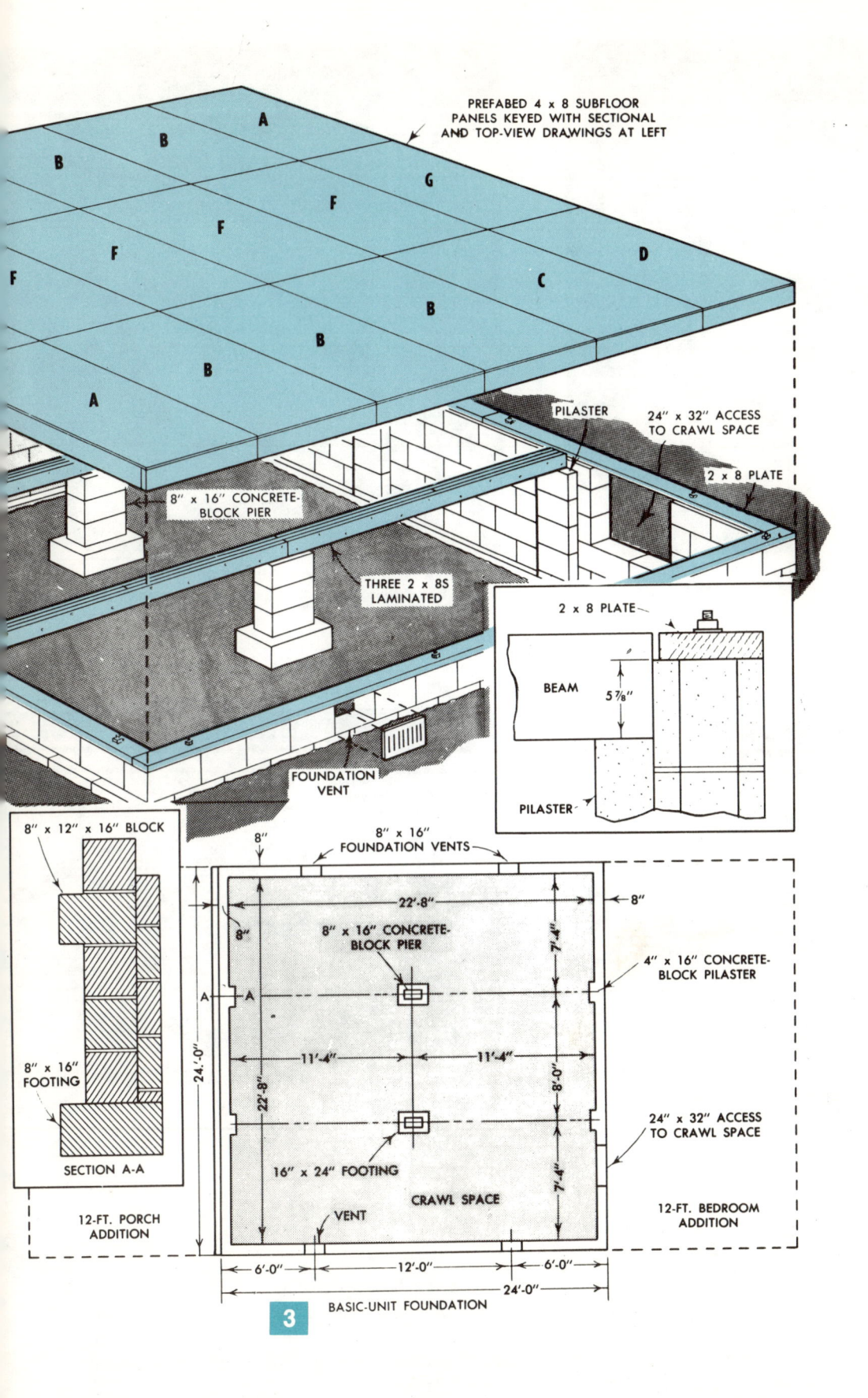

PREFABED 4 x 8 SUBFLOOR PANELS KEYED WITH SECTIONAL AND TOP-VIEW DRAWINGS AT LEFT

24" x 32" ACCESS TO CRAWL SPACE

PILASTER

2 x 8 PLATE

8" x 16" CONCRETE-BLOCK PIER

THREE 2 x 8S LAMINATED

2 x 8 PLATE

BEAM 5 7/8"

PILASTER

FOUNDATION VENT

8" x 12" x 16" BLOCK

8" x 16" FOOTING

SECTION A-A

12-FT. PORCH ADDITION

8" x 16" FOUNDATION VENTS

22'-8"

8"

8" x 16" CONCRETE-BLOCK PIER

4" x 16" CONCRETE-BLOCK PILASTER

7'-4"

11'-4"   11'-4"

22'-8"

8'-0"

24'-0"

16" x 24" FOOTING

CRAWL SPACE

VENT

24" x 32" ACCESS TO CRAWL SPACE

7'-4"

12-FT. BEDROOM ADDITION

6'-0"   12'-0"   6'-0"

24'-0"

3 BASIC-UNIT FOUNDATION

vacation homes

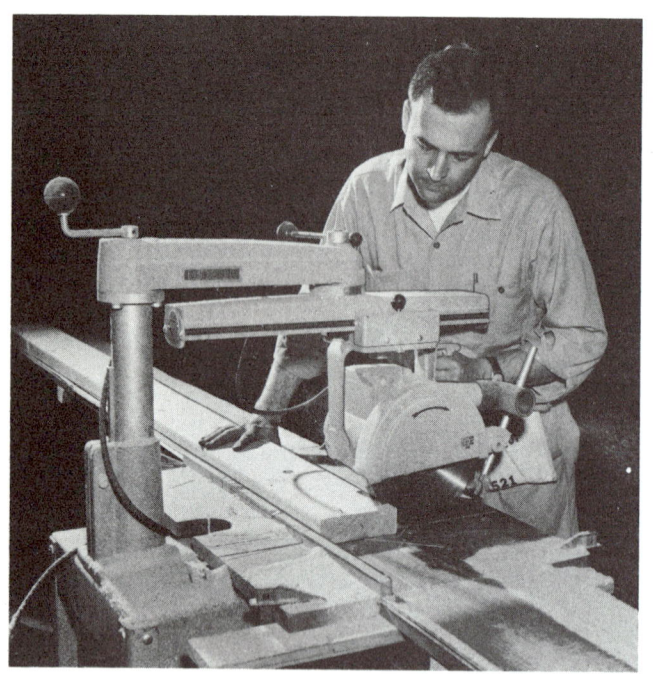

A radial-arm saw makes play of cutting duplicate floor members squarely and to the exact same length

Stop blocks automatically position longitudinal members in nailing jig in fast assembly-line method

Upright stops on jig quickly position closure members for nailing to ends of longitudinal members

Sheeting on some floor units center on edges of 2 x 6s to provide nailing ledges for adjacent units

prefab a vacation house, continued

walls of the basic home, several are identical, some are made right and left hand, others require only one of a kind. All are 4 ft. wide and 8 ft. long. As with the floor sections, it will pay you to take the time to rig up a building form for positioning and nailing the members together. Stop blocks located on the form as before will assure uniform spacing of the studs and identical overall dimensions.

There are several things to note in studying the

exterior wall sections individually detailed in Fig. 6. First, window and door sections, as well as wall section X-48SP, have doubled 2 x 6 headers across the top, whereas all others have conventional 2 x 4 plates, top and bottom. Second, with the exception of wall section WAF-4854-24, the 4 x 8 sheathing on each section overhangs the bottom plate ¾ in. This is done to prevent water from entering at the floor line and also to make the sections self-aligning during erection. The overhang at the bottom results in the sheathing being ¾ in. down from the top, but this is later covered with a 1 x 3 trim board. All wall sections are made simply to butt together when placed side by side, and except where noted otherwise, full 4 x 8-ft. sheets are applied as is without cutting. Here the exceptions, of course, are the door and window sections which require only a portion of a full sheet. Both the length and the number of studs required vary with each section, some requiring as few as three studs, others as many as five. True of all sections, the headers and the top and bottom plates are nailed to the ends of the studs, the headers being toenailed.

choice of materials

You have a choice of several different materials, both plain and textured, for sheathing. Vertical-groove plywood, called Texture One-Eleven, was used in prefabbing the walls of the pilot home. Similar textured panel boards are available in hardboard, also in coated insulating boards. Whatever is used, the material itself provides the exterior covering; nothing is applied to it. Where a plain panel board is used, battens will be necessary to cover the wall joints. However, with vertical-groove boards, battens are not necessary. The sheets have a rabbet along one edge which when butted against the square edge of the sheet in the adjoining wall section forms a matching groove and an invisible joint. In applying such material it is necessary to let the rabbeted edge of the sheet overhang the edge of the supporting frame a distance slightly less than the width of the rabbet itself. Thus when the wall sections are joined together, the overhanging rabbeted edge laps the 2 x 4 of the adjoining section, effectively sealing the joint between the two abutting sections. A simple gauge block can be used to assure a uniform overhang from top to bottom. In following this method, care must be taken in handling and stockpiling the prefabbed sections so as not to damage the overhanging edge.

Wall sections WAF-4854-24 and WT-4836 show the window sash in place. These, of course, would be installed on the job after the walls are up since there would be too great a chance of breakage if installed beforehand through transporting to the site and in nailing the sections together. Window sections are designed to accept stock sash. In the case of sections WAF-4854-24, the upper sash is fixed, whereas the lower sash opens inward. In the other window sections the windows are of the sliding, or bypassing, type.

The keyed floor plan, Fig. 5, shows where each of the individual wall sections goes to make up the four exterior walls of the basic unit, also the location of the interior walls. Note in the case of the interior walls that a plumbing wall is formed by two 2-in. walls positioned 8 in. apart. The space between provides room for the plumbing for the kitchen and bath. Fig. 7 details each interior wall section. With the exception of wall sections SP-48-119, which are assembled like the exterior walls, all other interior sections either are made of 2 x 4s placed flatwise or of 2 x 2s.

the load-bearing wall

Sections SP-48-119, along with two built-up beams of 2 x 8s, form the load-bearing wall for the roof. In actual erection, a second 2 x 4 plate, running the length of the wall, serves to align and tie the whole center wall together. The roof rafters at the ridge rest on this top plate. The two sections required for the interior load-bearing wall require five studs and are assembled right and left hand insofar as the notched upper corner is concerned. Actually they are both alike but are positioned when installed to provide support ledges for the two 8-ft. beams. This also is true of sections SP-42-119, both being alike but made right and left hand when it comes to facing them with paneling. It is best to leave the interior-wall sections uncovered for now; then face them later after installation of plumbing and wiring. Also, your interior paneling is material you would try to have delivered to the site by a lumber dealer in the vicinity. As each exterior and interior-wall section is completed, label it so you will know where it goes.

The floor and wall sections are all that are prefabricated, although there are other members which can be precut at home to save time on the job. These include the 26 roof rafters, the two beams for the load-bearing wall and the parts that make up the four rake panels which form the overhang at the gable ends of the roof. Roof

vacation homes

sheathing, foundation sill plates, floor beams and other lineal stock is material you would have delivered since it wouldn't pay you to cart it for any distance when it could be obtained in the area.

Now that the floor sections and the exterior and interior walls of your vacation home have been prefabbed, there's little else you can do at home to save time at the building site. While the rafters could be precut, it is more advantageous from a standpoint of transportation to have the rafters, along with other dimensional lumber you'll need, delivered to the site from a nearby lumber dealer and make the plate and ridge cuts on the job. The time saved in cutting them at home hardly would offset the problem of carting such long members (16 ft.) any great distance.

While waiting for the balmy days of spring, a thorough understanding of the general construction of the basic home will allow you to proceed without delay at the site. The sectional view from foundation to roof, Fig. 4, plus accompanying details, will orient you on how the floor sections rest on 2 x 8 plates bolted to the foundation wall and on two laminated beams supported on piers in the crawl space. By hiring someone in the area to put the foundation in for you, you'll be way

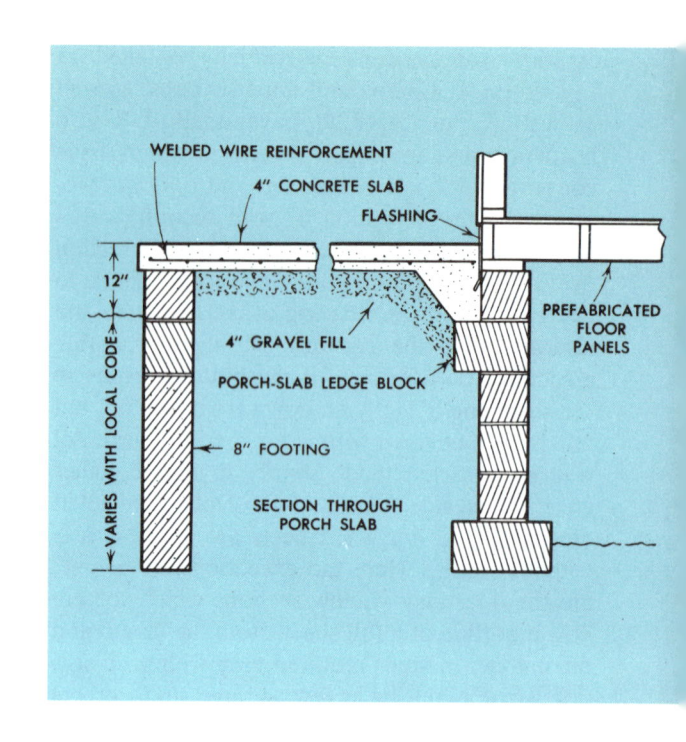

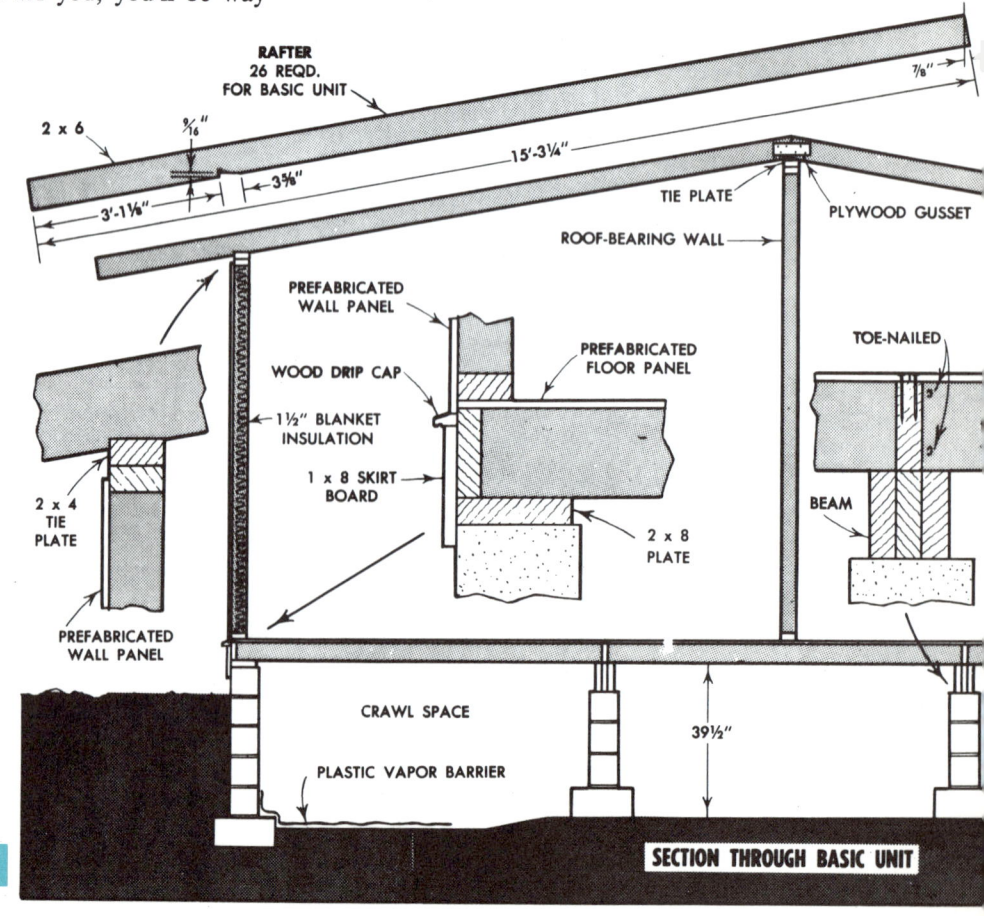

2866

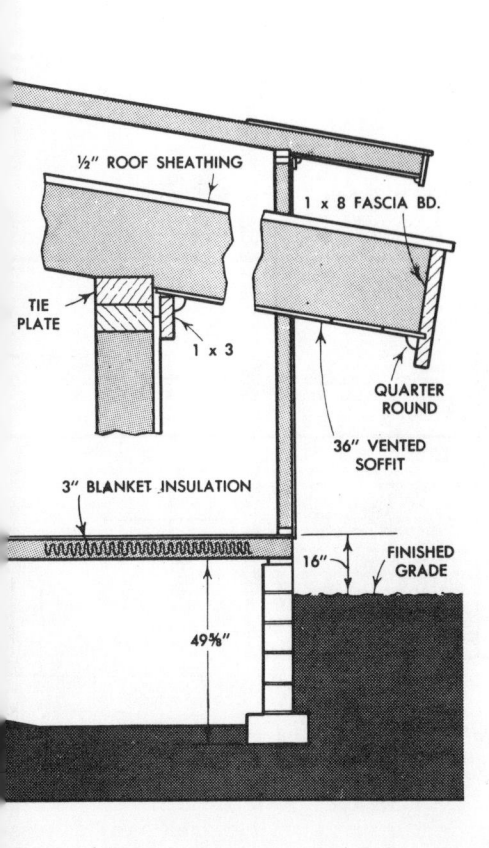

ahead timewise and can start setting beams and adding the plates the day you arrive. The sectional view also shows how the exterior wall sections hook over the floor sections and how the top of the walls are aligned and tied with a second top plate all around. You'll see how the lower edges of the wall sections are finished off with a drip cap and a 1 x 8 skirt board applied over tarpaper flashing and how the overhang is finished off with a 1 x 8 fascia board, a 36-in. vented soffit board and a 1 x 3 trim board, plus quarter round.

A total of 26 rafters are required for the basic house, eight of which are used to form the rake, or overhang, panels at the gable ends. The rake panels can be made up as separate units assembled on the ground and raised in position, or they can be framed in place on the roof. Cutting them involves notching for the wall tie plates and sawing at an angle to form the ridge cut. You'll notice that no ridge board is used. Pairs of rafters simply butt endwise and are held in line with ¾-in. plywood gussets placed on each side of the joint. Here, as with the rake panels, the 2 x 6 rafters can be assembled in pairs on the ground and lifted to the roof, or the plywood gussets can be added as the rafters are set 24 in. on centers and are toenailed to the tie plates of the outside walls and the central roof-bearing wall.

Before all this can be done, four triangular sections which form the gable ends of the struc-

vacation homes

prefab a vacation house, continued

ture must be prefabbed. These are identical, each measuring 11 ft.-8⅜ in., or half the total span of the end walls. In studying the framing of the rake panels detailed on page 2875, you'll see that long bevel cuts are required at one end and that a short fill-in stud is added at the opposite end to form a pocket for the 2 x 8 built-up beam which is a part of the roof-bearing wall. The cutting plan for the gable sheathing shows how two sheets (4 x 6 and 4 x 8) can be cut economically to cover all four gable sections. These are keyed to show where they go, three pieces being used in each case. Notice that the sheathing is applied so it overhangs the bottom edge 1 in. This is done so it laps the top wall plate and also to form a

Vertical-groove sheathing makes an attractive exterior siding. Here ⅝-in. plywood is being applied by driving the nails in the grooves where they are hidden. Note how the lower edge of plywood panel overhangs the bottom plate of 2 x 4 framework

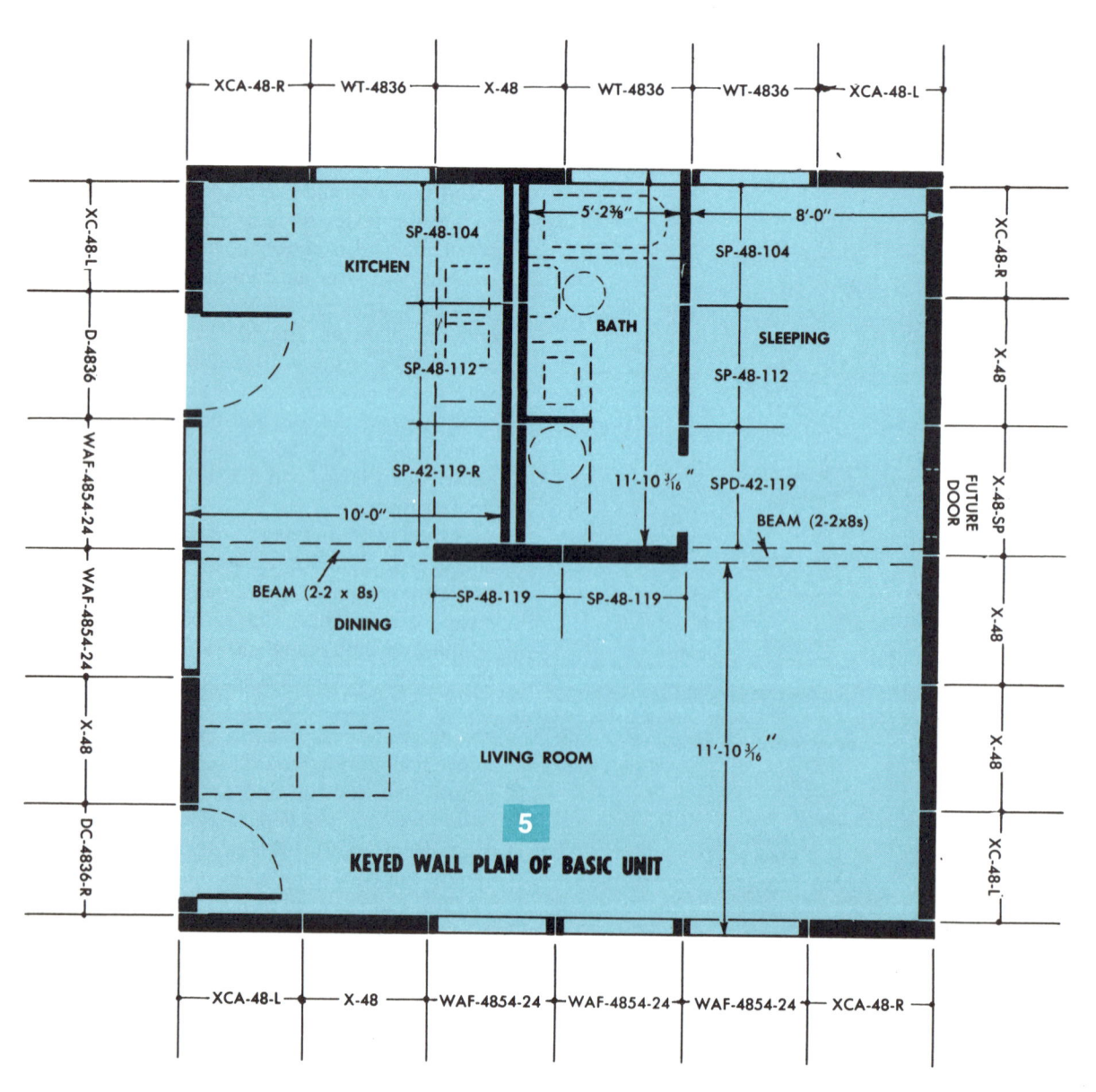

5 KEYED WALL PLAN OF BASIC UNIT

6 EXTERIOR WALL PANELS FOR BASIC UNIT

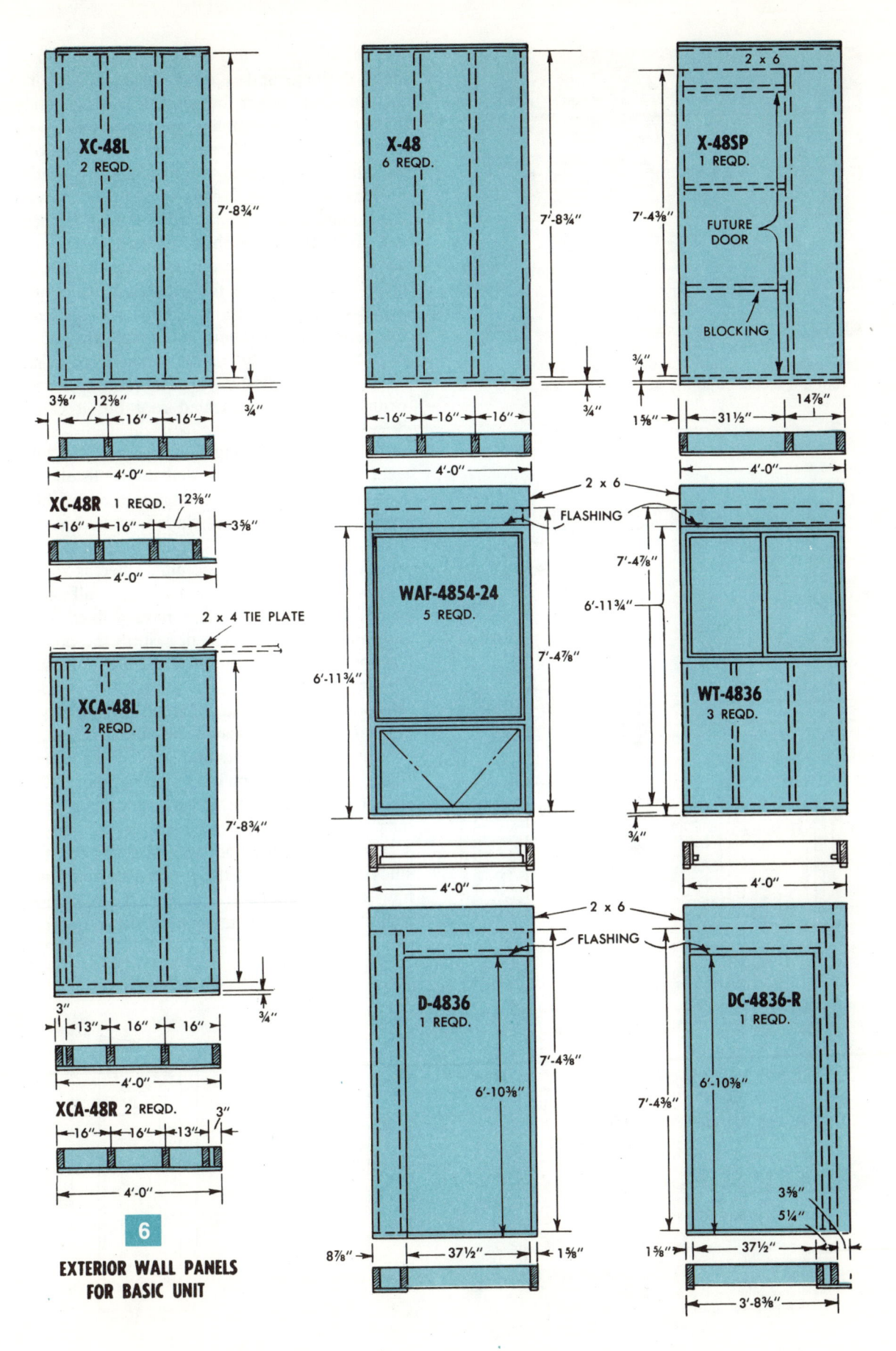

vacation homes

Rake panels which form the overhang at gable ends of roof are toenailed to the supporting gable plate

prefab a vacation house, continued

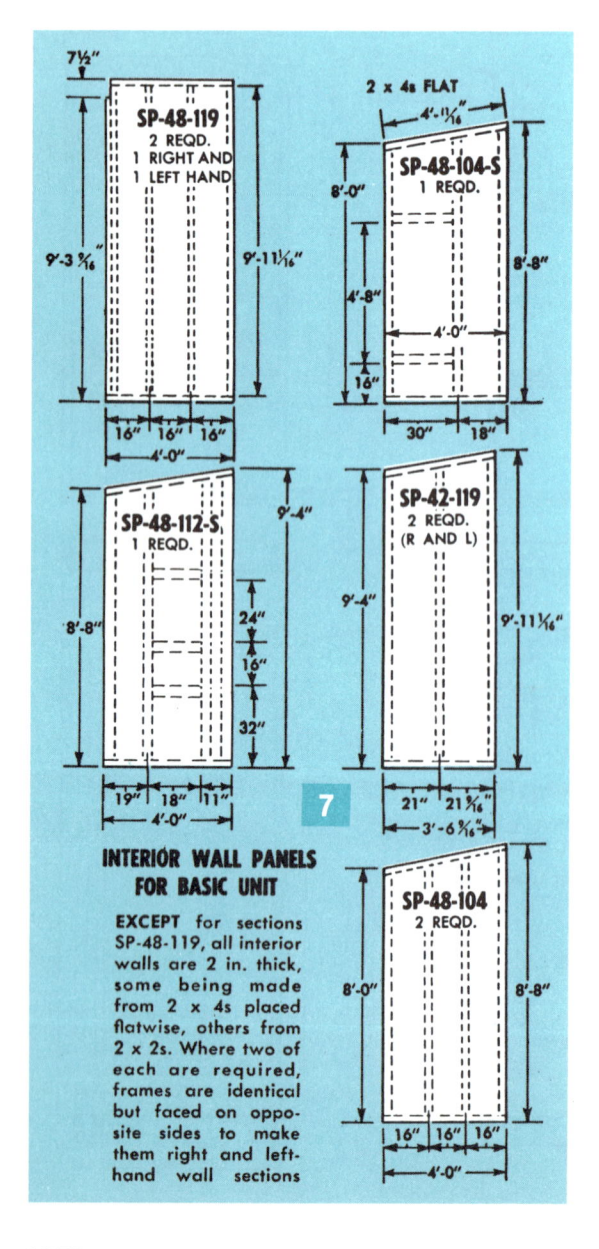

INTERIOR WALL PANELS FOR BASIC UNIT

EXCEPT for sections SP-48-119, all interior walls are 2 in. thick, some being made from 2 x 4s placed flatwise, others from 2 x 2s. Where two of each are required, frames are identical but faced on opposite sides to make them right and left-hand wall sections

waterproof joint when backed with a strip of metal flashing. Spikes driven through and into the top plate anchor the gable sections securely. The roof rake assemblies are supported by the gable sections, the former being centered over the latter and toenailed to it at each cross header.

Decking the roof can be done in the conventional manner, using roof boards or 4 x 8-ft. sheets and covering with asphalt shingles. Or you can add a roof of corrugated aluminum, fiberglass or other material. Here roof sheathing is omitted and 2 x 4 purlins (2 x 4 furring) are applied to the rafters 24 in. apart and lengthwise of the roof. Some difficulty may be encountered in providing adequate flashing around vent pipes and a chimney with a corrugated roof but it can be done.

To get your dwelling fully under cover you'll want to get the windows and doors installed as soon as possible. The openings in the prefabbed sections accept standard window units. Identical full-length windows are installed in the front and left elevations of the basic unit, whereas shorter half windows are used in the rear wall of the house. The full-length units have a fixed upper sash and a tilt-out casement sash at the bottom. The others are conventional double-hung sash. The two door openings are framed with standard jambs and headers and eventually trimmed with conventional casing, inside and out.

Whether you plan on adding the porch at some future date or not, you'll be wise to pour a 12-ft. slab if for nothing more than a patio for cookouts. Then if you should decide to add the screened porch, the floor will be ready for it. In studying the detail of the porch slab you'll note how a course of 12-in. block in the foundation wall provides a ledge to support the poured con-

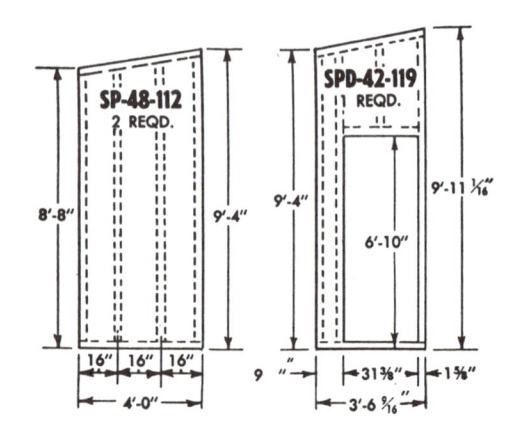

Here wall sections across the rear of the basic unit are being erected. Window sections normally would be faced with sheathing at the time of prefabbing. Note how the sections are braced to the floor to hold them plumb

crete. Besides being reinforced with welded-wire fabric, the slab is supported all around by concrete blocks resting on poured footings.

Once you have the foundation in and the floor and wall sections (which you prefabbed at home) delivered to the site, you are well on your way to completing your vacation home. Your biggest problem in getting the basic unit under cover will be adverse weather. But once that job is completed you are almost to the stage where you are ready to insulate.

There are several things, however, that must be done first. The kitchen and bath partitions must be in, nailers for the interior wall covering installed and the plumbing and wiring completed. The bathroom is designed to take a standard 5-ft. tub which means that the distance between the walls of the room must be placed just a little over 5 ft. apart. You'll note in checking the floor plan of the basic home that a plumbing wall for the sink and the bathroom fixtures is formed by erecting the 2-in. back-to-back wall sections 8 in. apart. It is recommended that both the wiring and the plumbing be installed by a professional tradesman to be sure that the installa-

C-clamps are used to hold the wall sections in line while spiking abutting studs together, above. Time can be saved on the job by priming window and door frames at home, below, before carting them to the building site

vacation homes

prefab a vacation house, continued

tions follow local code requirements in the particular locality.

Nailers must be fitted between the studs of all partition walls, namely, the central roof-bearing wall, the kitchen wall and the bathroom wall. These nailers, as their name implies, provide a place in which to nail when fastening the interior wall covering. They are merely scraps of 2 x 4 cut to fit between the studs and centered on a line 8 ft. up from the floor. In nailing them in place, you'll be able to drive through into the end of each block at one end, but at the other end you'll have to toenail.

Additional nailers must be fitted at the ceiling line of the two gable ends of the house. Here they are necessary to provide a nailing surface for both the furring strips which will eventually be applied to the rafters for fastening the ceiling tile and the soffit material on the underside of the roof overhang. You'll find it easier to install these gable nailers if it is done after the rake panels are in place and before the roof sheathing is applied. Short sections of 2 x 6 are cut to fit between the cross members of the rake panels and spiked to the top plate of the gable sections so that the 2 x 6 nailers overhang each side of the 2 x 4 plate an equal amount.

How thoroughly you insulate depends on

The pilot home has a roof of colorful corrugated aluminum supported by 2 x 4 purlins nailed to the rafters and spaced about 24 in. apart

While your future plans may not include the bedroom addition, you may someday plan to add the screen porch. Pouring the slab for it now will not only provide a patio you'll enjoy in the meantime, but a dry landing outside the door to help keep mud out of the house. Here gravel fill is brought even with the footing

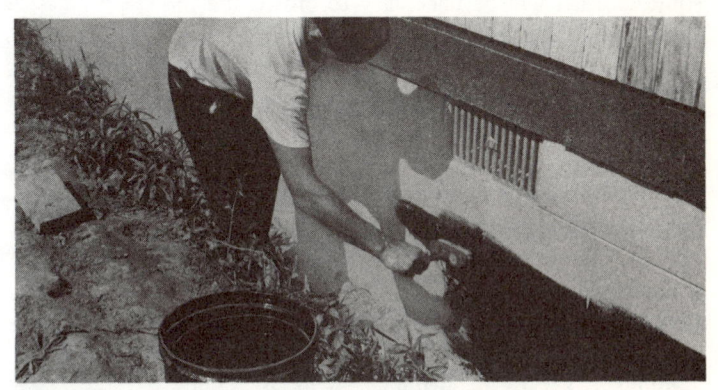

Before the foundation is back-filled, concrete blocks should be waterproofed with asphalt coating, above. Below, stock panels of vented soffit board come ready for nailing to the roof rafters

Here vertical-grooved plywood of the pilot home is being finished with two coats of redwood stain to contrast with the white trim

vacation homes

prefab a vacation house, continued

whether you plan to use your vacation home strictly as a vacation home whereby you would occupy it during the warm months, or as a year-'round home. In the latter case, it will pay to insulate throughout—the walls, the floor and the ceiling. But where the home is to be occupied during the summer months only, you can limit the insulation to just the ceiling. Here you'll save both time and money, but it should be remembered that since it is impractical to add insulation to the walls at a later date, it may in the end prove to be false economy.

In the case of the pilot home, the home was insulated throughout since it was to be used as a year-'round home. While 8-ft. bats were used in the ceiling of the pilot home and roll-type in the walls, the latter could be used throughout. Available in 50 and 75-ft. rolls, it would permit single lengths to be applied to the ceiling from the front wall to the back wall by feeding it up over the roof-bearing wall before stapling it in place. In some cases it will be necessary to crowd the insulation into spaces less than the standard 16-in. spacing, particularly in the walls. In other instances it will be necessary to cut the roll insulation in narrow strips.

If you use a corrugated aluminum roof as on the pilot home, it will be necessary to add a polyethylene vapor barrier to prevent condensation of moisture on the metal. This was applied in 12-ft. widths directly over the blanket insulation and stapled to the edges of the rafters. Meeting edges of the plastic were rolled before stapling to assure an airtight seal at the seams, and the plastic was brought down the side walls 4 or 5 in. to permit stapling to the top plate. This additional plastic barrier is only necessary where an aluminum roof is used. Bat or roll insulation with a foil facing is usually sufficient for a conventional-type roof of wood and asphalt shingles.

interior wall paneling

This brings you to the interior wall paneling. There's a great variety of panel boards from which to choose, both plain and fancy, prefinished and unfinished. A textured, vertical-grooved hardboard, which comes primed and ready for final painting, was used in the pilot home. Standard 8-ft. lengths are used to cover the 8-ft. side walls. In the case of the gable-end walls and the room partitions, you have the option (in the case of some materials) of using 10-ft. panels. The longer panels eliminate a joint

Knockdown window units are assembled on the job prior to installing in openings in prefabbed walls

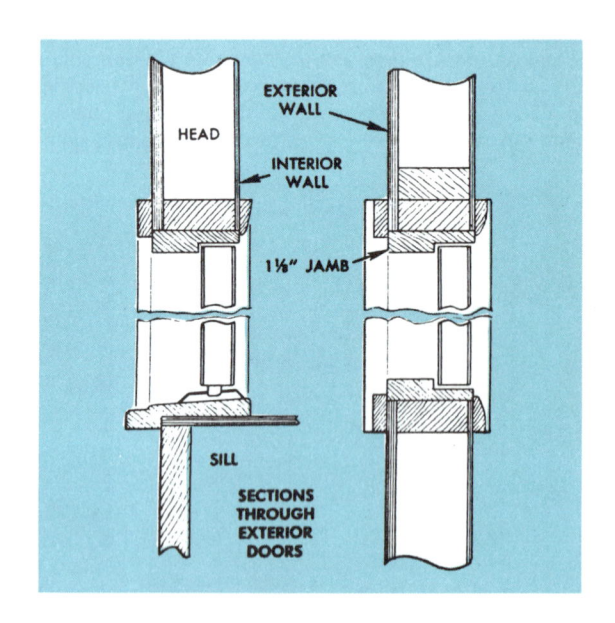

When wiring is in place in the exterior walls, blanket insulation is installed, stapled to studs

ROOF-FRAMING OF BASIC UNIT

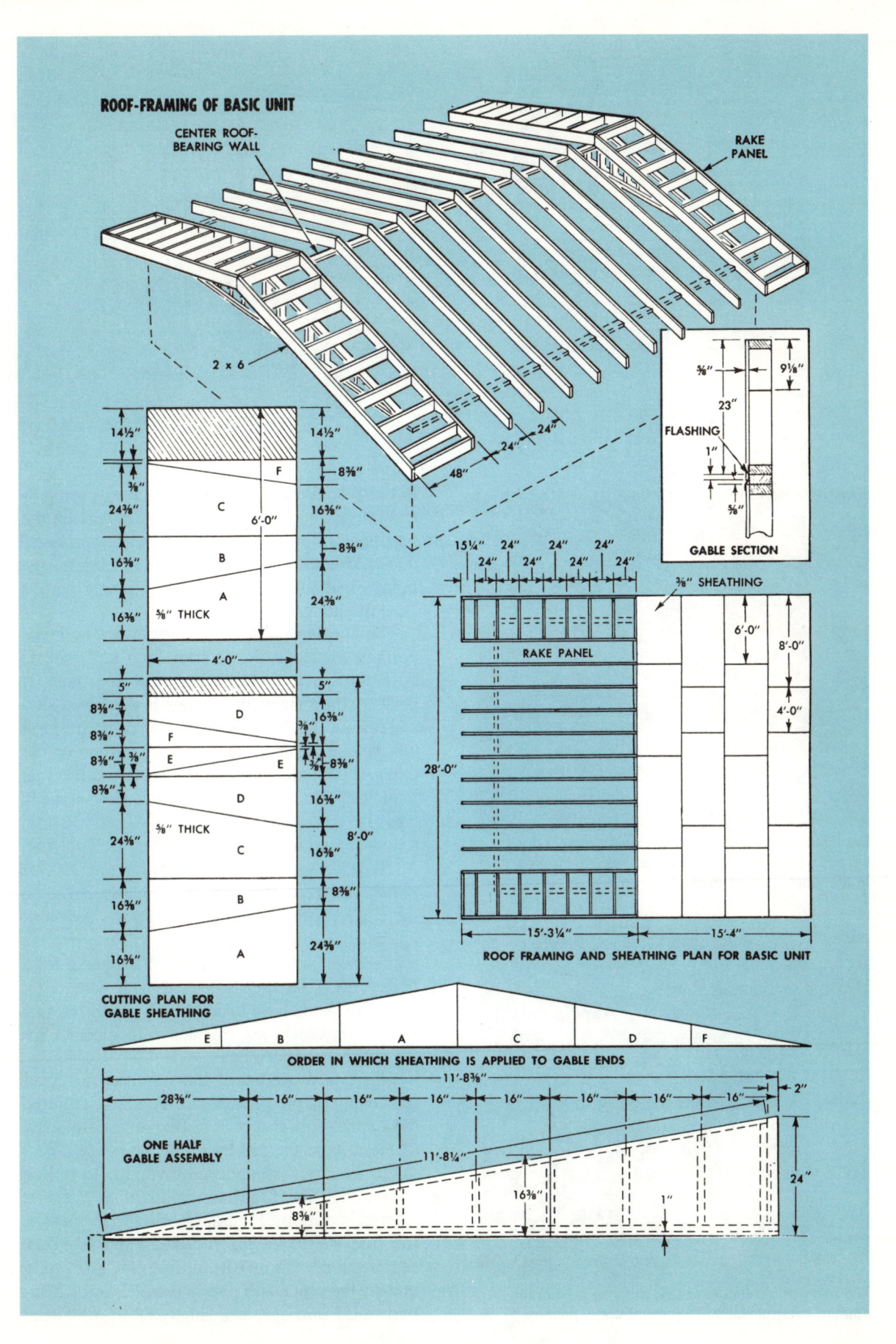

GABLE SECTION

CUTTING PLAN FOR GABLE SHEATHING

ROOF FRAMING AND SHEATHING PLAN FOR BASIC UNIT

ORDER IN WHICH SHEATHING IS APPLIED TO GABLE ENDS

ONE HALF GABLE ASSEMBLY

vacation homes

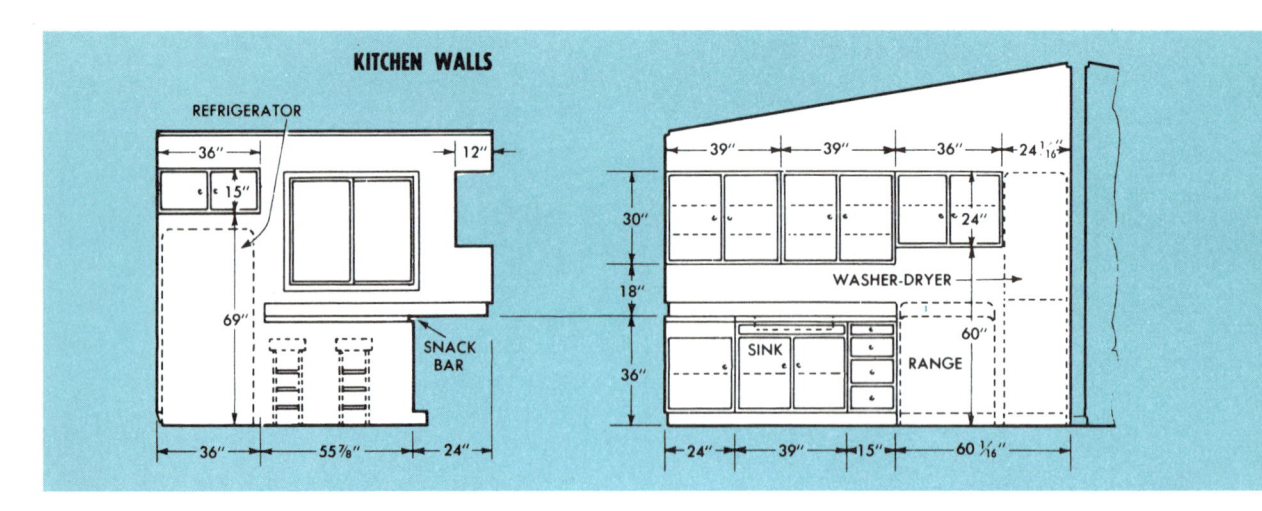

KITCHEN WALLS

prefab a vacation house, continued

Bat insulation in 8-ft. lengths is being installed between the roof rafters. The flanges are stapled to the sides of the rafters

The metal roof requires a polyethylene membrane applied over insulation to prevent condensation

at the 8-ft. level which you will have in using 8-ft. material, and also the need for nailers on the partitions. However, if the material you select does not come in greater than 8-ft. lengths, the point mentioned can be covered neatly with a stock molding.

The starting point of the first panel is unimportant; paneling can be started on any wall. It is important, however, where the first panel is positioned on the wall. As there is a doubled stud wherever wall sections butt, you must position the panel so that its edge centers on one or the other of the two studs and not center on the wall joint itself. In this way, the panel joint actually laps the wall joint. Whatever material you use, follow manufacturer's instructions for applying. A trick to remember in marking cutouts for switch and receptacle outlets is to rub chalk on the edges of the outlet boxes and press the panel against the chalked edges. This will transfer the outlines of the box to the back of the panel for a perfect fit. The nails supplied with some prefinished boards have heads which match the surface grain, others are supplied with special clips for concealed fastening.

Fiberboard acoustical tile was used to cover the ceiling of the pilot home. This first required the application of 1 x 3 furring strips crosswise of the rafters, the full length of the house. Spacing of the strips is important if you are to end up with border tile of the same width along opposite sides of the room. First apply the furring next to the side walls and the roof-bearing wall. Then center the next strip 10½ in. from the side walls, and do the same with a strip parallel to the bearing wall. From here you simply fill in with strips

BATHROOM WALL

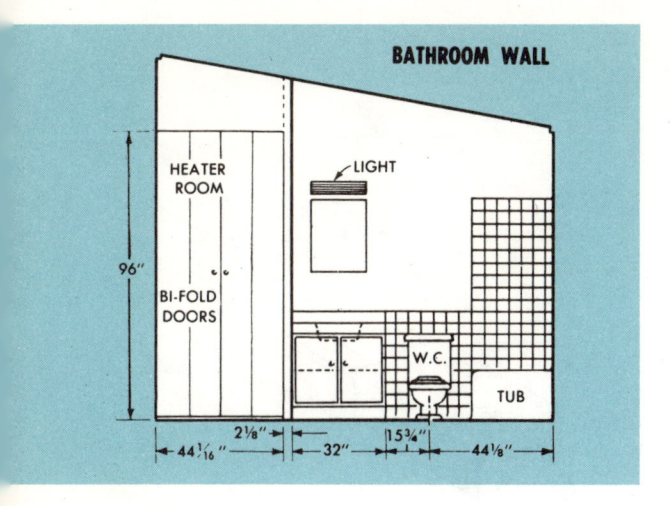

The electrical entrance cabinet is located in the closet housing the furnace and water heater

spaced 12 in. center to center. The joints of the tile were staggered rather than aligned, and to assure border tile of equal width along the gable ends of the rooms, half tile are used at the ends of every other row.

This means that the starting tile in the lower corner of the living room, for example, is cut so it measures 10 x 12 in. The next tile up the gable is a half tile, 6 x 12 in., followed by a full tile, then a half tile, and so on. Fiberboard tile cuts easily with a sharp knife, and goes on quickly with a staple gun. To assure straight rows, chalk lines should be struck on each furring strip and used in aligning each tile as it is applied rather than relying on the straightness of the tongue and groove of the tile.

Arrangement of the kitchen can be altered from that shown in the plans, insofar as the placement of the cabinets is concerned. Stock wall cabinets are available from mail-order houses in knockdown form and are priced at less than the cost of building them yourself.

As for heating, here again it depends on whether you plan to occupy your vacation home during cold weather. If not, installation of a portable, wall-type fireplace would help remove the first chill of fall evenings. Since the pilot home was to be occupied the year 'round, a compact gas-fired, forced-air furnace of 80,000 B.T.U. output, in addition to the fireplace, was installed in the crawl space, centrally located in the basic unit.

Pine trim was used throughout in finishing off the doors, windows and baseboard; cove molding added to the ceiling tile and the entire floor of the basic unit was covered with asphalt tile.

A gas-fired furnace in the pilot home was located in the crawl space, above. A packaged free-standing fireplace is shown being assembled

2877

clever ideas

Suet treat for wild birds will be a popular addition to your feeding station. Grind suet with birdseed, shape it into a ball and roll in more seed. Then drive a short dowel through the middle and tie a short twine hanger to one end.

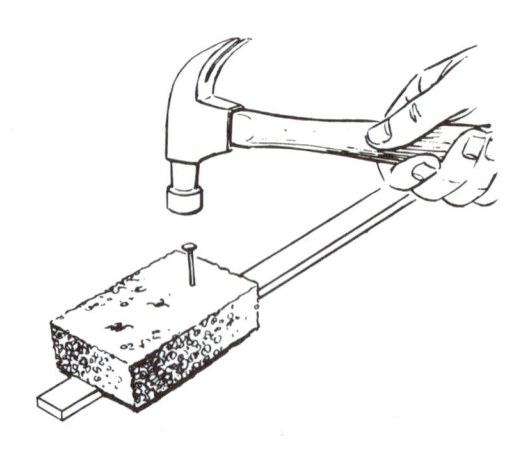

This paint dauber comes in handy when painting recesses in radiators and cupboards where it is almost impossible to use a brush. You can make one in minutes. Just nail a sponge to a thin wood strip with brads and dunk it in the paint like a roller.

A slat mat under your flower pots will protect the finish on your furniture from unsightly scratches. The mat shown above was made by gluing ice-cream bar sticks together, then painting the whole thing to match the pot.

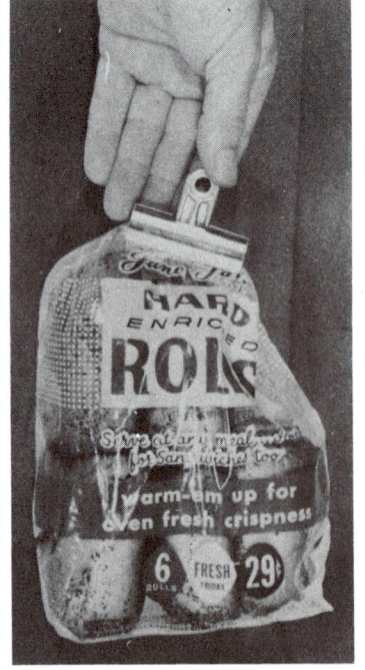

How do you close a plastic food bag to keep the rest of the contents fresh? Twisting the end never quite works. Next time try folding over the end and clamping it shut with a spring-type paper clip.

What to do until the plumber comes? Stretch-wrap that leaky pipe with a strip cut from an old inner tube and secure it with a small C-clamp. This will seal the leak effectively until a permanent repair can be made.

Project-a-plan

Here are the famous Project-a-plans—the *Popular Mechanics* system that makes you an artist in minutes. The method is simple. Cut the Project-a-plans from this page, following the dotted lines. Then coat each drawing with shellac, clear nail polish or even vegetable oil. Then mount each little drawing in a cardboard 35-mm slide frame. Put the frame in a slide projector and project it on the material on which you want to draw—poster board, plywood, etc. Set the material up against the wall like a screen, and make certain the projector is at right angles to the board. You can make the drawing any size you wish by moving the projector. Trace the enlarged outline on the material and you're all set. You can use this system for making signs and posters, enlarging designs for jigsawing and many other projects that require artwork.

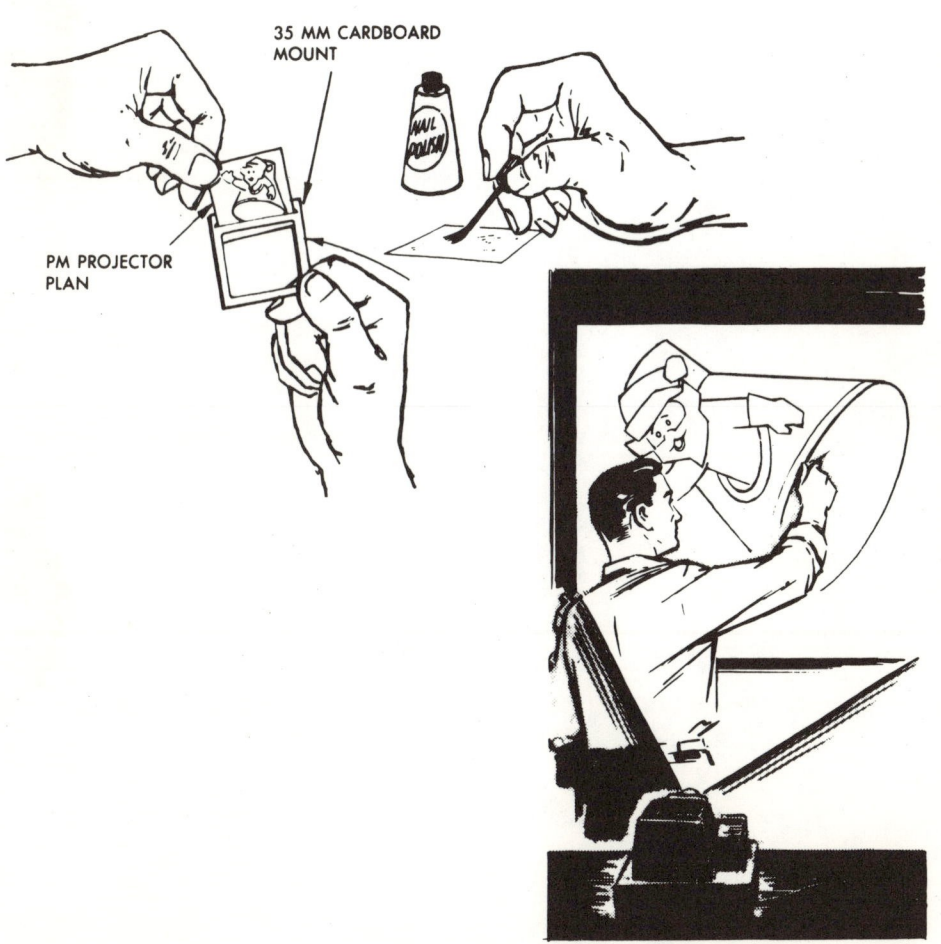

SEE "QUICK-CHANGE CARDBOARD PLAY MOUNTS," PAGE 2727